UCLA FORUM IN MEDICAL SCIENCES

Victor E. Hall, *Editor*

Martha Bascopé-Espada, *Assistant Editor*

UNIVERSITY OF CALIFORNIA, LOS ANGELES

BRAIN FUNCTION

VOLUME IV

BRAIN FUNCTION AND LEARNING

UCLA FORUM IN MEDICAL SCIENCES

NUMBER 6

BRAIN FUNCTION

VOLUME IV

Proceedings of the Fourth Conference, November 1964

BRAIN FUNCTION AND LEARNING

Sponsored jointly by the Brain Research Institute, University of California,
Los Angeles, and the United States Air Force Office of Scientific Research

EDITORS

DONALD B. LINDSLEY and **ARTHUR A. LUMSDAINE**

UNIVERSITY OF CALIFORNIA PRESS

BERKELEY AND LOS ANGELES

1967

EDITORIAL NOTE

The present volume contains the proceedings of the fourth in a series of conferences on Brain Function, supported by grants made to Dr. H. W. Magoun of the Brain Research Institute of the University of California, Los Angeles. The first and second conferences of the series, on *Cortical Excitability and Steady Potentials* and on *RNA and Brain Function*, respectively, were edited by Dr. M. A. B. Brazier and appeared as Numbers 1 and 2 of the UCLA Forum in Medical Sciences; the third conference, on *Speech, Language, and Communication*, of which Dr. E. C. Carterette was the editor, appeared as Number 4 of the Forum. The fifth conference, dealing with Brain Mechanisms of Aggression and Defense, was held November 1965, and shall appear as Number 7 of the Forum.

CITATION FORM

Lindsley, D. B., and Lumsdaine, A. A. (Eds.), *Brain Function, Vol. IV: Brain Function and Learning.* UCLA Forum Med. Sci. No. 6, Univ. of California Press, Los Angeles, 1967.

University of California Press
Berkeley and Los Angeles, California

PARTICIPANTS IN THE CONFERENCE

H. W. MAGOUN, *Co-Chairman*
Dean of the Graduate Division
Department of Anatomy and Brain Research Institute
University of California, Los Angeles
Los Angeles, California

DONALD B. LINDSLEY, *Co-Chairman and Editor*
Departments of Psychology and Physiology
and Brain Research Institute, University of California, Los Angeles
Los Angeles, California

ARTHUR A. LUMSDAINE, *Editor*[*]
Department of Education, University of California, Los Angeles
Los Angeles, California

RICHARD C. ATKINSON
Department of Psychology, Stanford University
Stanford, California

HERBERT G. BIRCH
Department of Pediatrics
Albert Einstein College of Medicine
New York, New York

MARY A. B. BRAZIER
Brain Research Institute, University of California, Los Angeles
Los Angeles, California

MELVIN CALVIN
Department of Chemistry, University of California
Berkeley, California

EMANUEL DONCHIN[†]
Department of Psychology, University of California, Los Angeles
Los Angeles, California

Present addresses:

[*] Department of Psychology, University of Washington, Seattle, Washington.
[†] Neurobiology Branch, National Aeronautics and Space Administration, Ames Research Center, Moffett Field, California.

Seymour Feshbach
Department of Psychology, University of California, Los Angeles
Los Angeles, California

Robert M. Gagné
School of Education, University of California
Berkeley, California

John Gaito
Department of Psychology, York University
Toronto, Canada

Robert Galambos
Department of Psychology, Yale University
New Haven, Connecticut

David A. Grant
Department of Psychology, University of Wisconsin
Madison, Wisconsin

J. P. Guilford
Department of Psychology, University of Southern California
Los Angeles, California

Raúl Hernández-Peón
Instituto de Investigaciones Cerebrales
Mexico City, Mexico

Ernest R. Hilgard
Department of Psychology, Stanford University
Stanford, California

Donald D. Jensen
Department of Psychology, Indiana University
Bloomington, Indiana

Arthur Koestler
London, England

Jerzy Konorski
Department of Neurophysiology, Nencki Institute for Experimental Biology
Warsaw, Poland

Lewis P. Lipsitt
Department of Psychology, Brown University
Providence, Rhode Island

NEAL E. MILLER[*]
Department of Psychology, Yale University
New Haven, Connecticut

NEIL O'CONNOR
Medical Research Council, Institute of Psychiatry, The Maudsley Hospital
London, England

KARL H. PRIBRAM
Neuropsychology Laboratories, Stanford University School of Medicine
Palo Alto, California

ERNST Z. ROTHKOPF
Bell Telephone Laboratories
Murray Hill, New Jersey

ROGER W. SPERRY
Division of Biological Sciences, California Institute of Technology
Pasadena, California

HERBERT A. SIMON
Graduate School of Industrial Administration
Carnegie-Mellon University
Pittsburgh, Pennsylvania

RICHARD F. THOMPSON[†]
Department of Medical Psychology
University of Oregon Medical School
Portland, Oregon

EDWARD F. ZIGLER
Department of Psychology, Yale University
New Haven, Connecticut

Present addresses:
[*] Rockefeller University, New York, New York.
[†] Department of Psychobiology, University of California at Irvine, Irvine, California.

FOREWORD

DONALD B. LINDSLEY
Co-Chairman

This Conference on Brain Function and Learning is one of several on re-lated topics which have been sponsored by the Brain Research Institute, University of California, Los Angeles, and the Office of Scientific Research, United States Air Force. The general plan in each instance has been to start with basic structural and functional considerations relative to the problem, usually the neuroanatomical and neurophysiological substrate, and then proceed to an elaboration of specific mechanisms determined in part by the substrate and in part by the environment and its special features of system-atic stimulus control and influence.

The recent success of biochemistry in establishing the elements of a genet-ic code utilized by biological memory, in the reduplication of the general features of morphology as expressed in inheritance, and in the specification of templates for cellular proliferation and immune reactions, has led to an interest in the extension of these approaches to the biochemical basis of learning and memory. It seemed, therefore, important to begin this confer-ence with a survey of the present status of the neurochemical approaches to learning and memory. This led, inevitably, not only to a consideration of the specific chemical change to be sought and measured, but to a discussion of what had been learned and remembered. The plasticity and flexibility of the nervous system as manifested in the dynamics of behavior-change offers tremendous challenges to the investigator and calls for a variety of tech-niques for the elicitation, measurement and assessment of such changes.

Accordingly, the next presentations are devoted to the electrophysiolog-ical, neurophysiological and behavioral indices and assessments of adapta-tion and change in the nervous system which might be correlated with bio-chemical transitions and transformations during conditioning and learning. This is followed by a résumé of the origins and present status of concepts and theories of conditioning and learning, and discussion of the method-ological basis for differentiating and sharpening the psychological aspects of the problem. In this respect, the advances in computer facilities have led to the increased use of mathematical models and to the development of artificial intelligence as an extraneural parallel and as a basis for testing ideas and concepts relative to learning and memory.

Following these basic and theoretically oriented approaches to an under-standing of conditioning and learning, a second group of presentations surveys two areas of high current interest and activity. The first, marking the recently renewed emphasis upon experimental child psychology, deals with the ontogenetic aspects of development and learning as revealed by the changing behavior of young children. The second emphasizes the variety and novelty of modern methods of programmed learning and teaching machines, a development of great interest, not only theoretically so far as this conference is concerned, but practically and empirically with respect to the demands of modern society for increased education and a rapidly expanding educable population.

The third group of presentations was deliberately planned to examine learning and learning potentiality in terms of contrasting groups and situations, namely the limitations imposed upon the mentally retarded by genetic accident or design, by trauma, by social and cultural deprivation, and contrastingly, the analysis of the factors constituting high mental endowment and creativity.

The nature of creativity is itself discussed by a renowned author, whose recent book, *The Act of Creation*,* tries to find common ground in the creative acts of artists, authors, inventors, scientists and others, and attempts to account for this communality historically, philosophically and empirically. The Conference thus comes to an end with Mr. Koestler's development of a theory of the creative process based on biological, neurological and psychological principles.

---

* Koestler, A., *The Act of Creation*. Macmillan, New York, 1964.

CONTENTS

NEUROCHEMICAL APPROACHES TO LEARNING

JOHN GAITO
York University
Toronto, Canada

Two neurochemical approaches to behavior have been quite prominent in recent years. One, which I would call the molar approach, has been presented by Rosenzweig, Krech and other workers at Berkeley (6), who have been concerned with acetylcholine-acetylcholinesterase activity. The other approach, at a molecular level, is concerned with the nucleic acids; most of the work in this area has been done by Hydén (21, 34, 36, 37, 39, 40). It is very interesting that these two approaches, which began at different levels, appear to be rapidly converging to a common ground.

I would like to devote my attention mainly to the molecular approach, pioneered by Holger Hydén (34, 36), who has some interesting experiments suggesting that RNA may be the substrate of memory. Unfortunately, careful consideration of the findings in this area (which I like to refer to as molecular psychobiology) gives little evidence to support such a contention (18, 24); multiple interpretations are possible for the data presented by Hydén and others in support of the idea of RNA as the memory molecule. Indeed, basic molecular biological considerations make it apparent that RNA is just one molecular event interposed in a sequence of events. I might add that Hydén has changed his ideas somewhat over the years (37); he was much more definite in his earlier than in his later papers.

Pribram: In defense of Hydén, it could be said he did not exactly call RNA the memory molecule; he has said it is intermediary between what goes on in the nerve and whatever the memory process is.

Gaito: In one paper (34) he used the term "substrate for memory". I am sure there is a problem of interpretation. Actually, Hydén started with an instructive theory that could be stated as follows: there is a particular RNA of specific base sequence; certain events occur during the passage of nerve impulses; these events change the particular RNA—a new molecule is made (34, 36). His thought has evolved toward a selectional theory, i.e., a number of species of RNA are available; some of these species are then released during the learning event (37).

Calvin: A later paper of Hydén's (41) has the statement, "In 1958, the senior author proposed a hypothetical 'mechanism of instruction' involving

1

the RNA of the neurons as a substrate molecule for storing information." In other words, he said essentially that the RNA is the tape on which the information of learning is stored.

Gaito: In any case, I think it is very difficult to assign an important role in memory to RNA, since it is just one step in a sequence of events. Nevertheless, the work of Hydén and of the many workers who have expressed similar ideas has provided data that can be used as a framework for further research, and shows interesting results that suggest some molecular transactions underlying learning and other behavioral events.

We have some information (34, 67, 69) indicating three important steps associated together, namely increments in the amounts of RNA, of proteins, and of lipids during functional activity of cells (learning, sensory stimulation, or motor activity). I would like to present a set of hypotheses related to such intracellular events, emphasizing that these hypotheses deal with only a small segment of the complex total sequence involved in learning. To incorporate these data into a meaningful model, I suggest a DNA activation approach. Let us say, for example, that we have events X_1, X_2, X_3 . . . X_n. X_1 could be stimulation at the periphery, that is, stimulation of receptors; X_n might be motor activity, or it could be something in the sensory or associational systems. On the basis of data from several authors and from the field of molecular biology (5, 22, 73, 75, 83) I would like to speculate about a particular segment concerned with protein synthesis (say, X_7 for DNA becoming activated, X_8 for RNA being synthesized, and X_9 for protein being made). What goes on before, i.e., X_6 and earlier, and what goes on afterwards at X_{10} and beyond, is obscure. Perhaps some of the later speakers will elucidate the rest of the sequence.

My first hypothesis is that during learning DNA is activated. There is a considerable body of information from molecular biology which suggests that DNA can be in a form either functionally active (synthesizing RNA) or functionally inactive (not synthesizing RNA) (5, 22, 44, 73, 75). For example, the puffing of insect chromosomes shows active DNA (5). Considering a puff from a biochemical point of view, increased amounts of RNA can be seen in that particular segment: the RNA/DNA ratio of the puffed insect chromosomal segment is greater in comparison with the nonpuffed area— the relative RNA synthesis is greater. Under the microscope these puffs can actually be seen in the chromosomes of various insects. The inactive chromosomal material is condensed; when it becomes active, it "opens up", and loops or puffs are seen coming out. These loops contain the RNA synthesis process. DNA has been activated.

My second hypothesis is that, upon activation, DNA brings about the synthesis of a number of RNA's in the presence of appropriate enzymes (RNA polymerases). I suggest the following seven:

a. Ribosomal RNA
b. Messenger RNA for the synthesis of ribosomal protein

c. and *d.* Messenger RNA's for the synthesis of the synaptic proteins choline acetylase (ChA) and acetylcholinesterase (AchE)

e. Messenger RNA for the synthesis of structural protein for axonal endings

f. Messenger RNA for membrane protein

g. Messenger RNA for enzymes for synthesis of membrane lipids.

There may be more—each of these may actually consist of more than one species—but I have tried to adhere closely to the existing data and to logical expectations, treating each portion as a single entity. Table 1 summarizes the suggested RNA's, their possible roles, and any related evidence.

To continue with the proposed sequence for protein synthesis, a type of messenger RNA in the cell nucleus receives the message from a DNA site in terms of a linear sequence of bases. This messenger RNA then moves to the ribosome (seen as a site in the cytoplasm—the Nissl substance of nerve cells). The consequent increase in ribosomal RNA is suggested by studies with bacteria which indicate that the amount of this RNA is related to growth (52): the ratio of ribosomal RNA to DNA over age increases with growth rate, while the same ratio for transfer RNA is constant, irrespective of growth. Further evidence for the synthesis of ribosomal RNA during learning is to be found in Hydén's data relating amounts of RNA per cell to age (36). Hydén studied the amount of RNA per cell of individuals from about three to about 90 years of age. The RNA, taken from the motor nerve cell in the spinal cord, was found to be on a rapidly rising curve which reached a peak at about age 40, a plateau up to about age 60, and then went down. It is to be assumed, of course, that the same pattern would be found for cortical nerve cells. If so, it would suggest that the increment measured is in ribosomal RNA, since this species constitutes 80 to 90 per cent of the RNA in the cell. In addition, ribosomal RNA is very stable, which is not necessarily true for messenger RNA (75).

Since the ribosome is an aggregate of RNA and protein (usually—at least in bacteria—in the ratio of one RNA molecule to ten molecules of protein), an increase in ribosomal RNA would imply an increase in ribosomal protein, coded by the corresponding messenger RNA. The ultimate result would be an increase in the number of ribosomes and in the rate and quantity of protein synthetized.

A third type of RNA, transfer or soluble RNA, retrieves amino acids and transports them to the ribosomal site for protein synthesis. A single transfer RNA is supposed to pick up a single amino acid.

Thus there are three types of RNA involved in protein synthesis (83): messenger RNA, carrying the basic message transcribed from DNA; transfer RNA, picking up the amino acid and carrying it to the ribosome; and ribosomal RNA, a constituent of the ribosome.

The remaining subhypotheses are related to synaptic and membrane events. The synapse is an important functional unit unique to nerve cells,

TABLE 1

RNA's Assumed to Be Synthesized Following DNA Activation During the Learning Process

Site or Structure Involved	Type of RNA*	Function	Evidence Suggesting RNA Type
Ribosome	Ribosomal RNA	Influences rate and amount of protein synthesized	Hydén data (36) 80 to 90% of cellular RNA Stable Molecular biology data—ribosomes related to growth (52)
	Messenger RNA for ribosomal protein	same	Required in the structure of ribosomes
Synaptic Area†	Messenger RNA for ChA Messenger RNA for AchE	Regulates amount and activity of Ach in depolarization of postsynaptic neurons during nerve impulse transmission	Data of Berkeley group (6) Neurophysiological data (19)
Synaptic Area†	Messenger RNA for structural protein required for the development of axonal endings	Effects new neural connections	Nerve cell culture studies (28) Data of Berkeley group (6)
Neural Membrane†	Messenger RNA for protein Messenger RNA for enzymes for lipid synthesis	Influences interneuron communication through synapses and more remotely	Palladin & Vladimirov data (67) Required if new connections develop or in growth of nerve cells

* More than one of each of the RNA types may be involved.
† These portions could relate not only to interneuron communication and structure but also to glia-glia and glia-neuron interaction and structure.

intimately involved, along with the membrane, in the electrical phenomena of brain tissue.

At the synaptic area, messenger RNA's for choline acetylase (ChA) and acetylcholinesterase (AchE) would be synthetized. These would, essentially, control and regulate the amount of acetylcholine available at the synaptic region to depolarize the subsynaptic membrane for the transmission of nerve impulses. I believe the findings of the Berkeley group are significant in this respect; the Krech-Rosenzweig data (6, 7) indicate an increase in AchE activity with experience, and these are experiments over long periods of time, in which some learning was certainly involved. Furthermore, basic thought in neurophysiology assigns to AchE the role of a synaptic transmitter substance (19), so that messenger RNA's for the enzymes controlling its synthesis and degradation would be required. Increasing amounts of choline acetylase and acetylcholinesterase would mean greater probability of nerve impulses and stimulation in other cells once certain cells are stimulated.

I further suggest that at the synaptic area messenger RNA for structural protein is required for the development of axonal endings. This is very conjectural. I have in mind a cell-assembly type of situation, in which it is hypothesized that new nerve connections are made to provide a permanent basis for memory. Consistent with this particular possibility are the results of the Berkeley group (6). There are indications that animals that have been in enriched environments for extended periods of time, 90 days or so, show thicker and heavier cortices, with the greatest thickness occurring in the visual cortex; lesser thicknesses and lesser weight occur in the somesthetic area. These findings presumably show that there is some particular growth as a function of experience; it may well be new connections. The nerve cell culture studies possibly suggest this as well: Geiger (28) found that ameboid movement and growth in nerve cells and glial tissue are functions of various chemicals and of electrical stimulation.

The last set of RNA's I am proposing as being synthesized during learning events is relative to the neural membrane. First, there is messenger RNA for protein, one of the constituents of membrane tissue; second, there is messenger RNA for enzymes that will control the synthesis of lipid, another component of the membrane tissue. If nerve growth occurs, there obviously will have to be increased amounts of lipid and protein for the nerve membranes that will encase all the new growth.

These messenger RNA's with their synthesized proteins would influence the intercommunication between neurons at the synapse. If we want to consider field effects such as the Landauer hypotheses (54), these messenger RNA's would also be relevant. If neurons or glia in one part of the nervous system are in tune with those in other parts, the particular proteins or lipids developed would then determine this tuning aspect.

I have suggested these possible RNA's as being involved in learning in order to account for the reported increases in RNA, proteins and lipids during functional activity of the cells (67). Of the various RNA's suggested, only ribosomal RNA need have great stability. The messenger RNA's could be degraded after performing their function of synthesizing the required proteins as long as the proteins showed greater stability. Thus, small increments of ribosomal RNA and proteins could occur over learning periods. Such increments might be too small to be detected following one learning period but could be sizable after extended learning situations.

Although the second hypothesis has been concerned with neurons, these RNA's and their associated protein syntheses could be related to the possible involvement of glial cells in learning events, as suggested by Galambos (25), Hydén (36, 37), Pribram (70) and Landauer (54).

These speculations, even though seemingly farfetched, can at least be stated in such form that they (or their deductions) can be tested by experimentation. We are heading in this direction at the present time but progress is extremely slow due to the involved chemical extractions and analyses, as well as related procedures.

Discussion

Konorski: Dr. Gaito, your first hypothesis stated that during learning DNA became activated. Could you define what you mean by "during learning"?

Gaito: I am referring to the event wherein an association is made between an action and its consequence—for example, pressing a lever and getting food. At the particular instant an animal makes this association, one or more segments of DNA in some part of its brain begin to synthesize RNA. All this would take place in the nerve cell—I cannot at this time specify where in the brain.

Konorski: I do not understand at which moment you can say that DNA is activated. Is it at the moment when the animal presses the bar, or at the moment when it eats, or at the moment afterwards when this is consolidated?

Gaito: Actually, I am not referring here only to such a learning sequence. In motor activity, also, there would be DNA molecules which would become active so that RNA would be synthesized, and protein would be synthesized to facilitate this motor activity. With regard to the learning event, it would have to be when the association is made.

Jensen: This seems to be the associational theory of learning in a particularly precise form. You speak of *when* an association is made. Just before this conference I spent two days discussing learning in several sessions on introductory psychology; the classic films by Guthrie & Horton (31) and by Liddell (57) were shown in each of the sessions; the Guthrie & Horton film is particularly relevant, since it shows sequences of trials by individual animals. I have watched these sequences literally dozens of times, yet I cannot see when an association is made by a particular cat. Rather, over an entire sequence of trials the stereotypy of behavior increases and the latency of the reinforced behavior decreases, but there is no single instant when this happens. I think that implicit in the discussion is a theory of learning to which Dr. Konorski is rightfully objecting.

Gaito: I do not necessarily think we have to consider this as RNA synthesis all at once. It can be a gradual process going on in time; the complete association or complete learning is not effected immediately. I am describing intracellular events only. The activation of DNA seems quite plausible from information available in molecular biological literature, such as the puffing of insect chromosomes I mentioned (5).

Donchin: What is the time scale for protein synthesis?

Gaito: It depends, among other things, on the organism involved. The event can occur within minutes.

Calvin: The one case in which it has been accurately measured is induced bacterial synthesis of enzyme (66). For example, if coliform bacteria are exposed to a particular molecule such as lactose, the exposure need last only a few seconds—lactose can then be withdrawn by dilution and three minutes later the enzyme capable of working on that particular substrate appears in the organism. So the entire sequence of events, presumably from the activation of the DNA, manufacture of the RNA, the passage to the ribosome, the loading of the transfer RNA and the production of the enzyme, takes about three minutes in the one case in which I know the full time scale. I do not know offhand of a time scale as well established in any other type of cell.

Miller: Going back to the Hydén curve for the variation with age in RNA per cell, what relevance does it have to learning? I believe some of the other Hydén data (41) may be more pertinent. Would such a curve be found for calcium or some other substance obviously not specifically related to learning? Calcium, which I would not say is the type of molecule in which memory is coded, is related to the functioning of the nerve cell. The curve for sex hormone might parallel the curve for intelligence more closely, rising rapidly up to adolescence and going down from then on.

Zigler: Most intelligence functions we know reach the asymptote much sooner, at about age 20, not 40.

O'Connor: We are dealing with learning, not intelligence. They should not be parallel.

Gaito: There should be some relationship, but they are certainly not the same. The particular function I described is also shown by cholinesterase activity, as was reported in one of the early papers on rats by Krech and his group (7). What I meant is that certain events underlie the learning situation.

Birch: Dr. Gaito, are you assuming that a given RNA produces a given amino acid chain?

Gaito: It codes for a particular amino acid.

Birch: Are you familiar with the evidence (15, 23, 78) that changes in the chain are obtained with changes in the concentration of an electrolyte such as magnesium, with the RNA remaining constant. For example, RNA which will produce a chain of phenylalanine will make chains of lysine when the magnesium concentration is changed. So the code is not specific to the RNA except when the surrounding circumstances are constant.

Gaito: There are molecular biology data that show that magnesium affects the ribosomal RNA (14, 83).

Birch: Two interpretations are possible: that magnesium affects the ribosomal RNA, or that it affects what the RNA code is doing.

Gaito: The basic aggregation of ribosomal particles is influenced. Variations in the concentration of magnesium cause these to break down into smaller particles or to aggregate into larger ones, which would then affect the protein synthesis (14, 83). Although I have used data outside learning, what I meant essentially is that during learning events it is plausible to expect an increase in ribosomes. Since ribosomes provide the vehicle on which protein synthesis occurs, I am postulating that an increment in the number of ribosomes affects the rate and amount of protein synthesized. To go a step further, we might hypothesize that perhaps the difference between maze-bright and maze-dull rats is that the maze-bright rats of the Berkeley strain (74) had more ribosomes available.

Birch: For which kind of maze? The maze-bright rats are bright for one kind of maze and dull for another. Do you mean to say that under one condition they have ribosomes and under the other they do not?

Gaito: No. Bright human beings would have more ribosomes than dull humans. Let me say that we take a number of rats that are bright in a number of mazes or in a number of situations.

Miller: I think Dr. Birch's point is that the Berkeley rats are not generally bright, but they are very specifically bright to a specific kind of maze (74). I think this makes the entire argument questionable.

Gaito: The fact that there is a large gap between these data and the actual learning event is what leads to hypothesizing. But most of these hypotheses can actually be tested; for example, we can test the hypothesis that there are more ribosomes.

Birch: Let us suppose your hypothesis is correct and is sustained: the maze-bright rats have more ribosomes than the maze-dulls. The maze-bright rats are brighter or are learning faster in an elevated maze, and are slower than the maze-dulls in an alley maze. Your hypothesis is then indeed in trouble.

Miller: Dr. Gaito's hypothesis should be made more specific. If I remember correctly, the Berkeley strain of rats, selected for successful alley-maze learning, is better at position learning but poorer at discrimination learning. A test would then be to predict that there are more ribosomes in the part of the cortex involved in position learning and fewer ribosomes in the visual discrimination area.

Guilford: Dr. Gaito, are you talking about particular learning episodes, or about learning activity or ability in general?

Gaito: I think, to be consient, we would have to say that a greater amount of ribosomes would be involved in other cases.

Birch: No, we would not. We would have to say that the ability to increase the number of ribosomes would be greater in one circumstance, and that for an instructed organism, in proportion to its instruction, we would have a larger amount of ribosomal substance.

Gaito: Greater ease of facilitation.

Rothkopf: If some animals perform poorly in a given maze, it may be due to a number of factors. The possibilities include slow acquisition of any habit, or quick acquisition of some habits which are not consistent with the training objectives. Each of these possibilities, as well as many others, may have a different correlate in the physiological substrate. We never measure learning—only performance. Hence, I would think that it would be unpromising to consult maze data for inferences about the chemical character of the substrate.

Miller: Are you saying that perhaps as a test we need a far simpler learning situation? One without a number of conflicting habits intermingled, so that facilitating one may impair performance, while facilitating another may improve it.

Rothkopf: Yes!

Jensen: The general finding in mammals in simplified learning situations tends to go against that suggestion. Often, differences in intelligence do not show up in simple situations: rats and children learn mazes at about the same rate; many species may show rapid conditioning of fear. It seems to me that we are in a dilemma. If we have a complex situation where we find differences, we have the problem of interpretation just mentioned. If we have a simplified situation, we sometimes find little difference in performance from one species to another.

Miller: I think you have a very good point there.

Konorski: I am somewhat at a loss. Dr. Gaito began with the question of what biochemical changes can be correlated with the process of learning, with the process of formation of associations. I cannot see a relationship with the problem of which rats are the better or poorer learners. We know that some animals are dull and some are bright; some animals may be bright in one problem and not in another.

O'Connor: I would like to supplement Dr. Konorski's earlier question about the exact point at which learning occurs. If an animal is learning a situation badly, it might presumably be building up more ribosomes in certain circumstances than an animal which is learning quickly.

Gaito: Actually, the ribosome is only one portion of the chemistry in-

volved in learning events. The animal's particular RNA's would merely make
more ribosomes available, so that the rate and amount of protein would be
affected.

The ribosomal aspect will be relatively easy to test; in fact, we are heading in that direction ourselves. Some of the other hypotheses will present
greater difficulty. At present we are concerned with the relative RNA synthesis, the fact that during functional activity of cells a rapid increase in
RNA occurs. We are using this particular aspect to determine the brain sites
involved in various forms of behavior, e.g., sensory stimulation, motor activity, or learning. We study the RNA/DNA ratio of a particular tissue of an
animal which has been subjected to a behavioral event and compare this
ratio with that of a control litter mate, i.e., one which did not have the same
training. A number of brain sites are taken: the cortex (sectioned into six
parts), the cerebral hemisphere without the cortex, the upper brain stem,
the lower brain stem (the brain stem sectioned just posterior to the inferior
colliculi), and the cerebellum. We also take two non-neural tissues as controls. The RNA analysis of non-neural tissue, something Hydén has not
done, would be an excellent control—events he described as occurring in
the nervous tissue may actually be similar to those occurring in the liver or
kidney, for example.

Pribram: Hydén has shown that they occur in some structures in the
brain and not in others (38). That at least is a partial control of the type you
are asking for.

Gaito: I meant that in learning experiments Hydén always shows base
changes in the particular site involved in the learning event. Obviously, he
does not show this in control tissue.

Galambos: Hydén and his colleagues report measurements of control
brain tissue in at least two papers that I recall. First, they report RNA base
ratio change in the cells of Deiters' nucleus in trained rats but not in cells
from the reticular formation of the same animals (40), even though the RNA
content rises in cells from both regions. Second, in the work on handedness
in rats (41), there is no altered base ratio in cortical cells ipsilateral to the
newly trained hand. Granted we are not told what happens to liver base ratios in either case, but I for one am satisfied at this stage with their evidence that something special happens in one brain region as compared to
another in the same animal.

Gaito: Hydén has used functional controls as well as learning animals
(39), and analyzed both. It would be a more definitive test if he were to include non-neural tissue. What if he were to find increments and also what
he reports as base changes in, for example, the liver?

Galambos: What if changes did occur both in liver and in some neural
tissue during learning, but not in other neural tissue during learning?
Would this be so much more informative than our present knowledge that

base ratios change in some neural tissue during learning but not in another neural tissue in the same brain?

Gaito: I think such controls would be more definitive. I am not disputing this.*

Miller: It might have been interesting if Hydén had analyzed base ratios in the muscles of the left and of the right arm. If he had found the same differences between the active and inactive arms, we would not have said that learned connections were being formed in those muscles; we probably would have thought that the difference was a function of activity rather than learning. This control would have been much more relevant than the liver.

Galambos: Hydén and Egyházi (21, 39, 40, 41) report many controls which show the relationship between mere activity and increase in RNA and/or protein in certain brain cells, but in these cases their measurements show no altered base ratio in nuclear RNA.

Miller: Are you saying that activity in the brain produces changes in the absolute amount of RNA but not in the base ratio of the RNA?

Galambos: Brain regions differ in this regard; this experimental demonstration is Hydén's great contribution, in my opinion.

Guilford: Does the RNA ratio increase also during simple perceptual activity, where there is little motor activity?

Gaito: I do not think anyone has ever investigated the ratios under perceptual conditions, but among Hydén's control situations in the learning studies there were some sensory conditions involving no motor activity. For example, in his experiments with animals learning to balance on a wire to get food (39), he found an increase in the amount of RNA in the Deiters' nerve cells, as well as an increase in what he calls altered base ratio. But in control animals (these were rotated horizontally and vertically) he found increases in RNA but not changes in the base ratio. This is somewhat pertinent to your question. He has not actually done motor-free perceptual experiments.

Konorski: Are the changes he obtained permanent, or do they vanish with the lapse of time?

* *Added by Dr. Gaito after the conference:* Pertinent to this topic, however, are the data showing that base changes in neural tissue are not unique to learning situations: Egyházi & Hydén (21) noted that the administration of a dimer of malononitrile, tricyano-amino-propene, caused an increase of 25% in the amounts of RNA and proteins in nerve cells and a decrease of 45% in glial RNA; the cytosine in nerve cells decreased by approximately 6%, while glial cells showed a 20% increase in this base; the guanine in glial RNA also decreased, by 25%. Geiger (27) reported that electrical stimulation of the cortex for 30 seconds brought about an increase in the cytosine and adenine content, whereas the amounts of uracil and guanine remained constant. Grampp & Edström (29) found that a six-hour excitation of crustacean stretch receptors did not affect the RNA content of the receptor cells, but the adenine/uracil ratio of the RNA increased significantly. Edström (20) showed that no changes in gross amounts of RNA occurred in either the axon or the myelin sheath of the Mauthner nerve fiber of the goldfish following spinal cord transection, whereas marked changes resulted in the adenine/guanine ratio; the greatest value—0.80—occurred two to three days after transection.

Pribram: The changes in the amount of RNA are present as long as the organism is exposed to that particular situation. They disappear within 24 hours after the organism is taken out of it (35), but if animals are exposed and removed, and then re-inserted into the situation, the changes reappear. Dr. Miller asks whether this is activity of neural tissue *per se,* but activity peculiar to the kind of task that we are talking about, or is it something hard to pinpoint called learning. I contend that if the activity is sufficiently specific to that particular task, it is as though the machine were being altered to enable it to produce the new responses; that is learning, to me. Therefore, I do not really see the relevance of the objection. I think it can be supervened by talking about learning.

Birch: Is the skill retained even after disappearance of the RNA? In other words, 24 hours after an animal learned something, when it has presumably re-equilibrated its RNA ratio and base characteristics, does it retain this learning?

Pribram: Yes. Then RNA is a labile substance, and it is the protein that is stable.

Birch: Would you argue that retention does not involve the RNA but, rather, the proteins which have been produced by the RNA?

Pribram: I would not even want to argue that. We should be clear on what the data are, and at least give Hydén credit for reliable data and clear interpretation and keep the two separable, as he does.

Feshbach: This raises questions with respect to Dr. Gaito's theoretical analysis. He postulates a set of structural and biological changes as occurring during the learning process. It is not clear, from his theoretical point of view, which changes are essential to what aspects of association, and which changes are merely correlated and irrelevant. What different kinds of facts do they presumably account for? Why do we have to have all these changes? Do they function as over-determinants or as antecedents for different kinds of phenomena?

Gaito: I said that the three events described are involved in any functional activity of cells, whether it be learning or just plain activity. For each of the different events, presumably, we would have different DNA sites activated; these would be specific to various sites of the brain and would function for different activities.

Assume we have a set of DNA molecules. Let us say site 1 is functional in motor tissue. In another type of tissue, another DNA would be activated to produce RNA and then protein. Thus DNA activation, RNA synthesis, and protein synthesis would be common to all situations, except that possibly there would be different messenger RNA's for the different types of activity and for different proteins. Or it might be that similar proteins are scattered throughout the brain; in this case the actual representation for memory and behavior would be right in the DNA molecule, and would merely need to be activated, indicating a kind of matching arrangement between stimulating conditions and specific sites in the brain, such as chromosomal sites.

Galambos: You are giving us an outline of what all cells in the body do, including brain cells. Would it not be more relevant to deal with the specific changes in brain cells of animals that learn? One thing we seem to know from the striking material accumulated is that, in the same brain, RNA with altered base ratio appears in some cells but not in others, even though these latter cells synthesize RNA and protein and become larger in size. This is the important result given us by the experiment.

Gaito: When you say altered base ratio, do you mean qualitatively different RNA's?

Calvin: They are chemically different.

Gaito: Not necessarily. Let me give you an example. What Hydén is doing is taking all the RNA in a particular cell.

Galambos: Altered base ratios are identified in RNA from the nerve cell nuclei he analyzes.

Gaito: It does not make any difference. More than one species of RNA are being produced there. For example, let us suppose that under the control condition the adenine ratio is 25 per cent for RNA species 1, and 30 per cent for RNA species 2. If these species are present in equal amounts, the content of adenine (or of any one base) would be pooled in the final results so that the ratio would come to be 27.5 per cent for adenine. If, under the learning conditions we are discussing, the RNA species are present in unequal amounts, we can find what appears to be a base change.

Calvin: The chemicals are different; they are different mixtures.

Gaito: We still have the same RNA's. They are not qualitatively different.

Calvin: Of course they are; both the mixtures and chemicals are different.

Miller: I think the source of the argument is a striking notion that Hydén emphasized earlier and still considers, but now plays down: that learning rearranges the atoms in a single molecule and, hence, changes it into a new molecular structure that stores the particular information learned (41). What Dr. Gaito is saying is that the change in base ratios does not necessarily prove that any completely new molecular structure has been created, because there is the possibility that somewhat different types of molecules which have been there all along are now being synthesized in different proportions; of course, we do obtain a different mixture, but not a new molecule with sub-groups rearranged to code specific bits of information.

Calvin: I have the impression that this discussion has attained a chemical level out of reach as far as the psychological problem is concerned. We are talking about chemical problems which as yet cannot even be attacked chemically, much less psychologically.

Grant: The same could be said for the psychological aspect. I think Dr. Birch raised a very interesting question. If we are considering substrates that vanish when the learning is retained, I think it is a relevant point; we can then talk about changes that are evanescent, and so on. I am beginning to wonder what we mean by substrate.

Pribram: Let me make Hydén's position clear, at least the most recent one I have heard about. It is essentially that DNA becomes de-repressed. This assumes, of course, that the DNA's potential is, for the most part, in a repressed state in most cells. When de-repression takes place, by whatever mechanism, it gives rise to RNA—this is the RNA Hydén thinks he is measuring. I believe that much he would maintain. His theories deal with what this means in terms of subsequent changes in protein and in nerve impulse transmission, and his ideas are subject to changes as new data become available. He is simply saying that here is a substance which he can show to be present under certain conditions and not under others. Whether or not you agree to call these the conditions under which learning has taken place, he *does* call them learning, and I agree with him. The RNA need not be present forever afterwards, any more than RNA continues to be present in the de-repressed cells that form our eyes or ears.

Grant: There are other temporary chemical changes that take place in an active part of the brain, such as serotonin levels that are rather localized. It is interesting that DNA and RNA have this marvelous coding system; I am sure, however, it does not exhaust the coding possibilities in proteins. It would be nice to find something that remains stable, appearing when the learning takes place, and staying there for about as long as the retention is demonstrable.

Jensen: Table 1 might indicate some such possibility in the RNA for structural protein for the development of axonal endings. If that RNA were used up, producing proliferation of endings, the endings would perhaps remain even though the messenger RNA might have disappeared within 24 hours. Does that sound reasonable?

Calvin: Yes. Actually, my feeling is that Dr. Gaito's proposal here has bypassed the initial presumption which I am sure is in all of our minds: at what level does the trace lie? Is it something one can see at the tissue level in the organization of cells, or is it subcellular? Is it distance across the synaptic cleft? Is it amount of acetylcholinesterase or choline acetylase at a particular cleft? Is the trace a circuit which is maintained by a structural residue, which in turn may have been induced by the total sequence of events described by Dr. Gaito—the RNA differences having long since disappeared while the structural differences remained? At what level? Can they be determined in terms of the sum action of ribosomes? Or in terms of mitochondria, their concentration or localization near the synaptic cleft, at either pre- or postsynaptic membranes? Would membrane thickness be a factor? Or each of the membrane's specific lipids? All of these could have been changed by the mechanism outlined by Dr. Gaito. The RNA may be gone but the structural change remains; if it is a switching mechanism that contains the learning or association you were asking for, then all of these things have been a part of it; they would have had to occur to produce the change, but they themselves have long since disappeared. Actually, the data quoted by Dr. Gaito do not correspond to the particular experiment on handedness mentioned by Dr. Galambos (41). Hydén made his analyses four days after testing; the change in handedness remained for nine months; he did not make an analysis after nine months.

Pribram: In the other experiment (35) there is no question; Hydén interrupted testing for 24 hours, then sacrificed, and the RNA change was gone from the Deiters' cell.

Calvin: There is no reason why the whole RNA pattern should have remained; the protein or lipid difference, or whatever difference, is still there.

Sperry: Is not the disappearance in Hydén's material (38) essentially the disappearance of a percentage difference within the nucleus? As soon as the altered RNA moves out of the nucleus into the cytoplasm it is no longer demonstrable, since the altered RNA constitutes such a small fraction of the total cytoplasmic population. This does not mean the altered RNA is no longer there, only that its production rate in the nucleus has returned to an indistinguishable level, and that the RNA produced during the burst of increased activity moved out into the cytoplasm, where it is lost as far as the demonstration methods go.

Pribram: Remember that Hydén demonstrated that, although these changes disappear immediately after cessation of activity in the neuron, in the glial cells they do not begin until cessation. Neuronal and glial RNA activities are reciprocal; when the neural RNA increases the glial RNA decreases, and rises only later, and then the change persists for as long as a week. Dr. Galambos has made most of us aware of the importance of glia, and central nervous system glia are homologous to Schwann cells in the periphery. It might well be that glial cells act as guides to neural growth, which is what the Schwann cells do in the periphery. Rose, Malis & Baker (71) have demonstrated that neural growth can take place in the central nervous system. The RNA changes may well be indicative of some change being induced in the glial cells; these may even be induced by the RNA to divide and thus allow the neural pseudopods to branch out to form new pathways. These are some of the possibilities (70).

Hilgard: We have been preoccupied mainly with the Hydén material. There seems perhaps to be a kind of skepticism, with respect to the Krech-Rosenzweig-Bennett results (53). If not, they could be very impressive regarding the permanence of modified structure. Are we implying we are unsure about those results?

Calvin: I do not understand what you mean by "permanent".

Hilgard: The brains of the trained animals are larger, and they presumably remain larger through adult life. If your point is that there is a residue of the RNA changes, perhaps we already have empirical demonstration for it. If we do not accept the results, I would like to hear someone say so. That is my reason for putting it as a question.

Pribram: Those thickenings in the cortex are not due to an increase in the number of nerve cells; this is as one would expect, since nerve cells do not divide. The number of glial cells does increase somewhat, though not enough to account for all of the increase in cortical thickness. The current guess is that nerve fibers also increase, and this is being checked.

Galambos: The Berkeley group reports (17) that rats raised in a "rich" environment (they play together, are active, and learn) show thickened visual cortex as compared to litter-mate controls kept in an impoverished environment. Altman & Das (1), using radioautographic techniques on brains from rats similarly raised in enriched and impoverished environments, show similar increases in cortical thickness as well as new nuclei in and around this thickened cortex. The newly formed cells are glial. Certain brain regions, the hypothalamus for example, show no increment of new nuclei in the experimental animals as compared to the controls. To a first approximation, then, the Berkeley observations seem to be confirmed by Altman & Das using a different technique.

Hilgard: In the behavioral sense, it is not only that the Berkeley rats had enriched environment, they were also brighter on the Hebb-Williams maze (53). There is a behavioral correlate of the larger brain. So, it is not just that the rats exercised more, or something of that sort; they really were brighter.

Pribram: One reason why the Berkeley data have been questioned is that originally they were obtained with regard to acetylcholinesterase, and there was uncertainty about the measurement of acetylcholinesterase and what it might mean. It turned out that the original work, although reliable, did not distinguish between cholinesterase and pseudocholinesterase. In the Berkeley experiments, pseudocholinesterase activity is what was actually enhanced, not cholinesterase. And pseudocholinesterase activity is not evidence of neural tissue function but of the activity of glia. So again we come full circle: all the roads lead to glia.

Sperry: In which way were the controls deprived? Were they kept in the dark?

Pribram: They were animals blinded by enucleation, and these subjects show a differential lack of growth in the visual cortex; there was also a group given much somatic but little visual experience, and which showed differential thickening of the somatic cortex. Some years ago, Lawrence Weiskrantz (84) did an experiment in which he deprived kittens of visual experience and found atrophy of the Muller cells in the retina. At the time this was just a finding *in vacuo*. It turns out that Muller fibers are the retinal equivalent of glial cells. And from Hydén's and other laboratories (10, 35) we have evidence that RNA activity of these "deprived" retinas is markedly distorted.

Sperry: It may very well be that the disuse atrophy effect is critically involved in memory. We have no way to tell at this time.

Jensen: In the paper by Bennett, Diamond, Krech & Rosenzweig (6) there were three groups: the Social Control (SC) animals which lived three to a cage, the Environmental Complexity and Training (ECT) animals which were housed in groups of ten and twelve with toys and were given formal training, and the Isolated Condition (IC) animals which were caged singly in a dimly lit and quiet room where they could not see or touch another animal, though they could hear and smell other animals. They found that the ECT group had more cortical tissue and greater acetylcholinesterase activity than the other two groups. The social control animals tended to resemble the isolated controls. The pattern of results seems to indicate that enrichment is more important than isolation, since the main difference was between the Environmental Complexity and Training group and the other two.

Sperry: Out in the periphery, disuse atrophy that would never be called learning can easily be demonstrated. Deeper into the centers, however, where association neurons are involved, there is no way to differentiate. Certain association neurons that are excited only by a unique pattern of experience could be maintained by activation; the effect would be difficult to distinguish from more positive types of cell alterations in learning.

Galambos: Atrophy with disuse of a structure, and hypertrophy with its use, are difficult terms to define. The point of these experiments, however, is that animals placed in situations where a good deal of activity (including learning) takes place do show morphological changes in brain for which the term "use-hypertrophy" seems appropriate.

Calvin: May I ask the neuropsychologists if they have already located in the brain areas that are associated with different kinds of activity, e.g., learning activity or certain types of motor activity? Has anyone examined the structural components of suitable portions of the brain—the same kind of examination at the cellular and subcellular level that Hydén has made at the molecular level? Have the same portions of the brain been examined either microscopically or electron-microscopically to detect a structural difference in the region in which Hydén (41) is claiming an RNA difference?

Galambos: Endlessly.

Calvin: They have seen nothing, is that right?

Galambos: These experiments we are talking about now are among the very few where morphological differences have been measured.

Calvin: At what level? Not the weight of the brain. That is not enough. Can one see differences in the synaptic structure or in the neuroglial relationships?

Galambos: You want an electron microscope or light microscope demonstration to show that in trained rat brain something is absent or present.

Calvin: I am looking for difference—I do not care whether absence or presence. The point is that Hydén (41) has been able to pick out surgically ten cells from a certain region and has been able to make a chemical analysis. That is really a nice feat. It should be a lot easier to do microscopically.

Pribram: No, it is not. There is no baseline. How can we tell the difference, if we do not know?

Calvin: There is the other side of the brain.

Pribram: What do we count?

Calvin: That is my question. We could either count the ribosomes or the mitochondria, or measure the lipid membrane thickness and compare the two sides of the brain just as Hydén did.

Pribram: There are a billion cells.

Calvin: Hydén looks at a billion molecules.

Pribram: He has quantitative methods; nobody has devised quantitative neurohistological methods.

Calvin: The internal control would be exactly the same.

Pribram: Hydén dissects out the neural cell bodies.

Koestler: I should like to ask a related question. According to Gastaut & Beck (26), when a conditioned reflex has been established, the EEG activity accompanying that reflex wanders down from the cortical level to lower midbrain formations. So one no longer has the structural changes in the cortex, but finds the EEG changes lower down. Is that confirmed?

Galambos: Yes. This began with the Yoshii, Pruvot & Gastaut paper (87).

Koestler: Is it also connected with the question of how the RNA base changes vanish but the learning does not? Gastaut's (26) answer was that it wanders downward—may the cytoplastic or structural change have gone down to lower levels? It is rather simple to go to the left or to the right. Could it go down to a lower level?

Galambos: Hydén & Egyházi's analysis of the Deiters' cell (39) takes the changes associated with learning to about as low a level as can be reached. It shows that there are altered base ratios measurable in the RNA of the nuclei of those nerve cells—and also of the glia surrounding them (40)—at the level of the first synapse in the vestibular pathways. I have heard people criticize the experiment "because everybody knows we do not learn in our Deiters' cells, in the medulla". The discovery of significant alterations in brain cells at this extremely low level in the neural axis during learning is most surprising. Is that your thought?

Koestler: Yes.

Calvin: Dr. Gaito has presented a very stimulating and suggestive hypothesis. I feel, of course, that its key lies at the beginning, with the electrical activation of the DNA, but he has already disclaimed any part of suggesting how that comes about. That kind of feedback would obviously be another essential prerequisite for maintaining the theory.

I would like to say a few words about another kind of presumption mentioned earlier, namely that the actual memory trace could conceivably lie in the structure of a single molecule or of something of such nature, and that it might very well be a nucleic acid molecule, which is an information-bearing type of structure.

Dr. Gaito's suggestions were, I believe, limited to the use of such informational molecules for some other effect on the structure of the learning apparatus, leaving the trace in some form other than necessarily the nucleic acid molecule itself. Nevertheless, the idea that the entire learning operation might in fact eventually reside in the unique structure of a nucleic acid molecule has been extant for some time.

This notion was encouraged substantially some years ago by some experiments on a very simple animal, the planarian worm, which I think are familiar to all of us. I first learned of these experiments three or four years ago through the intervention of Mr. Koestler, although he was not aware of it. At that time, the implication was that there was a transferable entity, a substance which would carry the learned operation. This seemed to mean that the learning process left its trace in a molecular structure which could be transferred from one organism to another. To a chemist, this was like saying, "Well, the door is now open, and you have only to extract the molecule, take it apart and map out what it is in order to learn the mechanism or equation. It is all written down in the molecule and you only have to eat it to get it."

The experiments with the Planaria worms, described as early as 1955 by Thompson & McConnell (79) and later by McConnell, Jacobson and their coworkers (62, 63, 64), have certain essential features in common. First, the animal could be trained, and such training, the result of some educational operation in the animal, could be objectively and quantitatively measured. Second, the planarian, being the kind of animal it is, could regenerate from a cut head or tail section, so that it was possible to determine whether or not that training was conserved in either the regenerated head or tail of the worm. The claim was that the regenerated organism retained some of the learning taught the original animal. As a third step, it was recognized that some varieties of these planarians are cannibals and can eat other worms of the same type. An experiment (64) was performed in which trained animals were cut up and fed to untrained animals, and the quantitative degree of training (a certain amount of ability to respond to a particular circumstance in a particular way) was transmitted to the animals which cannibalized the trained animals; those which were fed on naive or untrained animals did not show this conservation of training. These are the basic kinds of such experiments described in the literature.

About that same time we began our studies, in the thought they would provide us with the ideal tool to reach the possible molecular basis for training and the transfer of training.

As a first step we had to have worms that were trainable, and the training had to be quantitatively measurable and reproducible at will, so that we could measure the degree of saving, so to speak, or the training under various circumstances, in a variety of experiments. We therefore undertook to reproduce the training experiments. At that point, unfortunately, we were sidetracked: we spent some three years trying to train reproducibly all types and strains of these worms. The training techniques we used fall into five main categories which I shall mention briefly.*

Classical conditioning involved the shock, light-shock treatment. At first we used unpolarized, oscillating shock. Later on, when it was reported (2) that the shock had to be polarized, the worm's tail was subjected to the positive, and the head to the negative pole; otherwise the learning was extinguished.

The next experiment was *light habituation:* some planarians tended to respond to a flash of light, and the idea was that, if the flash were given frequently enough, they would become habituated to the stimulus and cease responding; instead of responding 40 per cent of the time, the worms would gradually habituate until the response disappeared entirely or fell to a low percentage.

The third technique, *maze training*, was carried out by running planaria through a maze consisting of a white hexagon with Y-shaped intersections offering six black arms. In order to make a correct choice, the worms had to stay on the inner white groove; a turn into the black arm would be punished by an anodal shock. Again, the training was counted as the number of successive correct turns made.

Operant conditioning was the next training experiment, in which the animal was subjected to a presumably aversive stimulus, namely a bright light. By going to a particular point in its pool, the worm could trigger photocircuits which would turn the light off for 15 minutes; the light would go back on after 15 minutes, and it would be switched off by returning to the same point. This activity was put on a recording machine, so we could read the records of the individual worms for days at a time.

The last training technique was of the *food reward* type, described in earlier literature (82). It was an experiment in which food was placed within reach of the planarian in the center of its pool; it could reach it in a very short time. There was apparently a chemical gradient in the water which enabled the worm to swim and find the food quickly. The time required for the planarian to get the food was recorded. The food was then placed in an increasingly more difficult position; since the worm has more difficulty reaching below the surface, the idea was to lower the food progressively, so as to make the worm reach food which it could not get if it were placed in the difficult position at the beginning. The time required to reach the food was recorded in an attempt to demonstrate a learned response.

---

* The techniques are more fully detailed in *Attempts to Train Planarians: A Summary Report,* by J. L. Alvarez, E. L. Bennett, M. Calvin et al., University of California, Berkeley.

In none of the five situations were we able to find a regime of any sort which unequivocally produced learning, nor could we account for failures in terms of any of the following: age, size, type, species, origin or strain of the planarian; the time of day or night; the season of the year; the food it received; or other variables which had been called upon to account for failures. However, I can say that occasionally an individual planarian would appear to be increasing its performance, but that increase would usually fall off. It was highly improbable that we could replicate the result. We could not do it individually with the worms, or statistically by just taking groups of worms and averaging their records. In neither case could we distinguish unequivocally between a trained and an untrained animal. When the naive animals were put into the test apparatus, the distribution of the naive and the trained animals was almost always equivalent on the same days. So there was no case in which we could use, in a quantitative way, this so-called *appearance* of a learning curve to indicate that anything had been transferred. We never did get around to doing any of the chemistry; we came to a standstill, I am sorry to say, on the training operation itself.

After several man-years of labor, we continue to report unsuccessful efforts to demonstrate, reproducibly and quantitatively, learning in planarians by classical conditioning, light habituation, maze learning, operant conditioning, or food reward. Until more adequate methods and useful descriptions of methods to train the planarian reliably and reproducibly are available, this animal appears to have little utility for proposed studies of the possible biochemical bases of learning. That is our conclusion.

Miller: I think you should be complimented, first, on your industry and, second, on your courage in reporting negative results. I fear all too often these are not reported because investigators feel that negative results must be due to some fault of their own.

Calvin: It took us three years to get up that much courage.

A. K.:[*] In the classical conditioning method, did you investigate the time relationships between the onset and length of the stimulus, the shock, and when the shock was followed? Did you vary it?

Calvin: We varied the voltage of the oscillating current. At first we used the Harvard inductorium to generate a random shock. Then we put a very carefully controlled oscillating frequency of known amplitude on the animal. On McConnell's advice, we tried random shocks; we used Barnes' (2) polarized cathodal shock; we tried all of these things day after day, with variations, but our results did not improve.

A. K.: As a graduate student I studied the time relationship of some planarians. I found learning, if one can call it that, with a two-second light stimulus and shock afterwards; rapid decrement could be on either side of the period.

Calvin: We did that, too. Mostly we used two- and three-second stimuli,

---

[*] An auditor at the Conference.

which is the timing reported by McConnell (63). Allan Jacobson in our laboratory also started with a two-second stimulus; two seconds of light without shock, and the third second light and shock together. That is the normal course.

Koestler: How much did your animals differ from one another? Four subjects, all behaving differently, are not much evidence.

Calvin: The curves on individual performance (Figure 1) show something of the variability of the animals on training; the circled numbers represent different worms. Some of them start out high and go down; some start low and then go lower. Figures 2 and 3 show results averaged for groups; again, there is no uniform trend.

Konorski: Our theme is "neurochemical approaches to learning", but none are possible where no learning occurs. I agree with Dr. Miller that negative results are often most important and should be reported, but there are also many workers who have obtained positive results. We know that in conditioning, as in other experimental methods, there are some tricky details,

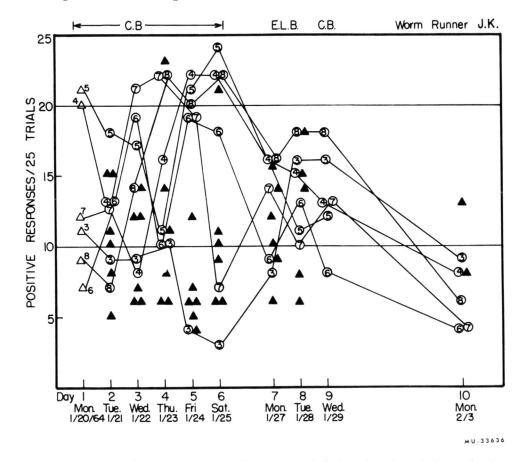

MU-33636

Figure 1. Scores of individual trainee *D. dorotocephala* (numbered circles) tested using cathode (tail) shock as the UCS. Original experiment, 2-sec. light and 1-sec. shock. *Abscissa:* days of training; *ordinate:* number of responses during the light stimulus, i.e., prior to shock. The isolated triangles represent the responses of naive subjects.

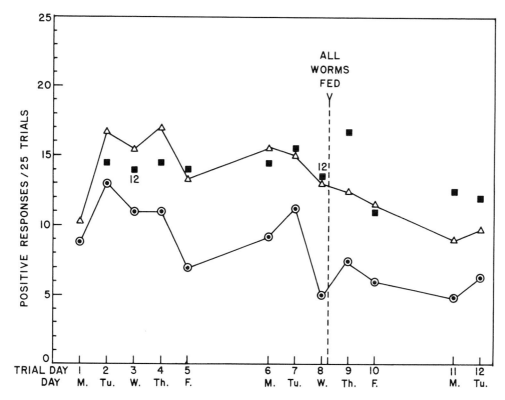

Figure 2. Responses on 25 trials of 8 trainee *D. tigrina* trained daily with cathodal shock as the UCS. Each "worm trainer" trained 4 planarians daily; the average scores are indicated separately by circles and triangles. The isolated squares present the results of 4 naive planarians tested each day (12 on trial days 3 and 8). The average score obtained for all naive planarians was 13 by one experimenter and 14 by the other.

some unwritten knowledge which often is not taken into account by another investigator. This may be the result of the negative effects of the experiments. The only question which should be asked here is how the positive results of other authors are explained, and whether or not there are some mistakes in statistics or in methodology. I have in mind particularly a paper recently published in *Science* (30), which reports discrimination of two responses.

Jensen: I am extremely pleased with the interest shown at this conference in the reductive substrates of learning. I think it is precisely this interest which led so many people, including Dr. Calvin, to be intrigued by the work done with Planaria. Unfortunately, the analysis of the data presented and the study of the general behavioral characteristics of planarians lead me, at least, to have considerable doubt about the nature of the phenomena reported (50).

I would like to return to Thompson & McConnell's original study (79). This work, published in 1955, is outlined in Table 2 and Figures 4 and 5. Table 2 shows that the study had four groups which were given different kinds of training: an experimental group (E) had light and shock paired, a

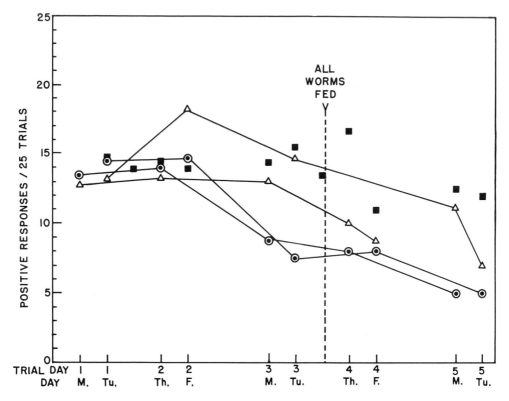

Figure 3. Responses on 25 trials for 24 trainee planarians (4 groups of 6) receiving cathodal shock as the UCS twice weekly. One group was tested on a Monday-Thursday schedule, and the other on a Tuesday-Friday schedule. These planarians were tested the same time as those for whom data are presented in Figure 2. Naive planarians were common to both groups.

light control group (LC) received light only, a shock control group (SC) received shock only, and a response control group (RC) received neither light nor shock. At one time these control groups might have been sufficient to indicate that associative conditioning had occurred, and for mammals they might even now be sufficient. But I would call attention to the fact that we are not dealing with mammals, but with animals which, in phylogenetic terms, are profoundly removed from and only distantly related to the higher vertebrates, differing greatly from them in behavioral physiology.

TABLE 2

Thompson & McConnell's Experimental Design (79)*

Group	150 Training Trials of	Data Obtained on
E	Light and shock paired	First 2 seconds of light in training trial
LC	Light only	First 2 seconds of light in training trial
SC	Shock only	30 special test trials
RC	Neither light nor shock	Mock trials (2 seconds without light)

* From Jensen (50).

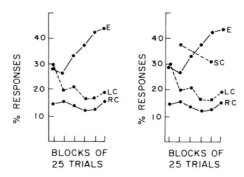

Figure 4. Percentage of responses for the Experimental (E), Light Control (LC), Response Control (RC), and Shock Control (SC) groups. *Left:* data presented as by Thompson & McConnell (79). *Right:* SC group added to same data to facilitate comparison with the other groups. (From Jensen, 50.)

Under such circumstances, absolutely precise control of confounding is necessary to show associative conditioning; variables which we unintentionally confound while working with mammals, and which are not important to mammals, may be important to Planaria. Controls that are adequate for experimentation with rats may not be sufficient for work with these lower organisms.

We should recognize that there are at least two types of confusion in the study by Thompson & McConnell (79). First, only the experimental group received both light and shock on every training trial. To test for the effects of association, that group should be compared to a control group also subject to light and shock on every training trial, but without pairing of the stimuli. No such control group is to be found in this experiment.

There is another more subtle type of confusion in the study, resulting from the fact that the data were obtained in different ways for the various groups. Data on the experimental and light control groups were obtained during the first two seconds of the light presented on training trials. The shock control group, on the other hand, received 30 special test trials, and only during those was light presented and data gathered. The response control group received neither light nor shock, and data were obtained, not from light given during special test trials, but from observation during arbitrary two-second periods called mock trials. The fact that data were obtained by three different procedures makes it difficult to interpret the differences between the various groups; nevertheless, comparisons were made and interpreted.

The data that were graphically presented in Thompson & McConnell's 1955 article (79) appear at the left on Figure 4: we see the experimental group increasing its tendency to respond, rising to something past 40 per cent responses, while the light control and the response control groups drop off or stay at a very low level.

While these data may superficially resemble what we would consider evidence of learning, there are only three groups shown. Where is the shock control group? The data from this group are presented not graphically but in tabular form, with the data for the experimental and shock control groups being presented in separate tables. Information from these separate tables is never directly compared; instead, it is pointed out that the group trained with light and shock showed a reliable increase over trials, and the group trained with shock alone did not, but the obvious comparison, between the amounts of responding to light stimuli by the two groups, is never made. To be sure, we can make the comparison ourselves. If the information from the separate tables is combined, we see that the group trained with light and shock averaged 13.8 responses in the first block of trials and 21.6 on the last block; meanwhile, the group trained with shock alone averaged only 5.6 responses to the light in the first block of trials and only 4.6 in the last block. At first glance, the direct comparison might seem favorable to the hypothesis that classical conditioning is occurring, but careful examination discloses that the number of trials involved differs for the two groups. There were 50 trials in the blocks for the experimental group and 15 trials per block for the shock control group. If we consider the data in terms of percentage (certainly the most trivially complex statistic to use in such a circumstance) and then plot the data graphically to compare directly the performance of all groups, we produce the graph at the right of Figure 4. We see immediately that the shock control group was superior to the experimental group during the first half of training and that the major effect in the experiment was that of shock. For both the experimental group and the shock control group the presence of shock apparently increased the response to the light; the most important result in this experiment was the effect of shock and not the effect of an association between light and shock.

The first thing that disturbs me about the Thompson & McConnell study (79) is that the data were not presented in a way that makes interpretation easy. I cannot help but wonder why direct comparisons were not made, why percentages were not computed, why trends were analyzed instead. The data were so presented that, "caveat lector", the reader must beware, which hardly seems the appropriate way to communicate scientific findings.

The second thing that bothers me is the fact that the experiment just criticized was used in other studies (63) by the same group of workers as justification for not running the shock control group or otherwise controlling for the effects of shock presentation.

Pribram: Why do the curves in Figure 4, right, cross?

Jensen: First, they do not appear to differ reliably. I would point out that there is a reason for expecting the performance of the shock control group to be lower than that of the experimental group: the shock control group received fewer light stimuli, and light of the intensity used might have been an activational stimulus. We will discuss this explanation when I attempt to describe the basic behavioral characteristics of Planaria. There is also reason to expect the shock control group to be higher in performance, since it might show less habituation to the light. Since two antagonistic processes, activation by light stimuli and habituation to light stimuli, may be involved, prediction becomes difficult.

Lipsitt: In defense of the basic Thompson-McConnell data, and with due respect to those who have failed to replicate the phenomenon, I think it is possible that really good evidence for conditioning can be found within these data, if statistically analyzed appropriately in terms of the interaction of the shock control group and the experimental group over trials. Apparently you have done only an overall analysis of the control *versus* the experimental group.

Jensen: I have already mentioned the confusion of number of light stimulations with other variables. The shock control group was given only 30 light stimuli, whereas the experimental group was given 150. We do not know what effect this difference had upon responsiveness.*

Lipsitt: I do not really think the way you have drawn the shock control group curve on that particular ordinate is appropriate, since only 15 trials are involved.

Jensen: The test trials were spaced over the entire 150 training trials. I simply represented them in the center of the halves to which the percentages referred.

Lipsitt: This representation might be rather misleading, since blocks of different sizes are being compared. Perhaps Thompson & McConnell took the graph at face value, and that is why they did not do it.

Jensen: The point is, they never presented the percentages, which are certainly relevant to the basic argument. The Thompson & McConnell study appears to be on the horns of a dilemma. If the data from the experimental and shock control groups are comparable, they should have been compared directly; if they are not comparable, the experiment provides no control for the effects of shock.

A study which makes an appropriate comparison between an experimental group which has light and shock paired and a control group with light and shock unpaired was performed by Baxter (3) and later published by Baxter & Kimmel (4). The experiment used a $2 \times 2 \times 2$ factorial design with three planarians per group; two types of pairing, two intensities of light, and two intensities of shock were compared. The data are shown in Figure 5. Over five days of training the tendency to respond to light increased in the group which had light and shock paired, and decreased in the group which had those stimuli unpaired.

A further source of confusion in the Baxter & Kimmel study is evident upon consideration of the events of a single trial: one group receives light and shock paired; for the other group the light and shock alternate. The first group has a full intertrial interval to recover from the effects of shock stimulation before the light is again presented; the control group has only half as much time between shock and the following light stimulus. To avoid this confusion it is necessary to have additional control groups or to test animals

---

* *Added by Dr. Jensen after the conference:* In 1961 I pointed out (48) that the four-group design used by Thompson and McConnell confuses interaction of CS and UCS presentation with the associative variable. Consequently, the analysis suggested by Dr. Lipsitt could not give unambiguous evidence of associative learning. Comparison of two groups, both of which receive light and shocks, but only one of which has them paired, is necessary to indicate unambiguously associative conditioning.

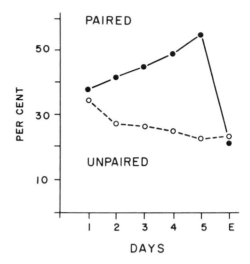

Figure 5. Performance of animals on five days of training and one day of extinction (E) as a function of whether light and shock were paired or unpaired (i.e., alternated). (Redrawn after Baxter & Kimmel, 4.)

under conditions where shock-to-light interval is not varied. Baxter & Kimmel (4) report some relevant data. After five days of training the animals were given a sixth day of testing under extinction conditions, with only the light being presented on each trial for both groups. Any short-term increment or decrement in performance resulting from shock stimulation would now be equivalent for the two groups. If this were a case of classical conditioning, we would expect an extinction curve for the paired group which might drop off rapidly to begin with, but would take some time to reach the same low asymptote reached by the unpaired control group. What actually occurred was that there was no difference in performance between the two groups during the day of extinction, when the shock was absent (E in Figure 5). There was an immediate decrease in the performance of the paired group to the level of the unpaired group on the last day of acquisition training. On the first block of ten extinction trials, the performance of both groups was intermediate (around 33 per cent) but during the remaining extinction trials it dropped rapidly. On the basis of the means for all fifty extinction trials, extinction performance of both groups resembles the performance of the unpaired group on the preceding day. Halas and coworkers (32, 45) have also failed to find differences in extinction.

We usually define learning in terms of operations and observations. When we call a phenomenon *classical conditioning*, we expect certain operations to be performed and certain kinds of data to result. With Planaria a very different pattern of data has resulted.

How can we explain the data? The first thing I did was perhaps not behaviorally characteristic of the American psychologist in the 1960's: I consulted the literature prior to 1950. If any of you expect to evaluate, interpret, or make decisions regarding studies on Planaria, I suggest you first become acquainted with the work published in 1903 by Raymond Pearl, who later became an important population geneticist. At that time he was a young instructor at the University of Michigan, the same institution where some of the studies we have criticized were later made. Pearl's monograph (68), published in English in a major biological journal, was 200 pages long, contained protocols rather than statistics, which was in keeping with the time, but it also contained a clearly stated theory of the behavior of Planaria. That theory was remarkably modern in its tone and physiologically reductive in its basic point of view.

Pearl indicated that there are two types of responses which Planaria can make: a large-magnitude turn from, or contraction to, a stimulus (negative reaction), and a small-magnitude turn toward a localized stimulus (positive reaction). He pointed out that any modality or stimulation can produce either of these responses, depending upon several variables, including the strength of stimulation and the physiological tonus or state of the organism. Pearl indicated that this tonus or state is a function of prior stimulation, and that repeated strong stimulation decreases the number of positive reactions and increases the number of negative reactions to any particular stimulus.

This would explain what happened in the Thompson & McConnell (79) study: the strong stimulation of shock changed the physiological state of the animal, its motivational state if you like, although I would rather not use the term "motivation" to refer to unknown processes in an animal which is profoundly different from mammals in its physiology and, I suspect, in its behavioral laws. By shocking a planarian we can change its physiological state and thereby temporarily sensitize it to the light, but strict temporal association between light and shock is not necessary for the effect.

There is recent evidence from work by Brown (11) in keeping with this explanation. Brown's interest began, as did Dr. Calvin's, with the role of nucleic acids in memory. In attempting to replicate and understand the behavioral changes he observed, Brown reached the same general conclusion from an analysis of his own data that I had reached from methodological criticism—that sensitization rather than any type of associative learning was indicated.

The criticisms I have made of the Thompson-McConnell work, if accepted, vitiate any interest in the cannibalism and RNA transfer experiments (60) for the purpose of understanding learning.

There are additional studies yet to be explained—those of Lee (55, 56) with operant behavior, and of Griffard & Peirce (30) with so-called discrimination learning.

Let us first examine Lee's experiment, in which a planarian was placed in a small plexiglass enclosure. An intense light was shined from above and a weak beam was directed from below onto a photocell; if the planarian interrupted the weak beam to the photocell, the strong beam went off. The criterion response was passage through the weak beam, and the reward was the removal of the strong light for a period of 15 minutes. Experimental animals, whose behavior influenced the strong overhead light, and yoked control animals, whose behavior had no effect upon it, eventually differed in operant rates of interrupting the weak light beam.

Pearl stated clearly in 1903 that both external stimuli and the physiological state of the animal influence a planarian's tendency to come to move and to come to rest. Pearl noted that Planaria "seem to be incapable of continuing movement more than a certain, not very great, length of time. Then a period of rest must intervene. Thus one may see a specimen which has been moving about come to rest, and after a length of time, varying from a comparatively few minutes to several hours, it will start into spontaneous movement again, and repeat the whole cycle over and over . . . if one stirs up a specimen, and sets it into activity again just as soon as it comes to rest, the periods of spontaneous activity will become progressively shorter, until finally the worm will only move a very short distance before coming to rest again" (68, pp. 532-533). Pearl also noted that probably the most important cause of the onset of rest in planarians of appropriate physiological state is the intensity of light. Animals entering areas of decreased light intensity are likely to cease locomotion and come to rest.

Lee's experimental procedure undoubtedly stimulated the planarians repeatedly and, accordingly, would be expected to produce a general readiness to come to rest. Thereafter, there was increased probability that the worms would come to rest shortly after the intense overhead light was extinguished. The temporal patterns of light stimulation administered to the pairs of experimental and control animals were exactly the same, but their *location* when the overhead light was extinguished differed markedly. When the light went off the control animals could be anywhere, but by virtue of the reinforcement contingency the experimental animals were invariably near the weak light beam at the perimeter of the chamber. If occasionally the planarians remained at rest for the 15 minutes of no overhead light, the experimental subjects would be found in the immediate vicinity of the light beam when the overhead light again came on. As a result, the experimental subjects would be more likely to interrupt the central light beam than would the control subjects, whose presence near the beam was not so ensured. "Extinction" would be expected whenever the removal of the reinforcement contingency removed the selective influence on position of the experimental subjects.

More recent research, indicating a further influence, has been reported by Ullyott (80). He showed that the initial response to light increase is an increased tendency to make turns (positive klinokinesis). The suggestion, then, is that there had been selection of the experimental animals' position, and therefore their responses to higher light intensity (movement and increased turning) were more effective in interrupting the trigger light beam from below than were similar responses by the control animals. Evidence relevant to this suggestion can be obtained by observing Planaria under appropriate conditions; they do indeed show the component reactions we have discussed.

Mlle. L. Seydoux[*] has attempted to replicate Lee's experimental situation. She obtained the basic result found by Lee, except that sometimes there was no "learning" curve of increased rate. The experimental animals often began immediately to respond at a stable, higher rate, which does not fit the hypothesis of learning. The curve was cumulative as in Skinnerian conditioning; the standard pattern reported by Lee (55, 56) is for the experimental animals to show a higher rate of beam interrupting than the yoked control animals.

I might add that other investigators, including J. Boyd Best (8, 9), who has reported instrumental learning in other instrumental situations, have also obtained immediate excellent performance without further improvement in situations approximating Lee's.

What I am trying to emphasize is the importance of considering all the data from a variety of sources, as well as the general behavioral characteristics of the animal. Consideration of all the possibilities leads to a very different point of view than study of the animals with overly specific questions in mind, thereby allowing the expectations of the investigators to produce misinterpretations.

This is a criticism that can be made of the discrimination experiment of Griffard & Peirce (30). In this study, individual planarians were placed in a plastic petri dish fitted with electrodes capable of being rotated about the perimeter of the dish. Direct current electrical stimuli were administered with the cathode placed at 45° left or right of the animal's axis, causing the planarian to turn toward the cathode. Two conditioned stimuli (light and vibration) were used, one being followed by cathodal shock producing a right turn, and the other by cathodal shock producing a left turn.

One problem with this experiment is the amount of shock used: three seconds of CS overlapped and ended with two and one-half seconds of shock; in the day's training a planarian received approximately 500 seconds of shock. We can ask what such strong, prolonged shock does to an aquatic invertebrate well supplied with mucus-secreting glandular cells. On the basis of a few observations made on the same species used by Griffard & Peirce, I can say that shock causes planarians to cease locomotion because they are stuck to the substrate. I suspect that what these investigators conceived of as discrimination was differential adhesion to the substrate; one side of the body was more firmly attached and therefore turning in one direction was easier than in another. It is interesting that in their data correct responses never exceed 50 per cent, which is consistent with the idea of asymmetrical adhesion. If we observe Planaria in this situation under a stereoscopic microscope at moderate magnification, we are impressed with the possibility that we are doing much more than giving noxious stimuli to the animal; we are also drastically changing its motility and very likely exhausting its metabolic resources. It is certain that Planaria are in poor health

[*] Institute de Physiologie, École de Medecine, Geneva, Switzerland.

after a large number of strong DC shocks. Because of the probable importance of changes in motility and physical condition resulting from the shock, it seems unwise to accept Griffard & Peirce's study as being indicative of learning.

I must admit that my work in this area of research is not based on a special interest in Planaria. While I am interested in lower organisms for phylogenetic reasons (49), I am still more concerned with the pattern of misinterpretation in this field of study—a pattern that borders on the production of myth. I am therefore pleased by Dr. Calvin's presentation of negative evidence and hope that future demonstrations of learning will be discussed and interpreted in the context of an appropriate behavioral theory. That theory, for lack of a better one, is to be found in Pearl's 1903 article (68).

Donchin: You have yet to explain Dr. Calvin's results. You have said that sensitization could occur under the conditions of the experiments with Planaria you reviewed. If this were the case, however, Dr. Calvin, who replicated the conditions, should have obtained the same "spurious" results.

Jensen: We have to consider the matter of great variability in planarian behavior. This was pointed out in 1903 by Pearl and more recently by Brown (11), whose data showed that animals which received shock training became more variable in their behavior. Brown found that animals did not become simply and uniformly more responsive to light as a consequence of receiving training with shock; their responsivity also became more likely to fluctuate, and therefore the shocked animals were more likely to reach a criterion of any given number of responses to light.

Hilgard: Is it fair to ask Dr. Jensen whether, with his tests, he would not expect greater uniformity than is shown by Dr. Calvin in Figures 1, 2 and 3?

Jensen: I do not think we know enough about the biology of flatworms to know how to culture them effectively, that is, how to maintain them in equivalent physiological status. When rats are put on 24 hours of deprivation, implicit in that operation are years and years of psychological lore, which we do not have for Planaria.

Calvin: The question asked earlier by Dr. Konorski was, since there are positive results, how do we account for them? My answer is that, if there are positive results and they are genuine, they should be described so that another investigator can repeat the experiments and hopefully obtain the same data. If they are not so described, they are not scientifically useful.

Jensen: Some advice which might be relevant was offered by McConnell in the 1964 *Worm Runner's Digest* (61). He commented: "We have, over the years, received many letters from individuals who have attempted to train planarians and who have encountered . . . difficulties. They write to us asking for the magic formula. Sadly enough, we don't have much magic to offer anyone, save for an admonition to keep at it, keep changing the experimental situation until the right conditions are hit upon". I would submit that that is an operational definition of selecting data—you know how it has to come out, you keep doing it until you get it, and then you publish.

Simon: Not if it can be retained once found. I think that remark is open to two interpretations, and you are taking the rather more damning one.

Jensen: Conditioning ordinarily requires a precise CS-UCS interval, but this work on Planaria does not. Association is not required; extinction is immediate. If the whole pattern of operation and data is not the same pattern we have in classical conditioning with mammals, then I say it is best not to call it classical conditioning.

Hilgard: I think we can be dissatisfied, but we do search for optimum conditions to indicate a phenomenon. I remember Yerkes (86), who did the early maze experiments on the earthworm, told me that his major problem was learning how to tame the worm.

Jensen: Unfortunately, no one else has learned how to tame the worm.

Hilgard: Nevertheless, Yerkes got the worm to lie quietly in his hand as he carried it from the burrow in the ground over to the maze. This took a little doing.

Calvin: I would like to add one more bit of information to this discussion. Two of the worm runners in our Planaria study originally trained the animals and then could not train them again.

Gagné: It is not clear to me what comments you have about the transfer that was found.

Calvin: My answer is that the evidence for training so far produced may be a statistical accident.

Gagné: I think my question really should be directed to Dr. Jensen.

Jensen: I can see no evidence from these experiments that what is transferred is anything specific. There is no control for this being a general sensitizing factor, for the possibility that perhaps a trained worm is a different kind of food than an untrained worm. It is one thing to say that specific engrams have been transferred, and quite another to say that some generalized tendency to respond has been transferred.

Gagné: Do you question that, after cannibalizing, these animals were different?

Jensen: There is a recent article by Hartry, Keith-Lee & Morton (33) reporting the effects of cannibalism of differently trained planarians by differently treated planarians; their results did not fit the interpretation that specific habits were transferred. Instead, a general response tendency was altered by feeding.

Zigler: Is that not impressive? How is this justified according to what you were telling us before?

Jensen: Just feeding Planaria has an effect. That is all we presently know about the effect of feeding on the physiological state of the animal.

Zigler: Not just feeding—we are talking about feeding animals that have had a certain kind of training.

Hilgard: The point of the study was that they could be fed naive animals, and they were able to learn by some criteria.

Jensen: Let me return to the idea that Planaria are able to learn. I feel we have no evidence of anything with the specificity that we naturally presume in the terms *associative learning* or *classical conditioning* or *operant conditioning*. We have nothing with the same basic structure in operations and observations that characterize the standard phenomena.

Koestler: May I remind you of Rosenthal's studies (72) on conditioning the conditioners. He told one group of his investigators that they were working with genius rats, and another group that they were working with stupid rats. In fact, both strains of rats belonged to the same garden variety. To make quite sure, Rosenthal went to the laboratory at night and switched the so-called stupid and genius rats. Nevertheless, the experimenters came up with statistically significant reports that the genius rats learned like geniuses and the stupid rats, like stupid rats. I do not know if the results have ever been disproved. Imagine Dr. Rosenthal appearing here tonight to explode a bombshell by saying, "All rat experiments which have been made are invalid, because this is what I did". It seems to me that the negative results, which are only partly negative (some of them are positive but made negative by your interpretation), are actually more interpretation than factual evidence. I would like to plead for the benefit of the doubt.

Zigler: I feel uncomfortable hearing this particular presentation without being able to ascertain Dr. McConnell's reply.

Jensen: My criticisms were originally given at a symposium (50) attended by Dr. McConnell.

Zigler: I am not saying you are doing it behind his back. It makes me uneasy because there is no one here to speak on the other side of the issue.

Jensen: I can only say I would have felt guilty had I not presented the opinion that I have reached. The strident character of the presentation is "just me".

Zigler: It surprises me that someone has not followed up McConnell's work in the light of Pearl's magnificent 1903 paper (68), which would allow control of all past mistakes. We would like to see the reported phenomena in the uncontrolled situation and note its disappearance in the controlled one. I would rather see the appropriate controls made than hear an impressive scholarly argument.

Birch: To my knowledge, scholarly arguments on various questions have appeared many times in the last 50 years. My first recollection is Jennings' (46) impression of the trap phenomenon as a manner in which the organism starts to approach an aspect of its environment, not because of any association but because of a change in the oxygenation gradient. Maier & Schneirla (59) spent considerable time on the principles of animal psychology, studying the problem of pseudoconditioning, for example, in fish and in certain lower forms.

Students in my laboratory have been working on the so-called Grabow-ski-Bramstedt disturbance, using paramecia in experiments similar to those published some years ago by Mirsky & Katz (65). The paramecia are placed in a well slide, only one half of which has been heated. With this setup we train the water rather than the paramecia, and get striking effects. Directional changes are produced even without the paramecia; very persistent gradients are produced, even in a water drop. Without stirring, the convection current itself is not enough to change the gradient, so the paramecia begin to make certain directional changes.

The Bentley (16) "learning" studies on paramecia were criticized in 1919 by Buytendijk (12), who indicated that the paramecium had, in effect, produced metabolites in the capillary tube; it then had a changed surface tension and an altered membrane characteristic, and would turn very readily. This is not a new idea.

This discussion is disturbing to me, not because of criticism of what I think are bad experiments and misinterpretations of the directional effects of stimulation; what is puzzling to me is why Dr. Calvin did not get systematic changes.

I have not worked with Planaria since 1948 or 1949; I was then more interested in certain features of metabolic gradient in regeneration than in behavior, but I did notice a number of striking phenomena. For example, planarians would respond differently to light on a fairly systematic basis, depending on their state of feeding; one kind of response to light gradient would be demonstrated if they had eaten little bits of liver: they would accumulate on one side of the dish if a light shadow was set up. I wonder what was wrong in Dr. Calvin's laboratory; he has not told us enough.

Calvin: We repeated experiments other investigators claimed to have done, trying to do them just as they had been described originally. We sought to improve them only after we failed to reproduce their results—then we obtained even more random effects.

Birch: What troubles me is that I am quite sure that the experiments in which directional effects have been found are, for the most part, well reported.

Calvin: I think it is the learner's learning.

Birch: No, I think it is something else in those laboratories that provides a specific basis, not for associations but for modifications in behavior, which may be direct modifications in the organism's behavior. From the data you have given, I do not know when the planarians are fed, nor how they are fed, nor when the experiments are done in relation to the level of light, noise, or activity in the laboratory.

Calvin: I would be glad to give you such data, but it would take too long. Ten people did the experiments; almost that many would be needed to describe them.

Birch: I cannot understand them, and that bothers me. I can see random behavior up to a point; there is a sufficient amount of uncontrolled "noise" in your experimental situation, for you do not provide directionalized stimuli for the organisms, and your setup maximizes their metabolic variability. But I can think of other laboratory situations in which inadvertent systematic effects are produced, not so much by the attitude of the investigator but by the style of organization of the laboratory. This presents an interesting problem.

Calvin: As a matter of fact, we even went so far as to suspect the microwave radiations from the fluorescent lights. Because someone suggested this might have an effect, I had a physicist tell me how much power, in which frequencies, was being radiated from those lights. Then we started using tungsten lights, back lighting at different intensities, and all of the different variables we could think of that might be directional.

Birch: You eliminated them?

Calvin: No, we incorporated them into the experiment to see if we could get some effect from them.

Jensen: I cannot help but think that the number of factual, positive results that have been published is relatively small. For those of us who feel uncomfortable about the possibility that a number of articles published in reputable journals involve misinterpretations, I can simply say that here is an example of the way science actually operates. There is latitude for error in interpretation as long as correction can occur. What we are trying to determine now is where misinterpretations have occurred and how to prevent them in the future.

Calvin: It is not a matter of interpretation; Dr. Birch is not questioning that aspect of the experiments. Of the 15 animals (out of hundreds) charted in Figure 1, two or three show a rising curve which leveled off and eventually decreased toward the end. On the assumption that animals of different behavior patterns should have individual and genetic differences, we tried selecting only the bright animals that showed a positive learning curve. The offspring of these animals, however, would again exhibit random behavior. But if the original animals instead of their offspring are used, and similar selections are made from other groups of animals, you can get what looks like learning curves and publish them. But we found no evidence of exhilarated response in charting the responses as they occurred, trying particularly to eliminate the experimenters' judgment as to what the animal is doing. This last we did in recording Lee's (55) operating condition: by using exclusively a recording machine, we did not look at the worms except to check that they were still moving, although their movement was shown by the machine.

Birch: Did you get any kind of curve?

Calvin: There were some positive curves.

Birch: I think there is a major discrepancy between your lack of findings and Dr. Jensen's effort to explain behaviors which do not occur; this is a great feat of the imagination if the behaviors do not occur.

Pribram: Did you analyze for RNA changes in those animals that did show a change in behavior?

Calvin: No; the point is, we could not get the learning curves a second time with the same animals. RNA analyses are very difficult and we will not undertake them until we can obtain reproducible training results.

Jensen: Remember that most of the positive studies that have been done involve one day's training and averaged curves; an individual animal's performance is seldom presented. That is what I mean when I say the whole pattern of data does not coincide with our ideas of conditioning. Let us look at the kind of data we can present. There is a dramatic difference between the types of data available for Planaria and for other invertebrates. At the Cambridge symposium where the substance of my present remarks was presented (50), beautiful films were shown on the learning of octopi, and there were dramatic demonstrations of learning-type phenomena in the digger wasp and in crustaceans. There is no doubt that these animals show massive modification of a very specific sort which can be analyzed and reproduced; no such massive and stable modifications have been found with Planaria, in which such differences are ephemeral.

Birch: I do not understand whether you are explaining McConnell's data, or data that you have obtained which replicate certain of the end-product features described by McConnell. If the latter, you have duplicated the end-product behavioral changes and you, too, are in disagreement with Dr. Calvin's inability to replicate stably those end-product changes.

Calvin: They can be found, as I showed you.

Birch: I do not mean for a couple of animals. It seems to me Dr. Jensen is not describing uniqueness.

Jensen: First of all, I am attempting to derive the data that have been presented from the information we have about the animal. Let me go one step further and say that the problem is that Pearl's (68) basic theory of the nature of the animal does not specify, nor do we have the information to specify, which physiological events are going to push the animal which way in what he calls "tonus".

Birch: Pearl speaks quite specifically about a biphasic theory; with Loeb (58), he is one of the first anticipators of this view. He finds that intense stimulation results in massive action and withdrawal to the degree that the stimulus is localized and that, when it is again directionalized but of low intensity, there is a tendency toward movement. Further studies on ameboid movement have been done by Hyman (42, 43), Child (13), and by many other investigators. The metabolic gradient theories are derived from such work. So, Pearl does make a prediction.

Jensen: I am saying that we cannot predict whether cannibalism will shift responsiveness in one direction or another. The data we have and the theory available from specific investigation of the animal form involved indicate that we must be careful in interpretation, and that careful interpretation has not characterized many of the studies which have been done.

To answer Dr. Birch's specific question of a while back, "If you know this, why not do the studies?", I can only answer that my reluctance comes from having been involved in this type of controversy once before, regarding the learning of paramecia with food reward on a silver wire (47). I received a certain amount of unpleasant response from other psychologists because I saw fit to say that I thought an interpretation was facile and unjustified. I hope that further involvement in this controversy will not be necessary; fortunately the data are starting to come in: we have studies by Brown (11), by Keith-Lee (33), and now we have the data from Dr. Calvin.

Zigler: Dr. Calvin's data bother us all. What we would like is for someone to show us the artifact—how to take it out and, perhaps, how to put it back in. The issue could then be put to rest.

Jensen: The problem is that there are too many possible artifacts. Light intensity, temperature, trough shape, dark adaptation, motility, length and origin of the planarian (regenerated head, middle, or tail), are all known to be important to responsiveness to light stimulation (11, 81), in addition to the influence of shock stimulation. One problem is that we do not have sufficiently precise descriptions of the original investigations to know which, or how many, of these possible artifacts were uncontrolled.

Zigler: At the Cambridge symposium you presented this material in McConnell's presence. Did he comment?

Jensen: We had nearly two hours of discussion in the course of the meetings, and we ended up designing an experiment which was apparently free of significant confounding of variables. That experiment is very similar to one often used in studying conditioning of dogs to aversive stimulation; it is a discrimination experiment in which a CS-positive is followed by a UCS, and a CS-negative is not. My expectation is that such a study would show a pattern of data other than that found with mammals, but this is a matter for future research.*

Sperry: I think the interesting material that has been presented tends

---

* *Added by Dr. Jensen After the Conference:* The experiment suggested at the Cambridge Symposium used touch as the UCS, and water vibration and light as the two CS. The experimental procedure was to involve discrimination training with one of the CS being followed by the UCS, extinction training with neither CS being followed by the UCS, and discrimination-reversal training with the other CS now being followed by the UCS. All data were to be obtained on test trials. Kimmel & Harrell (51) reported a somewhat similar study, except that shock was used as the UCS, neither extinction nor discrimination-reversal training occurred, and test trials were not given. Results were suggestive of associative learning only when the vibration stimulus was the CS-positive; when light was the CS-positive, training did not differentially increase responsiveness to light. Only four animals were run, and absolute levels of responsiveness were low. For a number of reasons, careful interpretation must be made of the differential increment in responses to vibration during pairing of vibration and shock. One consideration is that the design used confuses time since shock with type of CS, the CS-positive usually occurring longer after shock than the CS-negative.

to be concerned only indirectly with the fundamental problems of learning and memory. My inclination, as discussant, is to try to orient our thinking back toward the learning-memory problem in its more general form before we try to move into the more detailed aspects.

Regarding the general problem of the chemical or molecular basis of memory, my attitude at the moment is that the problem is not very relevant. This is only a provocative way of suggesting that the chemistry of memory is not of primary interest for the memory problem as we know it at the behavioral level. I like the comment on this subject made by Oliver Lowry, a neurochemist at the University of Washington, who pointed out at a meeting at the Salk Institute that the molecular approach to memory is rather like taking a television set and a computer, grinding them up and doing a chemical analysis to try to determine the source of all the pretty pictures and all the computations.

In my own case I have described the search for the chemical basis of memory as the search for a secret code of an unknown code for mental imagery that in itself is a will o' the wisp (77). The reasoning here is that, in trying to get at the chemistry of last year's memories, we must first translate these subjective images into brain dynamics. This is the first code; to solve it we are required to solve the mind-brain problem. Once this is achieved the dynamic brain states must be translated into a memory trace code, i.e., the frozen, static trace systems. Even the simplest principles of both these coding processes are completely beyond us at present. So far as the underlying chemistry goes, it is a situation with possibilities for unlimited confusion. The restraints on chemical imagination and chemical model building are simply nil, except for those imposed by cytochemistry and cytophysiology in general.

The main point I am trying to make is that the most interesting unknown aspects of memory lie in these coding problems, particularly the first, and that these are meta-molecular problems. Until these meta-molecular phenomena are worked out, the underlying chemistry is of little help in understanding the most interesting aspects of memory.

We can recognize two possible alternative types of answers to the chemical basis of memory: one is that there is a memory molecule and that mnemonic information is indeed coded at the molecular level; in this case the discovery of the chemical code for memory would, of course, be tremendously interesting and important. The other possibility is one in which the chemistry is a kind of universal change, with the coding of information at the network level, in the patterning of the distribution in the brain networks, in synaptic changes, membrane changes, and the like. In this case it would be nice to know what these cell changes are. To go a step further and analyze the chemistry of the membrane or endogenous changes involved is not particularly intriguing compared to other unknowns in memory. It is nothing like knowing where and how the information is coded. For decades, people who have thought about the problem have been inclined to think the information was coded mainly at the network level. It is only within recent years, of course, that the molecular theories have become popular.

Pribram: Even if it is found that there is a memory molecule or some molecular membrane change that indicates that a "memory" is stored, we still have another problem; molecular storage does not solve the question of read-out, i.e., recall.

Sperry: One of the difficulties with the new molecular approaches to learning and memory, it seems to me, is that they have ignored the two problems you have just mentioned. In doing so, they have ignored the great mass of the thinking that has been done in the past on the memory problem, as well as all the neurophysiological and psychological literature that is available, and have jumped directly into the molecules. Some passing effort is sometimes made to explain how these molecular changes are implanted, and how they are read out; but these are the most puzzling and the most intriguing parts of the problem, and nothing that I have seen is even remotely satisfactory as an answer.

Pribram: I do not share your negative attitude. As of ten years ago or little longer, there was not one constructive statement that could be made about whether anything at all is going on in the brain as a function of some change in behavior. There was not a single experiment to cite. Then along came Galambos, Hernández-Peón, John, the Killams, Hydén, and others. It is very exciting to me to see almost any neural change that can be reliably correlated with a change in experience and in behavior, even if we cannot yet understand what that correlation signifies.

Sperry: But let us not confuse the physiological level (which I would regard as the more important level for explanation) with the underlying molecular substructure. I guess it is the reductionistic philosophy that can be read into headlines like "The Chemical Basis of Memory" that particularly bothers psychologists. In regard to the RNA changes associated with learning, as demonstrated thus far, I personally am inclined to wait until the Calvins and Jensens move in on these problems and look at them a little more closely.

Take one simple example along this line: the problem of timing in learning and memory is extremely important. In establishing conditioned reflexes, just the timing of the two stimuli being paired is critical: put them together simultaneously, in what might seem to be the best conditions for molecular association, and there is no conditioning; one stimulus must precede the other by half a second or so. It is important to relate these timing factors to the explanatory molecular or physiological level. Also, the synapse is commonly thought to be a key location for the molecular changes. I think we tend to overlook the possibilities for trace changes in the endogenous properties of neurons involved in their pulse pattern detection and firing properties. This could be, and perhaps is, a better place to look for the cellular or chemical changes that may be involved, rather than in the synapse and network alterations.

Galambos: It is a little strange to hear you emphasizing "pattern detection" and "firing properties" in connection with this problem you have worked on for so many years. This new molecular biological approach to the nervous system seems to be so much more relevant. I am thinking, of course, of your elegant regeneration and transplantation experiments. Long ago you considered (76) the various ways a given nerve cell could know how to go to the right place to get itself connected. If I remember correctly, you thought it an inescapable conclusion that some chemical relationship between the presynaptic and postsynaptic element was responsible for the connections finally accomplished.

Now, if all chemical events in a nerve cell ultimately stem from its DNA read-out through RNA of various sorts, then the chemical recognition, which your experiments and those of Weiss (85) and others have so magnificently demonstrated, is obviously also determined by the DNA-RNA reactions in the neuronal nucleus.

Sperry: Certainly, there is no question but that the morphological network patterning of the nervous system is based very largely on this differentiation of the nerve cell population which, of course, is based on DNA and RNA mechanisms. But also the physiological endogenous properties of different nerve cell types, insofar as they are inherently determined, are also dependent on this same system for cell lineage and differentiation. Both types of trace change that I discussed, the connectional synaptic changes as well as those affecting endogenous firing properties, would involve this system. It further follows that the two types of possible chemical answers I have mentioned, one where the type of chemical change is a universal, common to all memories, and the other in which all the information is coded within the molecule, are two extremes. Between these two, there are intermediate possibilities in terms of interaction between the different types of chemically specific nerve cells that might influence either the connections or the endogenous physiological timing properties. The chemoaffinity or neurospecificity effects envisaged here are, of course, highly diverse, but this kind of thinking is still a long way from anything that could be called the coding of mnemonic information into a memory molecule. The profound changes that the language of the chemists in the Neurosciences Research Program group has undergone in the past two years is revealing. Whereas initially everything was going to work out in macromolecules, the language is coming around now to where it is almost the same as that used by psychologists and the rest of us. The chemistry they are now looking for is the chemistry of the synaptic change and the "switching factor". It is quite a shift from the early idea that memory is coded in the DNA or RNA molecule.

Calvin: I am inclined to think that Dr. Sperry may be right in his statement that the memory trace is a pattern rather than a molecule, and I differ from him only in the amount of interest I attach to the chemical basis of that pattern. Assuming for the moment that the trace is a pattern, whether of synaptic interactions or various other microstructural features, the chemical basis upon which this pattern has been produced is of great interest to me. I have the feeling that, as an intermediate step, we need to find some simple cellular system which shows a definitive response, either behaviorally or electrically, such as the relationships the physiologists are now finding associated with learning. If we could find some way to translate that kind of electrical activity into molecular changes which, in turn, might effect structural changes, and so on, the whole sequence of events would be a great step forward.

Sperry: To bolster further your argument against my own, I think that it is very possible that the chemical approach to the organic basis of memory in general will arrive at the answer first, because we know so much about the cell, and because the alternative possibilities are more limited than are the physiological network approaches. Perhaps we will arrive at the nature of the memory trace more quickly by working up through cytochemistry than by working down through the tremendously complicated organizational system. Whether the answer will be recognized when seen by the molecular approach is another question. And this, of course, does not alter the fact that knowledge of the chemical, membrane, or cellular changes involved in learning and memory may still leave as obscure as ever most of the more interesting informational features of the problem.

Miller: We have the problem of getting the information from the neuron language, which is a series of pulses, into the molecular language, which is a structure of atoms. Furthermore, the energy levels required to change the structure of such molecules is high—more in the order of X rays than of nerve impulses. Finally, it is hard to imagine how vast amounts of information coded into a single large molecule, on the analogy of the genetic code, could be read out quickly in the impulses of neuron language. I am not against RNA being involved in learning—for example with the same kind of release from suppression being involved in each memory trace and the information depending on where in the nervous system this change occurs. I am objecting to the different idea of the "tape recorder molecule" with the potentiality of encoding an entire book in one big molecule.

REFERENCES

1. ALTMAN, J., and DAS, G. D., Autoradiographic study of the effects of enriched environment on the rate of glial multiplication in the adult rat brain. *Nature*, 1964, **204**: 1161-1163.
2. BARNES, C. D., and KATZUNG, B. G., Stimulus polarity and conditioning in Planaria. *Science*, 1963, **141**: 728-730.

3. BAXTER, R., *Classical Conditioning in the Planarian*. Thesis, Univ. of Florida, Gainesville, 1961.

4. BAXTER, R., and KIMMEL, H. D., Conditioning and extinction in the planarian. *Am. J. Psychol.*, 1963, **76**: 665-669.

5. BEERMANN, W., and CLEVER, U., Chromosome puffs. *Sci. Amer.*, 1964, **210**(4): 50-58.

6. BENNETT, E. L., DIAMOND, M. C., KRECH, D., and ROSENZWEIG, M. R., Chemical and anatomical plasticity of brain. *Science*, 1964, **146**: 610-619.

7. BENNETT, E. L., ROSENZWEIG, M. R., KRECH, D., KARLSSON, H., DYE, N., and OHLANDER, A., Individual, strain and age differences in cholinesterase activity in the rat brain. *J. Neurochem.*, 1958, **3**: 144-152.

8. BEST, J. B., and RUBINSTEIN, I., Environmental familiarity and feeding in a planarian. *Science*, 1962, **135**: 916-918.

9. ———, Maze learning and associated behavior in Planaria. *J. Comp. Physiol. Psychol.*, 1962, **55**: 560-566.

10. BRATTGÅRD, S.-O., The importance of adequate stimulation for the chemical composition of retinal ganglion cells during early post-natal development. *Acta Radiol.*, 1952, Supp. **96**: 1-80.

11. BROWN, H. M., *Experimental Procedures and State of Nucleic Acids as Factors Contributing to "Learning" Phenomena in Planaria*. Thesis, Univ. of Utah, Salt Lake City, 1964.

12. BUYTENDIJK, F. J. J., Acquisition d'habitudes par des êtres unicellulaires. *Arch. Néerl. Physiol.*, 1919, **3**: 455-468.

13. CHILD, C. M., *The Origin and Development of the Nervous System from a Physiological Viewpoint*. Univ. of Chicago Press, Chicago, 1921.

14. DATTA, R. K., and GHOSH, J. J., Studies on the stability of brain cortex ribosomes. *J. Neurochem.*, 1964, **11**: 595-601.

15. DAVIES, J., GILBERT, W., and GORINI, L., Streptomycin, suppression, and the code. *Proc. Nat. Acad. Sci. USA*, 1964, **51**: 883-890.

16. DAY, L. M., and BENTLEY, M., A note on learning in paramecium. *J. Anim. Behav.*, 1911, **1**: 67-73.

17. DIAMOND, M. C., KRECH, D., and ROSENZWEIG, M. R., The effects of an enriched environment on the histology of the rat cerebral cortex. *J. Comp. Neurol.*, 1964, **123**: 111-119.

18. DINGMAN, W., and SPORN, M. B., Molecular theories of memory. *Science*, 1964, **144**: 26-29.

19. ECCLES, J. C., Neuron physiology—introduction. In: *Handbook of Physiology; Neurophysiology I* (J. Field, H. W. Magoun and V. E. Hall, Eds.). American Physiological Society, Washington, D.C., 1959: 59-74.

20. EDSTRÖM, A., Effect of spinal cord transection on the base composition and content of RNA in the Mauthner nerve fibre of the goldfish. *J. Neurochem.*, 1964, **11**: 557-559.

21. EGYHÁZI, E., and HYDÉN, H., Experimentally induced changes in the base composition of the ribonucleic acids of isolated nerve cells and their oligodendroglial cells. *J. Biophys. Biochem. Cytol.*, 1961, **10**: 403-410.

22. FRENSTER, J. H., ALLFREY, V. G., and MIRSKY, A. E., Repressed and active chromatin isolated from interphase lymphocytes. *Proc. Nat. Acad. Sci. USA*, 1963, **50**: 1026-1032.

23. FRIEDMAN, S. M., and WEINSTEIN, I. B., Lack of fidelity in the translation of synthetic polyribonucleotides. *Proc. Nat. Acad. Sci. USA*, 1964, **52**: 988-996.

24. GAITO, J., DNA and RNA as memory molecules. *Psychol. Rev.*, 1963, **70**: 471-480.

25. GALAMBOS, R., A glia-neural theory of brain function. *Proc. Nat. Acad. Sci. USA*, 1961, **47**: 129-136.

26. GASTAUT, H., and BECK, E., Brain rhythms and learning. *New Scientist*, 1962, **13**: 496-499.

27. GEIGER, A., Chemical changes accompanying activity in the brain. In: *Metabolism of the Nervous System* (D. Richter, Ed.). Pergamon, London, 1957: 245-256.

28. GEIGER, R. S., Subcultures of adult mammalian brain cortex *in vitro*. *Exp. Cell Res.*, 1958, **14**: 541-566.

29. GRAMPP, W., and EDSTRÖM, J. E., The effect of nervous activity on ribonucleic acid of the crustacean receptor neuron. *J. Neurochem.*, 1963, **10**: 725-731.

30. GRIFFARD, C. D., and PEIRCE, J. T., Conditioned discrimination in the planarian. *Science*, 1964, **144**: 1472-1473.

31. GUTHRIE, E. R., and HORTON, G. P., *Cats in a Puzzle Box* (silent film, 1938). Psychological Cinema Register, 1963-65:23 (Item PCR-21), The Pennsylvania State Univ., University Park.

32. HALAS, E. S., JAMES, R. L., and KNUTSON, C. S., An attempt at classical conditioning in the planarian. *J. Comp. Physiol. Psychol.*, 1962, **55**: 969-971.

33. HARTRY, A. L., KEITH-LEE, P., and MORTON, W. D., Planaria: memory transfer through cannibalism reexamined. *Science*, 1964, **146**: 274-275.

34. HYDÉN, H., Biochemical changes in glial cells and nerve cells at varying activity. In: *Biochemistry of the Central Nervous System*, Vol. III (O. Hoffmann-Ostenhof and F. Brücke, Eds.). Pergamon, London, 1959: 64-89.

35. ———, The neuron. In: *The Cell*, Vol. IV (J. Brachet and A. E. Mirsky, Eds.). Academic Press, New York, 1960: 215-323.

36. ———, Satellite cells in the nervous system. *Sci. Amer.*, 1961, **205**(6): 62-70.

37. ———, Biochemical and functional interplay between neuron and glia. *Rec. Adv. Biol. Psychiat.*, 1964, **6**: 31-54.

38. ———, Activation of nuclear RNA of neurons and glia in learning. In: *The Anatomy of Memory* (D. P. Kimble, Ed.). Science and Behavior Books, Palo Alto, 1965: 178-239.

39. HYDÉN, H., and EGYHÁZI, E., Nuclear RNA changes of nerve cells during a learning experiment in rats. *Proc. Nat. Acad. ci. USA*, 1962, **48**: 1366-1373.

40. ———, Glial RNA changes during a learning experiment in rats. *Proc. Nat. Acad. Sci. USA*, 1963, **49**: 618-624.

41. ———, Changes in RNA content and base composition in cortical neurons of rats in a learning experiment involving transfer of handedness. *Proc. Anat. Acad. Sci. USA*, 1964, **52**: 1030-1035.

42. HYMAN, L. H., Metabolic gradients in Amoeba and their relation to the mechanism of amoeboid movement. *J. Exp. Zool.*, 1917, **24**: 55-99.

43. HYMAN, L. H., Physiological studies on Planaria. III. Oxygen consumption in relation to age (size) differences. *Biol. Bull.*, 1919, **37**: 388-403.

44. IZAWA, M., ALLFREY, V. G., and MIRSKY, A. E., The relationship between RNA synthesis and loop structure in lampbrush chromosomes. *Proc. Nat. Acad. Sci. USA*, 1963, **49**: 544-551.

45. JAMES, R. L., and HALAS, E. S., No difference in extinction behavior in planaria following various types and amounts of training. *Psychol. Rec.*, 1964, **14**: 1-11.

46. JENNINGS, H. S., *Behavior of the Lower Organisms.* Indiana Univ. Press, Bloomington, 1962.

47. JENSEN, D. D., Experiments on "learning" in Paramecia. *Science*, 1957, **125**: 191-192.

48. ———, Operationism and the question "Is this behavior learned or innate?" *Behaviour*, 1961, **17**: 1-8.

49. ———, Hoplonemertines, myxinoids, and vertebrate origins. In: *The Lower Metazoa; Comparative Biology and Phylogeny* (E. C. Dougherty, Z. N. Brown, E. D. Hanson and W. D. Hartman, Eds.) Univ. of California Press, Berkeley, 1963: 113-126.

50. ———, Paramecia, Planaria and pseudo-learning. *Anim. Behav.*, 1964, Supp. **1**: 9-20.

51. KIMMEL, H. D., and HARRELL, V. L., Differential conditioning in the planarian. *Psychon. Sci.*, 1964, **1**: 227-228.

52. KJELDGAARD, N. O., and KURLAND, C. G., The distribution of soluble and ribosomal RNA as a function of growth rate. *J. Molec. Biol.*, 1963, **6**: 341-348.

53. KRECH, D., ROSENZWEIG, M. R., and BENNETT, E. L., Effects of environmental complexity and training on brain chemistry. *J. Comp. Physiol. Psychol.*, 1960, **53**: 509-519.

54. LANDAUER, T. K., Two hypotheses concerning the biochemical basis of memory. *Psychol. Rev.*, 1964, **71**: 167-179.

55. LEE, R. M., Conditioning of a free operant response in Planaria. *Science*, 1963, **139**: 1048-1049.

56. ———, *Free Operant Conditioning Technique for a Lower Organism: Planaria.* Thesis, Univ. of Maryland, College Park, 1963.

57. LIDDELL, H. S., *Conditioned Reflexes in Sheep* (silent film, 1928). Psychological Cinema Register 1963-65: 28 (Item PCR-19), The Pennsylvania State Univ., University Park.

58. LOEB, J., *Forced Movements, Tropisms, and Animal Conduct.* Lippincott, Philadelphia, 1918.

59. MAIER, N. R. F., and SCHNEIRLA, T. C., *Principles of Animal Psychology.* McGraw-Hill, New York, 1935.

60. McCONNELL, J. V., Memory transfer through cannibalism in planarians. *J. Neuropsychiat.*, 1962, **3**, Supp. 1: 42-48.

61. ———, Worms and things. *Worm Run. Dig.*, 1964, **6**(1): 1-5.

62. McCONNELL, J. V., CORNWELL, P. R., and CLAY, M., An apparatus for conditioning Planaria. *Am. J. Psychol.*, 1960, **73**: 618-622.

63. McCONNELL, J. V., JACOBSON, A. L., and KIMBLE, D. P., The effects of re-

generation upon retention of a conditioned response in the planarian. *J. Comp. Physiol. Psychol.*, 1959, **52**: 1-5.

64. McConnell, J. V., Jacobson, R., and Humphries, B. M., The effects of inges-
tion of conditioned planaria on the response level of naive planaria: a
pilot study. *Worm Run. Dig.*, 1961, **3**: 41-47.

65. Mirsky, A. F., and Katz, M. S., Avoidance "conditioning" in Paramecia.
Science, 1958, **127**: 1498-1499.

66. Moses, V., and Calvin, M., Lifetime of bacterial messenger ribonucleic acid.
J. Bacteriol., 1965, **90**: 1205-1217.

67. Palladin, A. V., and Vladimirov, G. E., The use of radioactive isotopes in
the study of functional biochemistry of the brain. In: *International
Conference on the Peaceful Uses of Atomic Energy*, Proceedings, Vol.
12: *Radioactive Isotopes and Ionizing Radiations in Agriculture, Physiology, and Biochemistry*. United Nations, New York, 1956: 402-408.

68. Pearl, R., The movements and reactions of fresh-water planarians: a study
in animal behaviour. *Quart. J. Micr. Sci.*, 1903, **46**: 509-714.

69. Pevzner, L. Z., Nucleic acid changes during behavioral events. In: *Macromolecules and Behavior* (J. Gaito, Ed.). Appleton-Century-Crofts, New
York, 1966: 43-70.

70. Pribram, K. H., The new neurology: memory, novelty, thought, and choice.
In: *EEG and Behavior* (G. H. Glaser, Ed.). Basic Books, New York,
1963: 149-173.

71. Rose, J. E., Malis, L. I., and Baker, C. P., Neural growth in the cerebral
cortex after lesions produced by monoenergetic deuterons. In: *Sensory
Communication* (W. A. Rosenblith, Ed.). Wiley, New York, 1961: 279-
301.

72. Rosenthal, R., and Fode, K. L., The effect of experimenter bias on the performance of the albino rat. *Behav. Sci.*, 1963, **8**: 183-189.

73. Sampson, M., Katoh, A., Hotta, Y., and Stern, H., Metabolically labile
deoxyribonucleic acid. *Proc. Nat. Acad. Sci. USA*, 1963, **50**: 459-463.

74. Searle, L. V., The organization of hereditary maze-brightness and maze-
dullness. *Genet. Psychol. Monogr.*, 1949, **39**: 279-325.

75. Sonneborn, T. M., The differentiation of cells. *Proc. Nat. Acad. Sci. USA*,
1964, **51**: 915-929.

76. Sperry, R. W., Problems in the biochemical specification of neurons. In:
Biochemistry of the Developing Nervous System (H. Waelsch, Ed.).
Academic Press, New York, 1955: 74-84.

77. ———, Summation. In: *The Anatomy of Memory* (D. P. Kimble, Ed.). Science
and Behavior Books, Palo Alto, 1965: 140-177.

78. Szer, W., and Ochoa, S., Complexing ability and coding properties of synthetic polynucleotides. *J. Molec. Biol.*, 1964, **8**: 823-834.

79. Thompson, R., and McConnell, J. V., Classical conditioning in the planarian
Dugesia dorotocephala. *J. Comp. Physiol. Psychol.*, **48**: 65-68.

80. Ullyott, P., The behaviour of *Dendrocoelum lacteum*. *J. Exp. Biol.*, 1936,
13: 253-278.

81. Van Deventer, J. M., and Ratner, S. C., Variables affecting the frequency
of response of Planaria to light. *J. Comp. Physiol. Psychol.*, 1964, **57**:
407-411.

82. Van Oye, P., *Nat. Rev. Wet. Tijdschr.*, 1920, 1(2).

83. Watson, J. D., Involvement of RNA in the synthesis of proteins. *Science*, 1963, **140**: 17-26.

84. Weiskrantz, L., Sensory deprivation and the cat's optic nervous system. *Nature*, 1958, **181**: 1047-1050.

85. Weiss, P., Selectivity controlling the central-peripheral relations in the nervous system. *Biol. Rev.*, 1963, **11**: 494-531.

86. Yerkes, R. M., The intelligence of earthworms. *J. Anim. Behav.*, 1912, **2**: 332-352.

87. Yoshii, N., Pruvot, P., and Gastaut, H., Electrographic activity of the mesencephalic reticular formation during conditioning in the cat. *EEG Clin. Neurophysiol.*, 1957, **9**: 595-608.

ELECTRICAL EVENTS IN THE BRAIN AND LEARNING

ROBERT GALAMBOS
Yale University
New Haven

My assignment is to review the efforts to discover, through electrophysiological methods, the location of Lashley's engram. Let me begin with a few general remarks that will provide a starting point. First, I would have you consider the so-called learned *versus* unlearned dimension in behavioral responses. A first principle of genetics holds that the phenotype is the product of the genotype interacting with its environment; this rule applies to behavior as well. For instance, if I, with my particular genetic constitution, had been sufficiently deprived of iodine in infancy, I would have developed into a mentally deficient cretin.

Most of us would probably agree, however, that behavioral responses do indeed come in two major varieties: unlearned and learned. Certain species-specific behaviors, such as breathing at birth in the mammal and spinning a cocoon in the silkworm, are distinguishable from behavior that clearly depends upon an interaction between an individual and its environment, such as learning to drive an automobile in the 20th century as opposed to learning to handle a team of horses in the 19th. Yet most samples of human and animal behavior do not drop easily into the definite categories of innate as opposed to learned. An organism seems to acquire its behavioral repertoire as much because it is built to do so as because it is able to learn, or adapt, to the unique constellation of environmental circumstances it encounters in life. Our analysis, as I see it, must deal not merely with how the brain stores and retrieves the learned responses; those species-specific responses offer equally important challenges and problems.

It could be, as many now feel, that the basic mechanisms responsible for all durable behavior, whether clearly innate, clearly acquired, or a combination of the two, will ultimately prove to have many common features. The terms "molecular neurology" (F. O. Schmitt) and "molecular psychobiology" (J. Gaito) give names to these efforts to link memories of all types with the genetic machinery within brain cells. The currently popular and promising moves along these lines lie outside the scope of my presentation.

Next, let us consider the brain within which the memories reside. Figure 6 shows in diagram form afferent and efferent sensory systems, along with the integrating centers within a typical brain. It lays out for us the field of battle, so to speak.

First, we see the sense organs (eye, ear) which are activated by the interaction with the environment, as well as the system of nerve fibers connecting them through synapses to the highest levels of the brain. These are the classical afferent pathways. A second major system, intensively studied during the last 15 years, is the reticular formation, which parallels the classical afferent pathways, receives input from them and terminates at essentially the same cortical levels. A third collection of fibers and nuclear masses comprises the so-called limbic-midbrain system. Fibers from several sources enter paleocortical structures such as hippocampus and amygdala and, in turn, send nerve fibers through the hypothalamus to the midbrain reticular areas.

The functions of these three major systems, as generally accepted these days, have been neatly summarized by Dr. Brazier (5): transmission of the message to the brain (the classical afferent system); awareness of its arrival (the reticular formation); the memory of its arrival (the limbic-midbrain circuit).

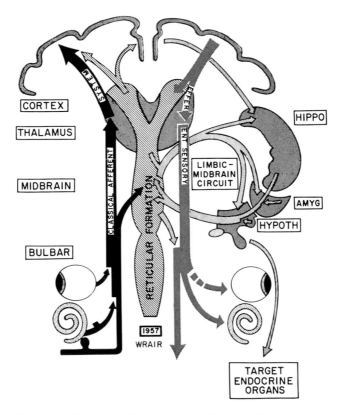

Figure 6. Diagram showing several neuronal systems on which electrophysiological studies related to learning have been performed. (From Galambos & Morgan, 14.)

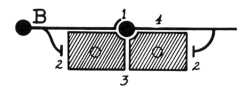

Figure 7. Neuronal models of fundamental units required for brain function. A: The neuroneuronal synaptic model. B: Same, but with glial cells added. (From Galambos, 13.)

Figure 6 also shows a system of descending sensory pathways arising in the cortex, synapsing at all levels en route downward, and terminating around sensory cells of the corresponding sense organ. Since the only known function of these descending or efferent pathways at the sense organ is to inhibit activity, it has been suggested that they operate in orienting or attentive behavior as a negative feedback loop that prevents entry of sensory stimuli which the organism is not at the moment using.

I wish someone could point out in this diagram exactly where interactions occur during memory deposition and retrieval. Perhaps someone can do so, even though the diagram is highly schematic and completely disregards the corticospinal, extrapyramidal and cerebellar motor pathways. As for me, I shall be able to give only a small part of the story, reminding myself throughout that this diagram shows existing possibilities for the brain of a mammal, such as cat or man; it does not tell us where things could happen in the very dissimilar brain of the bee, who learns through the dance of another bee how far and in what direction to fly to find the flowers and the nectar.

Grant: I am curious about the order of magnitude of the number of axon terminals upon a single cell.

Galambos: This depends upon the site. A good example would be the cat cochlear nucleus, which anatomically has two parts, an anterior and a dorsal. The ratio of contacts between incoming VIII nerve fibers and a postsynaptic element in the anterior ventral cochlear nucleus is approximately 1:1, whereas in the dorsal cochlear nucleus an incoming fiber ends in common with tens or hundreds of others upon a single postsynaptic element.

Now I would like to direct your attention briefly to the two models of brain—all brains, including the bee's—that control the thinking of physiologists who study learning problems. In part A of Figure 7 we see the neuroneuronal connections by way of synapses, the functional unit of the nervous system accepted by most physiologists over the last 50 years. Part B of the figure depicts the same neuroneuronal model, to which those constant companions of neurons, the glial cells, have been added. We can take our pick, these days, of which model to use in our thinking about brain function.

These two models or concepts of what the fundamental unit of brain function might be permit only certain logical possibilities regarding where the durable change of learning could reside. The durable change might, for example, be entirely intraneuronal: one could equate learning with synthesis of a unique ribonucleic acid in the neuronal nucleus, and a new protein inside the nerve cell—one memory, one molecule, so to speak. On the other hand, the durable change might be interneuronal; that is, the learning experience might in some manner permanently alter the synapse through which the neuronal messages pass, altering its properties in some way. The various popular synaptic theories of learning based on this possibility proposed over the last 75 years are, I am sure, familiar to you.

A third idea might be that learning is essentially a non-neuronal event in which experience alters the glial cells in some manner, the engram being stored in them, and thereafter they instruct, control or direct the neurons to respond merely passively in some pattern appropriate for retrieving the acquired response.

Finally, there are what might be called the glia-neuronal possibilities, in which the durable change of learning is thought to involve both glial cells and neurons; experience would alter both of them, and a new interaction between them would provide the key to how learned responses are stored in and retrieved from the brain. This last view you will recognize as the model of Svaetichin (39) and Hydén (30, 31), among others.

Thus we have several conceptual possibilities that can be used in planning experiments to determine where the durable changes of learning might be located. Many variants on these themes and expansions of them are of course possible, but we need not consider them here.

Next, let me review the electrical activity displayed by brains. Besides the familiar EEG, or brain waves, other electrical phenomena less generally known to experts outside the field of electrophysiology are under study. Prominent among these are the standing (or D.C.) potentials that can be measured when one brain region is compared to another. Many properties of these standing potentials, including the way they vary with different natural states of the organism and with other measurable external events, have recently been summarized (3). I shall refer to recent investigations that have attempted to relate these D.C. changes to learning and to performance.

The term *evoked response* covers another class of electrical brain events (4, 16, 33, 43). A light flash or skin shock will produce, after a suitable delay, a minor electrical explosion (evoked response) under electrodes placed in or upon the brain. These evoked responses have interesting properties, not the least of which is their tendency to vary in size despite the constant strength of the stimulus. Small responses appear in animals exposed for long periods of time to monotonously repeated flashes or clicks of constant strength, and they can become impressively large in size when the stimulus is given meaning through conditioning procedures of the sort Pavlov employed with such success. Labile evoked responses have been brought more or less under experimental control, and the subtleties and nuances associated with this fact constitute a body of information I shall consider briefly later.

Besides these three electrical phenomena (spontaneous brain waves, standing D.C. potentials, and evoked responses), it has become evident in recent years that an active brain changes its ability to conduct electricity. Experiments (1) show currents to flow through brain tissue more easily at some times than at others, and this variability of the brain as an electrical conductor is related in interesting ways to the correct and incorrect performance of learned responses.

I would like to list some of the main facts about learning that seem to me to have emerged from the electrophysiological studies thus far, in the hope that inserting a summary at this point rather than later will help orient our discussion. I hope the professional psychologists among you who detect the serious flaws and limitations in this classification will nevertheless permit me to continue. I am trying to orient nonexperts, not revolutionize psychological terminology.

Three phases are encountered during learning processes: acquisition, performance, and extinction. *Acquisition* refers to that period of time during which the learning experience is presumably modifying the brain physiology. A rat, when first put into a maze, acts as if it does not know what the experimenter would have it do. During the acquisition phase, it discovers what is expected, acquires necessary skills, achieves insights and does all of those other things that convince us that some impressive changes must be going on in its brain.

Performance refers to the behavior itself. Our measures of performance during acquisition will show the rat doing something progressively faster, or more skillfully, or with less errors. Performance is graded from zero at the start of training to a maximum at the end of it. A given level of performance presumably reflects the progress of the brain changes we wish to understand and, also, the degree to which the memory can be retrieved from the storehouse inside the brain.

Extinction, as I want to use the term, refers to the drop in performance from high to low, when the experimenter deliberately alters the situation, as for instance by failing to provide food at the end of the maze. As the animal's performance drops in extinction, we infer some alteration in the durable brain change set up during acquisition, and we would like to measure this.

During acquisition, in animal experiments, spontaneous EEG patterns change in an orderly way regarding amplitude, frequency, and phase relationships (2, 6, 11, 17, 35, 37, 41). These changes have been studied in the limbic system, the cortex, thalamus and reticular formation. Hence most of the systems in Figure 6 seem to be involved in learning as judged by observed alterations in amplitude, frequency and phase relations of the spontaneous EEG patterns. Second, when learning is complete, many brain regions finally achieve characteristic, stable electrical patterns locked to the conditioned stimulus; this is true for both the spontaneous (2, 6) and the evoked electrical activity (4, 16, 33). Third, in the hippocampus, an impedance change of 5 to 10 per cent comes to be time-locked to the conditioned stimulus (1). Fourth, some involvement of the DNA-RNA mechanisms of neurons and glial systems is suggested by evidence of both a direct (30, 31, 32) and indirect sort (10).

In the next phase, correct performance is highly correlated with the presence of both the hippocampal impedance change (1) and the characteristic specific electrical patterns built up during acquisition (2, 33). If performance is incorrect or absent, these specific electrical events are also absent. Second, the value of the normally present transcortical D.C. potential is critical, for performance will be impaired or lacking when the steady potential is manipulated experimentally as, for example, in spreading depression (7), or by local surface-negative polarization (35). Furthermore, direct measurements show sizable brain D.C. shifts to the conditioned stimulus in

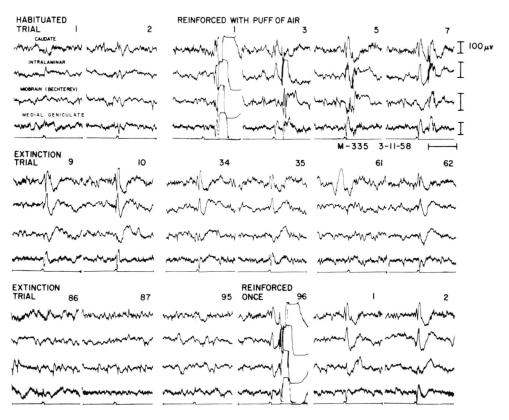

Figure 8. Evoked responses from four brain regions of a monkey during training. Click stimulus indicated on bottom lines of each record segment. Note increased response to click at all electrode sites during reinforcement, and progressive decline in amplitudes during extinction. Records in lower right demonstrate reconditioning with one reinforcement. (From Galambos & Sheatz, 16.)

trained animals (3) and in man (42).

In extinction, as the learned response disappears, the above mentioned electrical events disappear; with relearning, they return.

To turn now to the evoked response role in learning: typically, a monkey or cat is placed in an instrumental or a classical conditioning situation, the conditioned stimulus being a click or light flash, the reinforcement a puff of air, or food, or shock. The animal is habituated for hours or days, the stimu-

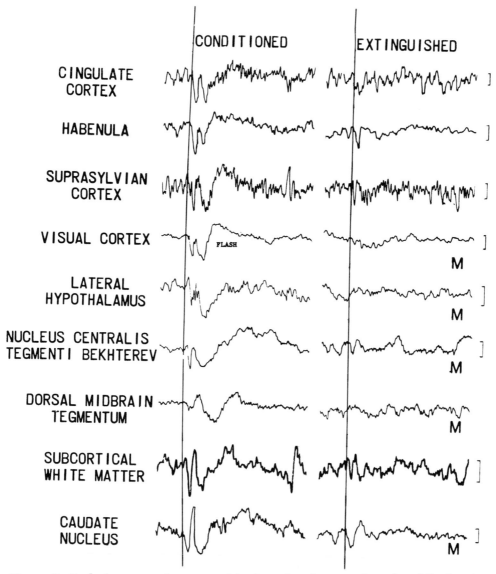

Figure 9. Evoked response from several brain regions in cat and monkey (M), showing enhanced response in the conditioned state as compared to the extinguished. Vertical lines indicate moment of stimulation (the CS) which in all cases except one (flash) was a click. Unconditional stimuli were variously puffs of air, food reinforcement, or shocks. (From Galambos & Sheatz, 16.)

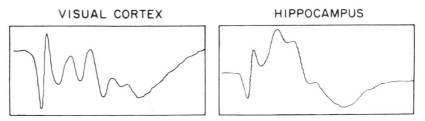

Figure 10. Cortical and hippocampal evoked responses to flash in unanesthetized cat, showing similarity in wave shape. (Adapted from Brazier, 5.)

lus (in our case a click) being presented at regular intervals, perhaps every five seconds. The experiment begins with association of the click with, say, a puff of air, and the brain events evoked by the click are recorded throughout from electrodes implanted in the head.

Figure 8 shows the results of one such experiment (16). Recordings with bipolar electrodes in the caudate nucleus, hypothalamus, midbrain reticular formation, and medial geniculate body show how the responses evoked by the click vary during conditioning. In the habituated animal clicks evoke small responses, and when the clicks are reinforced with air puffs the electrical responses grow systematically in each channel to an overall impressive size. The air puff reinforcement is now discontinued, and we enter the extinction phase. If we compare the amplitude of evoked responses appearing in the early extinction trials with the habituated control amplitudes, we will probably agree that the brain has indeed been changed, at least insofar as its ability to generate electrical activity is concerned.

In extinction the response diminishes in size until after approximately 100 such unreinforced clicks: then the evoked responses are small in size again. At this point a single reinforcement restores the evoked response to large size.

Figure 9 shows some responses recorded through bipolar electrodes from a variety of brain regions. They illustrate the points I wish to make: first, response amplitude to a stimulus of constant strength varies; second, amplitudes can regularly be enhanced by reinforcement with food, shocks, or puffs of air delivered in the Pavlovian manner; third, the actual wave shapes recorded seem to have many common features, regardless of the site of the recordings or the type of stimulus employed. These facts—response lability and conditionability, as well as the similarity in wave shape at all brain locations—pose difficult problems to the electrophysiologist, whose present theories regarding the generation of such waves seem inadequate to handle the facts.

Proceeding to the computer recordings of evoked responses, I have taken the liberty of reproducing some of Dr. Brazier's records (5) in Figure 10, which shows computer-averaged responses from unanesthetized cat visual cortex and hippocampus to 240 flashes. Each record covers 150 msec. The records from both the visual cortex and the hippocampus show rather complicated events. Clearly, there are marked similarities between these records up to a time of the order of 70 msec., at least. I submit this figure as a demonstration that the evoked responses in different brain regions can, under certain circumstances which we do not understand, remarkably resemble one another.

Discussion

Brazier: Do point out that the latencies of the evoked responses you just mentioned are different, however.

Galambos: The initial latencies are indeed somewhat different, but from the originals I could not decide to what extent. How much would you say?

Brazier: In the unanesthetized cat the latency from the flash is usually about 12 msec. to the beginning of the response in the visual cortex; it may be as long as 20 msec., and sometimes longer, in the hippocampus. There is great variability according to the exact position of the electrode. The order of magnitude of the amplitude in the cortex is probably 100 μV.

Simon: Do the electrical events disappear even in circumstances where there is substantial saving on retraining?

Galambos: They are not present when the response is extinguished.

Hilgard: I think this is an important point. We do have to distinguish between extinction and forgetting. I think you ought to have something in your list for a more permanent retention; otherwise you link brain activity with performance rather than with the accumulated changes that persist.

Lumsdaine: One prevalent concept of forgetting is that it takes place not just through passive fading, but as a result of the organism learning an incompatible response. The question now is a factual one: are there any data comparing the electrical activity under two conditions of performance decrement, one accomplished by extinction, and another accomplished by retraining the animal to an incompatible habit?

Galambos: Some experiments on hippocampal rhythms in which animals are reversal-trained will interest you. A door opens and the cat sees two alleys, one lighted, the other dark. If the correct choice for food reinforcement is the lighted alley, the hippocampal brain wave is recorded as the animal makes his choice. A stable hippocampal rhythm time-locked to the door-opening develops during this training, and persists during repeated performance trials.

If the signals are switched, so that the cat must choose the dark alley in order to be reinforced, the time-locked brain waves are at first enhanced, then disappear, and finally return when the animal regularly goes to the dark alley instead of the lighted one (2).

Lindsley: Dr. Galambos, your definitions seem somewhat too specific. For example, you said performance may represent an increase in the speed of activity; it could be the reverse. Similarly, the electrical changes you mentioned could be the reverse, or there could be differential electrical activity at the same time. That is, there might be increased negativity in one place and increased positivity in another.

Galambos: I said there were characteristic patterns and did not specify the polarity of these patterns, whether activity present in the control situation disappeared, or changed, or anything else.

Lindsley: But relative to specific changes, you said that during extinction they go away. They may or may not, it seems to me. Actually, we may be recording some specific activity in one area. This activity may effect another change in another area still involved in the performance process. In other words, there can be slowing down of learning to inhibit an act as well as to speed it up.

Galambos: I think I summarize the available data correctly when I say that both inhibition of response and performance of response will have related to them a particular constellation of electrical brain events as measured in different parts of the brain. There might be activity increase here and decrease there for inhibition, as compared to some different pattern for a learned lever-press. I wish merely to state the main generalization I see in all of these data, which is that a reasonably stable pattern of electrical brain activity correlates rather highly with whatever particular performance the animal displays.

Miller: In many instances there is first widespread electrical activity and then, as the animal acquires skill, the activity is more concentrated in a given region. Now, when you start extinction, is the foregoing sequence simply reversed? That is, does the activity become more widespread, or does the concentrated activity simply disappear?

Magoun: In that connection, I would like to make reference to the initial stages of extinction, since data (34) suggest that it involves the introduction of activity of a different sort, rather than the simple disappearance of what was going on before. Large slow waves and spindle bursts can be recorded from the cortex at the beginning of extinction, suggesting that this represents one category of Pavlovian internal inhibition and is associated with the EEG synchronizing discharge of the nonspecific thalamocortical system, which is active also during the excitability-reducing stages of satiety and light sleep.

Galambos: If I am correct, the question was whether during extinction some new and different electrical events occur, and Dr. Magoun has answered it. My point was that when the animal has undergone extinction the characteristic events previously related to performance of the conditioned response do not appear to the stimulus.

Pribram: You said that during performance certain characteristic changes take place, and that they can be altered by D.C. stimulation. But in most of the experiments in which these changes have been produced, the animals were still undertrained. Only at the 70 to 80 per cent level can one still manipulate the performance by electrical stimulation to the brain. Once 90 per cent or better performance is established, this is no longer the case. Is that correct?

Galambos: That is my understanding (3).

Since spreading depression experiments are important for my argument, I would like to outline one for you (7). A rat is trained to perform a certain task; the transcortical D.C. potential is then abolished by any of several means; the animal is now unable to perform the learned task. When that standing potential returns some minutes later, the behavior returns. Because of experiments like this, we can argue that the standing potential is important for performance of learned responses.

Pribram: Bureš* has pointed out one additional interpretation: there may be a change of state in these subjects so that they act like certain curarized preparations: what they learn in one state they do not remember in the other state. This is a possible, although farfetched, interpretation. My own feeling is that you are correct. When changes are produced which are so massive as to involve the entire hemisphere, performance is "abolished". But anything short of this seems to be effective only during more labile phases, i.e., during acquisition.

Galambos: A number of investigators are currently trying to relate learning and memory to the standing D.C. potentials. That is the point I wanted to make.

Pribram: Let me describe an experiment Chow and I have just done. We made a lesion on one side of the brain which, when bilateralized, affects visual discrimination performance. Because of anterior commissure interconnections, one would expect a D.C. shift in the homologous area of the opposite side of the brain to occur immediately following the unilateral procedure. Thus we wanted to see if we could find any decrement in performance *immediately* after the unilateral surgery. We used intravenous barbiturate anesthesia and tested the monkey within two hours after the completion of surgery, and from then on every hour for the next 12 hours. There was no decrement in performance.

Galambos: Perhaps you used the wrong test.

Pribram: No; it was a series of visual discrimination performance tests and the cortical area involved was the inferior temporal gyrus.

Brazier: Although I know nothing about learning theory, I am always surprised that the electrophysiological events are apparently so widely accepted as evidence of acquisitional learning, or something like that. Does it never bother you that this may be something quite different, such as the stress the animal is under, and hence you cannot get this change when the animal has reached 100 per cent? It is then no longer under stress. Are these not just the autonomic changes?

Pribram: That is just the point I am trying to make. We have not yet es-

---

* Personal communication.

tablished the necessary connection between electrical brain events and behavior.

Brazier: I heard Dr. Bureš recently at a symposium in East Berlin, where
he was challenged on the same point, in reference to spreading depression.
I think he was well aware that it is a matter of opinion as to whether electrophysiological events are directly related to acquisition, or whether both
phenomena occur at the same physiological state of the brain, including the
impedance changes.

Koestler: Returning to a question I asked earlier, but did not formulate
explicitly, and which seems to me relevant to the kind of problems which
point to the coalescence of physiological and psychological observation, I
would like to call your attention to the experimental work published by
Gastaut & Beck (18) about two years ago. It applies only to acquisition, retention and performance, not to extinction. In this experiment, a cat is conditioned to a light stimulus. During learning, there is a very clear and
specific electrical pattern on the cortical and reticular levels. With progressive facilitation, this pattern becomes weaker on the cortical level, but
seems to wander downward to limbic and even lower midbrain structures. So
it seems, at least to the psychologist, that a kind of law of least effort is operant: as long as you learn something, you have to concentrate, with focal
awareness; once you have learned it, you do it with your muscles on unconscious levels. That would also mean that the engram, whatever it is, would
follow this kind of downward traffic to older, phylogenetically more primitive levels; this would partly answer the question as to why the RNA
changes vanish, whereas the acquired trick or skill remains intact. Could it
have wandered downward toward more primitive levels, to give the cortex
freedom for other things such as the acquisition of a new skill?

Gastaut & Beck reached the following conclusion: "Can it be that once
we have learned something we no longer rely so much on our cortex and
reticular formation? Those things we do 'without thinking', or when we are
sleepy, or intoxicated, may depend more on the older primitive parts of the
nervous system such as the limbic structures, thus releasing higher centres
such as the cortex for other tasks. . . . Common sense indicates such a possibility; electrophysiology suggests it" (18).

Pribram: If we take seriously the machine analogy of the memory mechanism we might say that a large number of neural structures participates
during the construction of additions to the machine. But once the additions
have been made, fewer elements are required again to make the modified
performance. For instance, all an adding machine has to do in order to mul-
tiply is to repeat and repeat and repeat. The order "repeat so many times"
has to be constructed into the machinery, but once construction is completed the machine essentially adds just as it did before.

Grant: If these electrical events show a certain level before acquisition, a
progressive change during acquisition, then remain during performance

phases, but disappear during extinction, it might be that these changes are more closely related to readiness or even to attention, than to the learning mechanisms themselves. They are end products of the learning process, with certain other things involved but, surely, if they disappear during extinction (and we know there will be spontaneous recovery), they are perhaps not quite the same as the associative phase of learning.

Galambos: May I try to give some perspective to these electrophysiological data? I know of no one who claims to know exactly how they are related to the brain events occurring during deposition and retrieval of the memory trace. Electrical stimulation and recording are merely two of a number of tools used by physiologists in the search for the durable change in the brain during learning. Drs. Sperry and Pribram, for instance, are experts on the ablation approach, an equally valid and useful one. The electrophysiologist, however, studies what he can study, namely the electrical events in the brain, and he does so with increasing elegance and precision thanks to superb equipment, computers, and so on. During the past ten years, electrophysiologists have applied their techniques to the learning problem; I have outlined their results here. But some of them have become disillusioned about the relationships they find in the brain in association with these various phases of learning. Something is escaping them.

Grant: Speaking as an outsider, I think it is most remarkable that so much has been done. You should not be disappointed.

Galambos: Electrophysiologists would be absolutely delighted to discover that their electrical events are related precisely to acquisition, performance and extinction. But so far we have only fairly good correlations, and not the conclusive answers we would like.

Jensen: Do you have data in which you have controls for sensitization, that is, where you presented unpaired stimuli?

Galambos: Yes, in experiments where click alternates with flash at five-second intervals. If we reinforce the click alone and observe what happens to the response to both flash and click, we will see enhanced responses to the click but not to the flash. If we now extinguish the animal to the click, and then reinforce the flash, evoked responses to flash increase in size, while those to click do not. If the phenomenon were due only to sensitization, would we not expect the responses to both stimuli to increase in amplitude? At any rate, when Dr. Sheatz and I (16) did these studies, we felt that we had excluded sensitization as the responsible factor.

But there is more to the story. What I have described applies to events in certain brain regions; in the very same animal it can be demonstrated in other brain regions that, regardless of which stimulus is reinforced in such an experiment, all responses increase in size. We found several instances where some brain regions acted in accordance with sensitization or pseudoconditioning notions, while in another region of the same brain "true" conditioning seemed to be taking place (16).

Grant: It might be interesting for you to do some straight sensitization training without the discrimination feature because, behaviorally, we know that in quite a variety of experiments the degree of generalization is greatly circumscribed in a variety of ways if discrimination training is given. Perhaps this is not apropos of what you are looking for, but you might find the results of such an experiment useful.

Galambos: Yes. This would involve giving just the shocks without relation to the stimulus. We have done it, of course, in which case responses to all stimuli can show high amplitudes. Sometimes everything increases, but at other times a stimulus delivered to a highly excited animal completely fails to evoke a response.

Lindsley: Dr. Galambos, regarding the question of sensitization, or perhaps attention as opposed to learning, we have done experiments with human subjects in which they receive alternate clicks and flashes of light. We instruct the subject, for example, "Now you are going to get both of these stimuli alternately, but pay attention only to the flashes." In this case, the average evoked potential to flashes will be higher in amplitude, and the responses to the clicks will be diminished, although they will be present. We can do just the reverse by saying, "Now pay attention to the clicks and ignore the flashes." Then the response to clicks is enhanced. There is no particular learning involved; we are simply instructing the subject to direct his attention to one or the other stimulus. In your particular experimental situation, the size of the responses reflects perhaps that the animal has learned to attend to your conditioned stimulus.

Galambos: I merely stated that, if we subject an animal to a simple conditioning procedure and observe the electrophysiological phenomenon associated with it, we will find changes in evoked response amplitudes similar to those I described. What the changes have to do with learning is an important, interesting, and unsolved question (16).

Lindsley: The point I wanted to make is that, if you are speaking about durable changes that have been induced, they might not necessarily be changes as reflected by the size of the electrical activity. Perhaps it is simply a matter of whether the animal is attending, or learning to attend, to that stimulus or to another.

Lumsdaine: Would you point out, from your experience, some specific differentiating features in any of the loci between the conditioned and extinguished waves that are more or less characteristic?

Galambos: Notice the reticular formation (tegmentum) in Figure 9; it is barely noticeable in the right column (extinguished), but very long in duration, and polyphasic (down-up-down) in morphology after conditioning. That is the characteristic pattern.

Now look at the response from the caudate nucleus. Again, the click produces a small response during extinction, and a large one when the animal is conditioned. Furthermore, both the time relationships and the morphology of this response resemble what can be seen elsewhere in the figure.

Guilford: During the extinction phases, does it make a difference whether there is an actual response?

Donchin: From Dr. Lindsley's laboratory we have data bearing on Dr. Guilford's question. A subject is presented with near-threshold flashes of light; if he detects the flash, he makes a "correct" response, and if he does not detect it, he makes an "incorrect" response. If averaging techniques are applied to the EEG recorded during the experiment, correct responses are found to be associated with average cortical evoked potentials, while the incorrect responses are not.

In another experiment (9), we recorded reaction time to flashes of light, and found that fast reaction times were associated with average evoked potentials of higher amplitudes than the potentials associated with slow reaction times. These, of course, were not conditioning experiments, but at least they show some covariation of electrocortical response with specific behavioral responses.

Hernández-Peón: I would like to discuss briefly some points which have been presented by Dr. Galambos, and to point out some gaps in the knowledge of the neurophysiology of learning.

Obviously, functioning of the central nervous system involves neural events at the axonal, synaptic and subsynaptic levels, as shown in Figure 11. The electrical changes at the axonal level have been studied extensively by electrophysiological methods. A very important step at the synaptic level is associated with the release, diffusion and action of chemical substances

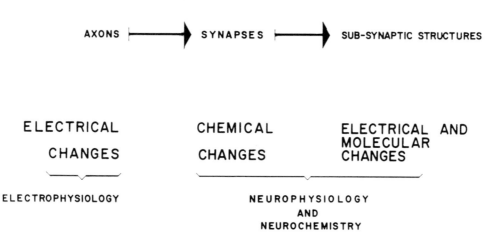

Figure 11. The sequence of the neural events in learning involves electrical changes propagated along the axons, chemical changes occurring across the synapse, and electrical and molecular changes occurring at the subsynaptic structures. Whereas the electrical axonal changes are well known, much remains to be learned about synaptic chemical and subsynaptic molecular processes.

upon the subsynaptic membranes. At the subsynaptic level there are, again, electrical and molecular changes.

While investigators of the neural mechanisms underlying learning have been particularly interested in molecular changes, as Dr. Gaito has shown, very little attention has been paid so far to the chemical synaptic changes. I would like to point out this gap, which may be important in the neural events involved in learning.

In order to understand the neural mechanisms of learning, we need to know which parts of the brain are most importantly related to the different aspects of learning. First, a distinction must be established between the changes associated with positive learning and those associated with negative learning.

By *positive learning* we mean the process involved in the acquisition of a response to a stimulus which did not evoke it before. By *negative learning* we imply the process by which, through repetition, a stimulus becomes ineffective in evoking a response. The simplest example of "positive learning" is that associated with the classically conditioned responses described by Pavlov, and the simplest example of "negative learning" is habituation.

Lipsitt: I wonder if, by the term "negative learning", you mean to include both habituational processes and those kinds of arrangements which we refer to as extinction, and whether there are any discernible differences in electrical activity for the two kinds of processes if, indeed, they are different.

Hernández-Peón: We do include habituation and extinction under that term. Since it seems that the same electrophysiological manifestations are present in both, we think we are dealing with the same process.

I will refer to the functional role of the brain stem reticular formation essential for wakefulness in the plastic changes occurring during acquisition of a conditioned response, and to the possible relationship of some plastic changes associated with extinction and a brain system responsible for the onset and maintenance of sleep.

Most of you are probably familiar with experiments (24, 25) in which we showed that the neocortex is not essential for the acquisition of a simple conditioned response, whereas a small tegmental lesion in the midbrain, which does not impair wakefulness, can eliminate this simple type of conditioned response. Figure 12 shows a cat from which the neocortex had been previously removed. Two types of conditioned responses were established: a salivary CR (preceded by the conditioned orienting response) to a visual stimulus, and a flexor response to a buzzer previously associated with an electric shock applied to one leg. Both the orienting and salivary responses to the visual CS, as well as the flexor CR to the buzzer, disappeared after a midbrain tegmental lesion.

Although these experiments point out the importance of the midbrain reticular formation in the plastic changes associated with the simplest and

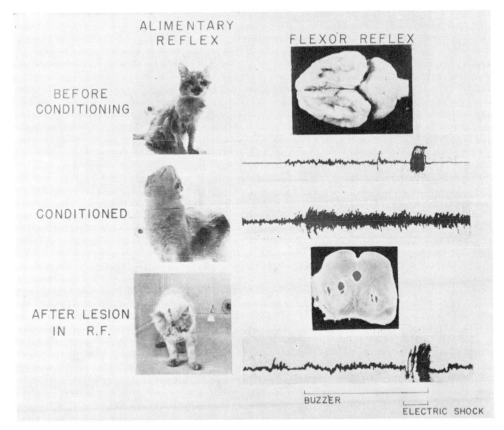

Figure 12. A neodecorticated cat which was easily conditioned to the presentation of food (a piece of fish presented within its visual field) and to a buzzer associated with an electric shock. After a small tegmental midbrain lesion, both alimentary and flexor conditioned responses disappeared. (From Hernández-Peón & Brust-Carmona, 23.)

earliest type of conditioning, it cannot be concluded that plastic association occurs at this level. However, using the electrophysiological technique, Buser, Jouvet and I (8) have obtained some evidence supporting this interpretation.

We recorded the evoked responses from the midbrain reticular formation, using as the CS two clicks separated by an interval of 500 msec. In the naive animal, at that interval, the second evoked response was always smaller than the first (Figure 13). After association of the clicks with a nociceptive electric shock, there was enhancement of not only the first evoked potential but of the second as well, showing a change of excitability at this level. This change seems to be rather permanent, for the potentials did not always return to the original magnitude even during prolonged extinction; furthermore, they were quickly disinhibited by a single application of the nociceptive stimulus. These results, and some others, indicate that the changes occurring during plastic association are more stable than the changes occurring during plastic inhibition, as in the case of extinction.

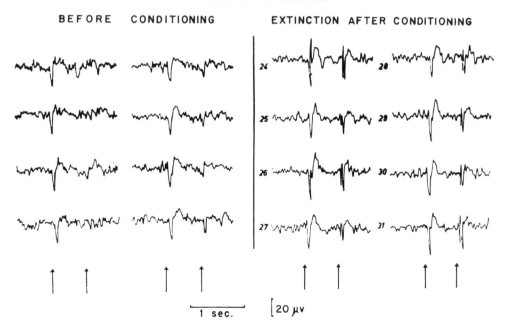

Figure 13. Auditory responses recorded from the midbrain reticular formation, evoked by pairs of clicks separated by an interval of 500 msec. In the naive animal before conditioning, the second potential of each pair was always smaller than the preceding potential. By associating the pair of clicks to a nociceptive electric shock, both the first and the second potential of each pair became enhanced. During extinction those electrical changes persisted longer than extinction of the behavioral orienting conditioned response.

Grant: Is there more activity on the second response during extinction?

Hernández-Peón: There is more excitability than prior to the conditioning situation, but during conditioning, of course, the second potential very often had the same amplitude as the first. In our opinion, this means that the hyperexcitability during conditioning must involve release of a tonic inhibition. In other words, the reduction of the second potential obtained during the control preconditioning period is not the result only of refractoriness, as is usually assumed.

Konorski: How soon after the beginning of conditioning does the second click begin to evoke the increased response?

Hernández-Peón: Very soon. We sometimes observed the changes during the first session after 15 or 20 association trials; they certainly appear during the first session.

Hilgard: Are there behavioral signs? There is a diminution of some kind of overt response. Does this persist? Is there no longer correlation with the overt response to the conditioned stimulus? In other words, is there something that is really disappearing, while something else is remaining constant?

Hernández-Peón: Yes, there is some correlation with the orienting responses to the clicks, which were actually enhanced simultaneously with

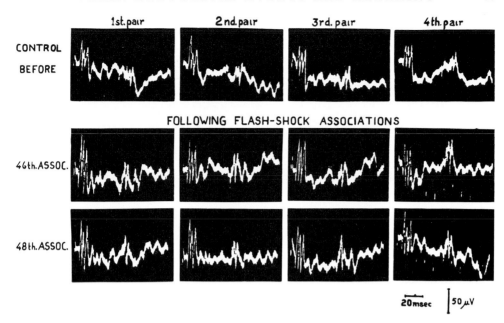

Figure 14. Photic evoked potentials recorded from the optic tract in a cat. Four pairs of flashes separated by an interval of 60 msec. at a rate of 1/sec. were used as the CS. A nociceptive electric shock, presented simultaneously with the 4th pair of flashes, was the UCS. After 46 associations, a significant enhancement was observed in the first and second potentials of each pair, particularly in the 4th pair.

the evoked reticular responses. The orienting reaction diminished during the extinction period. However, extinction of the reticular evoked potentials developed more slowly than extinction of the overt behavioral response.

By utilizing a pair of stimuli as CS, it is possible to show hyperexcitability changes at a level as far down as the first synapse—for instance, in the retina. Figure 14 illustrates an experiment made in collaboration with Palestini and Davidovich (36), in which the conditioned stimuli were a series of four pairs of flashes which evoked potentials from the optic tract, thus representing activity from the retina. Again, the second potential of each pair was much smaller than the first. However, after 46 associations of the flashes with an electric shock applied to the cat's leg, the second potential of each pair became enhanced as well as the first. This was most clear for the pair of flashes overlapping in time with the electric shock. These results indicate that the changes of excitability produced by conditioning can be reflected away from the brain by centrifugal fibers.

We have seen that during extinction, in addition to the diminution of the evoked responses, other electrical phenomena appear which were not previously present. Very often, slow waves were triggered by the conditioned stimuli during extinction; this answers Dr. Miller's question. Figure 15 illustrates an extinction experiment in which responses evoked by series of four flashes of light at a rate of 1/sec. were recorded from the visual cortex. Previously, the four flashes of light were associated with a nociceptive electric

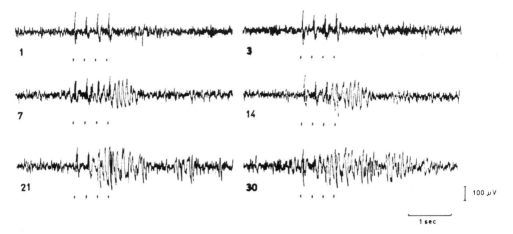

Figure 15. Photic evoked potentials recorded from the visual cortex of a cat during extinction. At the 7th trial of the non-reinforced visual stimulus, slow waves were triggered by the fourth flash. At the 14th trial the slow waves were triggered by the third flash, and at the 21st trial the slow waves began to be triggered by the second flash.

shock, as mentioned before. During the seventh non-reinforced trial, slow waves were triggered by the last flash of each series of four representing the CS. As more flashes were presented without reinforcement, the slow waves were triggered even by the first flash of each series. The temporal development of those electrical changes recorded during extinction indicates that plastic inhibition is a cumulative phenomenon.

Cortical slow waves were also triggered by the non-reinforced stimulus during other manifestations of internal inhibition, such as delayed inhibition. In the experiment illustrated in Figure 16 the same CS (four flashes of light) and UCS (electric shock) were used. As the UCS was separated from the CS, slow cortical waves were triggered first by the fourth flash, then by the third flash, and so on.

When we observed these phenomena, we wondered about the source of the inhibitory influences that develop during internal inhibition. A reasonable assumption, because of the identity of the cortical manifestations of internal inhibition and those of sleep, is that both processes must have a common source from a hypnogenic brain pathway. In attempting to map out this pathway by electrical stimulation, we soon realized that there was extensive anatomical overlapping of hypnogenic and arousing structures. We therefore decided to approach this problem by the method of neurochemical stimulation, which, at the same time, might provide some insight into the possible synaptic transmitters involved in these events.

By introducing minute crystals of acetylcholine through cannulae permanently implanted in cat brains, we have been able to map out a circumscribed anatomical pathway, the activation of which produces all the behavioral and electrographic manifestations of sleep (19-22, 26-28, 40).*

* This research was supported by the National Institute of Mental Health, USPHS (Grant MH-10003-01) and by the Foundation's Fund for Research in Psychiatry (Grant 64300).

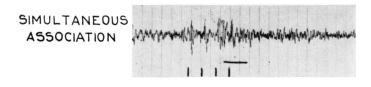

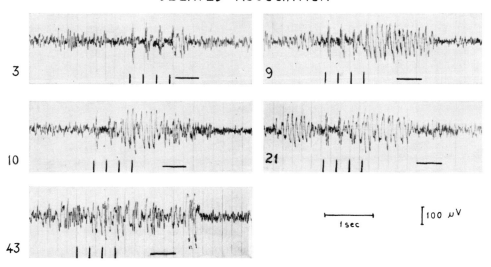

Figure 16. Photic evoked potentials recorded from the visual cortex of a cat during delayed association of the CS (four flashes of light) and the UCS (nociceptive electric shock). As the UCS was delayed, slow waves began to be triggered, at first by the fourth flash, later by the third flash, and so on.

There are two main components in the sleep system: an ascending component starting at the spinal cord, which goes up through the medulla oblongata and pons to the midbrain, and a descending pathway arising from certain cortical areas, such as the anterior cingulate gyrus, the orbital surface, and the pyriform cortex, and which descends along the limbic-midbrain pathway to join the ascending pathway at the level of the pons (Figure 17). In an attempt to test the hypothesis that some manifestations of internal inhibition (such as "neuropil habituation", extinction, delayed inhibition) are mediated by the sleep system, we decided to test whether interruption of that pathway impairs plastic inhibitory phenomena.

In preliminary experiments carried out in collaboration with Rojas-Ramírez, we have found that localized lesions in the posterior pontine tegmentum, which prevent the appearance of slow waves during spontaneous light sleep, also impair habituation of the arousal response to an olfactory stimulus, as tested by recording the "arousal discharges" of the olfactory bulb (29). On the other hand, habituation of arousal is favored by a lesion in the anterior pontine tegmental region which diminishes vigilance.

These results, showing that localized lesions in the caudal brain stem can change the pattern of habituation, support the idea that activation of the

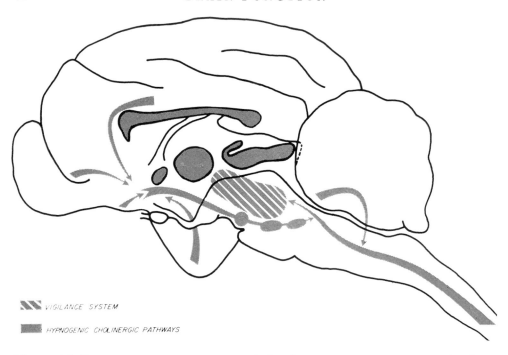

VIGILANCE SYSTEM

HYPNOGENIC CHOLINERGIC PATHWAYS

Figure 17. Diagrammatic representation of the sleep system traced by acetylcholinic stimulation of the central nervous system. This hypnogenic pathway is made up of two components: a spino-bulbo-pontine component starting from the spinal cord, represented by the ascending arrow impinging upon the vigilance system (hatched), and a descending component represented by the arrows originating at the cingulate gyrus, the orbitofrontal cortex, and the pyriform cortex, converging upon the descending limbic-midbrain circuit.

hypnogenic pathway may be involved in some manifestations of plastic or internal inhibition.

We are beginning to test experimentally a last hypothesis: just as the sleep system is made up of an ascending component of spinal origin and a descending component of cortical origin, which join at the brain stem level, the vigilance system, which plays a fundamental role in plastic association, is probably also made up of two components—an ascending component starting at the spinal cord, with maximal development at the brain stem level, and a descending component represented by corticofugal projections.

Indeed, we have found that adrenalin locally applied in the gray substance of the spinal cord elicits arousal and prolonged wakefulness. It would perhaps be wise to keep in mind that the processes of plastic association and plastic inhibition can take place at all levels of the central nervous system, from the spinal cord up to the cortex.

Brazier: Both Dr. Galambos and Dr. Hernández-Peón have raised questions about the parts of the brain associated with learning. The work I was trying to do on systems in the brain was related to some problems on coding in the nervous system, because I was trying to differentiate what neuronal activity was necessary for (and I am fully aware of the trap in the word I am going to use) *conscious* experience.

It seems fairly clear to me that there are three neurophysiological systems necessarily operating, if the organism is to have full conscious experience. The message coming in from the environment, whether internal or external, has to reach the cortex; it has to come in and report that an event has taken place. We know that the message goes up a specific afferent system. We also know that it gets there perfectly well in very deep anesthesia. In fact, this was how the electrophysiologists first found the evoked potential: before they had computers to increase the signal-to-noise ratio, they used anesthesia to abolish the noise. They very clearly perceived the signal that the message had reached the cortex.

The next stage is that the organism has to be aware that this has happened. I do not have to expand on this, since it was principally Drs. Magoun and Lindsley, our co-chairmen, who elucidated this phenomenon, showing that it is the midbrain system that has to be open and operating in order for the organism to be aware of a message having come in.

Now it seems to me there is a third process necessary for the organism to be *conscious* that this happened. The arrival of the message and awareness of it in the specious present is not enough; there has to be some mechanism in the brain that retains this information. The work of many investigators suggests that the limbic system, which Dr. Galambos pointed out in Figure 6, may be the third system, and the one responsible for this process.

In my current work I am testing these systems by using drugs to make reversible pharmacologic lesions. The suggestion that came to me from observation in man, or perhaps I should really say in woman, is well known to any of us who have witnessed women being delivered under scopolamine and morphine. We can observe that the afferent system is open and that the awareness system is open. Yet, when it is all over, the patient says to the doctor, "I want that anesthetic for all my babies." There has been no retention. Scopolamine is thus a drug which will selectively knock out the retention system without knocking out the awareness of the arrival of the stimulus. It is not an anesthetic.

In my current work I therefore am testing the theory that this retention is in the limbic system and am exploring whether the evoked responses die out in the hippocampus while they are still present in the midbrain and in the cortex.

Now, the first question I would like to put to the psychologists present is, do you feel that all three of these systems have to be open for learning? I am sure there are experiments in which investigators have attempted the training of animals with only one or two of these systems present and active. So I wonder whether, whatever the word *learning* means—and I am very unclear about it—this actually might make some kind of neurophysiological approach to an analysis of the underlying mechanisms. Also, such an analysis might perhaps help to differentiate between changes that are going on, whether they be chemical or structural or electrical, during the process of learning, as contrasted with the state of having learned. There was discussion earlier about how long Hydén's chemical changes lasted, and so forth. Do we necessarily have to demand that the changes we find during the processes of learning have to be the same as those found in the state of having learned?

I would like to ask a second question of Dr. Galambos. Have you considered looking at your material or designing your experiments with a model drawn from information theory in mind? As we all know (and I am now using the term in its strictly defined sense), information is conveyed by the degree of probability; the higher the probability of the occurrence, the less information is transferred. Surely this conceptual model has some application to the problems of learning, or at least to training, because what we do not know, what is novel, conveys information; the least probable event carries the most information. We physiologists read and hear so much about training experiments in which repetitive tasks are given, in which the methodology actually includes repetitive unchanging conditions. I wonder whether an approach by probabilistic theory might not be fruitful. Would you like to comment on that, Dr. Galambos?

Galambos: As far as I am concerned, any experiment, if undertaken by a serious worker, regardless of his theoretical bias, is worth doing. But behavioral responses, especially those innate ones, have a very high probability of occurrence.

Brazier: I am talking about the probability of the occurrence of the stimulus, because this is what the mind or brain is assessing. I am suggesting that the brain reacts differently to a highly probable stimulus than it does to a stimulus of low probability.

Galambos: Yes, and the point I wanted to make is that, if we were to study responses with a probability of practically 1.0, such as, for instance, the knee-jerk (unlearned) or imprinting (learned), the brain organization underlying them might be rather easy to uncover without using the statistical and probabilistic notions certain people currently feel to be the most fruitful approach to an analysis.

We are obsessed and perhaps even blinded, it seems to me, by the search for what happens in the brain during learning. Certainly, some new organization is achieved in the brain of an animal that makes contacts with its environment and thereafter responds differently to a stimulus. But I remain unconvinced that this brain reorganization is, in principle, dissimilar to those built-in ones that exist to account for spinal cord reflexes, the hypothalamic regulation of temperature control, and similar highly predictable behaviors.

Understanding the events that underlie the very highly probable responses may well provide the clues to understanding what occurs in those less probable responses to stimuli that we encounter in learning situations (12).

Pribram: There is an experiment Sutton and coworkers (38) have done, using the average evoked potential technique. They gave human subjects visual stimuli in a predictable and in an unpredictable order, and obtained vast differences in the afterwave of the average evoked response recorded from the occiput. "Certainty" and "uncertainty" of expectation give rise to different brain wave patterns.

Magoun: May I follow this up a little further? The increase of amplitude and distribution of input signals, associated with orientation to their novelty, is stimulated also by the introduction of reinforcement at a time when this novelty has worn down and the signal has diminished.

Activity of the central neural system for orientation to novelty, as well as that involved in reinforcement, tend to increase the amplitude and generalize the distribution of input signals and, presumably, thereby promote learning in the brain. Do these utilize identical neural mechanisms? Are the mechanisms dissimilar, but parallel in their end results? What kinds of generalizations can we draw concerning these two ways of promoting an increase of amplitude and distribution of input signals in learning, one depending upon evocation of the orienting reflex, and the other being a consequence of reinforcement?

Galambos: This will not answer your question exactly, but it may be helpful. My colleagues and I were at first greatly intrigued with the alterations in response amplitude associated with conditioned stimuli and reinforcement, but as time went on it became increasingly clear that factors difficult to measure—what people call vigilance, attention, or orienting to novel stimuli—were also involved in controlling the evoked response amplitude. I was convinced at one point that this electrical explosion, which we called the *evoked response characteristic* of the trained animal, was merely a watered-down version of the startle pattern seen electrophysiologically (and behaviorally) after a loud sound. I still feel there is some continuum here that relates evoked response amplitudes to stimuli that provoke startle, attention, orienting, and conditioned responses. Further work on evoked responses, especially with fine-grained computer analysis, may well reveal the differences one suspects exist, and thereby clear some badly muddied water. At the moment, however, I do not think anyone can specify unique distinguishing features of the evoked responses to novel, as opposed to conditioned, stimuli.

Lindsley: I should like to comment on one point that Dr. Brazier brought up. Sometimes we are focused on the stimulus of the moment, and then its effect seems to move to a lower level. I remember an experience I had after sleep deprivation. On this occasion I had stayed up all night doing some work and then began dictating letters. Several times I found that the last sentence I had dictated now escaped my memory. Pressing the button to go back and pick up the last sentence, I found I understood it perfectly well, but my short-term memory system did not retain it; I had to press the button immediately again to get the last sentence. In other words, as Dr. Hernández-Peón has said, the vigilance system in this case is reduced to such a point that temporary storage is not retained.

Dr. Donchin has described to me another situation in which his wife, whose primary language is Hebrew and who later learned English, was coming out from under the influence of anesthesia; she would speak Hebrew to him but believed that she was speaking English, the more recently acquired language. In this case there is a lack of identification or conscious awareness of what has been recently learned, as opposed to that which has been stored a long time in the learning and memory system.

Hilgard: There is a contradiction there between the availability of the memory and the storage; English was not lost. We are doing some experiments very much like Dr. Brazier's on amnesia following barbiturate intoxication, which is similar to the scopolamine effect. But while there is complete amnesia for the experience, we are often able to recover some of it under hypnosis. It is not so much that what is learned under the drug is lost, but rather that it is not available for recovery. I think this becomes a very interesting problem.

Jensen: Has anyone ever given patients the drug a second time and said, "Now, tell me about your last delivery"? Perhaps we have the curare situation, where memories acquired under a drug are available only under the influence of the drug. Does this seem like a reasonable thing to do?

Hilgard: It is reasonable, and you will usually find that the memories will not be available. We have run a half dozen cases recently and none of them had the memories available.

Pribram: That is with barbiturate, but not with scopolamine.

Koestler: I wanted to say something in connection with the problems you raised. By definition, classical conditioned reflexes are automatisms. A complex skill learned by a human being, such as playing the piano or typing, requires at the beginning a maximum of concentration and gradually becomes automatic. If it is repeated under monotonous conditions, it becomes more and more stereotyped, more and more rigid, until it is like a chain of conditioned reflexes; but it does not start like that. This parameter is missing in the discussion. We discuss learning, memory formation and recall in terms of conditioned reflexes in the classical sense because, I repeat, they are automatisms by definition, whereas acquired human skills may become automatic after a while. But a part of the story is missing.

REFERENCES

1. ADEY, W. R., KADO, R. T., DIDIO, J., and SCHINDLER, W. J., Impedance changes in cerebral tissue accompanying a learned discriminative performance in the cat. *Exp. Neurol.*, 1963, **7**: 259-281.

2. ADEY, W. R., and WALTER, D. O., Application of phase detection and averaging techniques in computer analysis of EEG records in the cat. *Exp. Neurol.*, 1963, **7**: 186-209.

3. BRAZIER, M. A. B. (Ed.), *Brain Function, Vol. I: Cortical Excitability and Steady Potentials; Relations of Basic Research to Space Biology.* UCLA Forum Med. Sci. No. 1, Univ. of California Press, Los Angeles, 1963.

4. ———, Information carrying characteristics of brain responses. *EEG Clin. Neurophysiol.*, 1963, Suppl. **24**: 55-67.

5. ———, Role of the limbic system in maintenance of consciousness. *Anesth. Analg.*, 1963, **42**: 748-751.

6. BREMNER, F. J., Hippocampal activity during avoidance behavior in the rat. *J. Comp. Physiol. Psychol.*, 1964, **58**: 16-22.

7. BUREŠ, J., BUREŠOVÁ, O., and ZÁHOROVÁ, A., Conditioned reflexes and Leao's spreading cortical depression. *J. Comp. Physiol. Psychol.*, 1958, **51**: 263-268.

8. BUSER, P., JOUVET, M., and HERNÁNDEZ-PEÓN, R., Modifications, au cours du conditionnement chez le chat, du cycle d'excitabilité au niveau de la reticulée mesencephalique. *Acta Neurol. Latinoam.*, 1958, **4**: 268-278.

9. DONCHIN, E., and LINDSLEY, D. B., Cortical evoked potentials and reaction times. *EEG Clin. Neurophysiol.*, 1965, **18**: 523.

10. FLEXNER, J. B., FLEXNER, L. B., and STELLAR, E., Memory in mice as affected by intracerebral puromucin. *Science,* 1963, **141**: 57-59.

11. FREEMAN, W. J., Correlation of electrical activity of prepyriform cortex and behavior in cat. *J. Neurophysiol.*, 1960, **23**: 111-131.

12. GALAMBOS, R., Changing concepts of the learning mechanism. In: *Brain Mechanisms and Learning* (A. Fessard, R. W. Gerard and J. Konorski, Eds.). Blackwell, Oxford, 1961: 231-241.

13. ———, A glia-neural theory of brain function. *Proc. Nat. Acad. Sci. USA,* 1961, **47**: 129-136.

14. GALAMBOS, R., and MORGAN, C. T., The neural basis of learning. In: *Handbook of Physiology; Neurophysiology III* (J. Field, H. W. Magoun and V. E. Hall, Eds.). American Physiological Society, Washington, D.C., 1960: 1471-1499.

15. GALAMBOS, R., and SHEATZ, G. C., Electrical responses evoked in the brain of the normal animal. *Fed. Proc.*, 1961, **20**: 326.

16. ———, An electroencephalograph study of classical conditioning. *Am. J. Physiol.*, 1962, **203**: 173-184.

17. GALEANO, C., Electrophysiological aspects of brain activity during conditioning. A review. *Acta Neurol. Latinoam.*, 1963, **9**: 395-413.

18. GASTAUT, H., and BECK, E., Brain rhythms and learning. *New Scientist,* 1962, **13**: 496-499.

19. HERNÁNDEZ-PEÓN, R., Sleep induced by localized electrical or chemical stimulation of the forebrain. *EEG Clin. Neurophysiol.*, 1962, **14**: 423-424.

20. ———, Attention, sleep, motivation, and behavior. In: *The Role of Pleasure in Behavior* (R. G. Heath, Ed.). Hoeber, New York, 1964: 195-217.

21. ———, A cholinergic limbic forebrain-hindbrain hypnogenic circuit. *EEG Clin. Neurophysiol.*, 1964, **17**: 444-445.

22. Hernández-Peón, R., Central neuro-humoral transmission in sleep and wakefulness. *Prog. Brain Res.*, 1965, **18**: 96-117.
23. Hernández-Peón, R., and Brust-Carmona, H., Functional role of subcortical structures in habituation and conditioning. In: *Brain Mechanisms and Learning* (A. Fessard, R. W. Gerard and J. Konorski, Eds.). Blackwell, Oxford, 1961: 393-412.
24. Hernández-Peón, R., Brust-Carmona, H., Eckhaus, E., López-Mendoza, E., and Alcócer-Cuarón, C., Functional role of brain stem reticular system in salivary conditioned response. *Fed. Proc.*, 1956, **15**: 91.
25. ———, Effects of cortical and subcortical lesions on salivary conditioned response. *Acta Neurol. Latinoam.*, 1958, **4**: 111-120.
26. Hernández-Peón, R., and Chávez-Ibarra, G., Sleep induced by electrical or chemical stimulation of the forebrain. *EEG Clin. Neurophysiol.*, 1963, Supp. **24**: 188-198.
27. Hernández-Peón, R., Chávez-Ibarra, G., Morgane, P. J., and Timo-Iaria, C., Cholinergic pathways for sleep, alertness and rage in the limbic midbrain circuit. *Acta Neurol. Latinoam.*, 1962, **8**: 93-96.
28. ———, Limbic cholinergic pathways involved in sleep and emotional behavior. *Exp. Neurol.*, 1963, **8**: 93-111.
29. Hernández-Peón, R., Lavin, A., Alcócer-Cuarcon, C., and Marcelin, J. P., Electrical activity of the olfactory bulb during wakefulness and sleep. *EEG Clin. Neurophysiol.*, 1960, **12**: 41-58.
30. Hydén, H., and Egyházi, E., Nuclear RNA changes of nerve cells during a learning experiment in rats. *Proc. Nat. Acad. Sci. USA*, 1962, **48**: 1366-1373.
31. ———, Glial RNA changes during a learning experiment in rats. *Proc. Nat. Acad. Sci. USA*, 1963, **49**: 618-624.
32. ———, Changes in RNA content and base composition in cortical neurons of rats in a learning experiment involving transfer of handedness. *Proc. Nat. Acad. Sci. USA*, 1964, **52**: 1030-1035.
33. John, E. R., Ruchkin, D. S., and Villegas, J., Experimental background: signal analysis and behavioral correlates of evoked potential configuration in cats. *Ann. N. Y. Acad. Sci.*, 1964, **112**: 364-420.
34. Magoun, H. W., *The Waking Brain*, 2nd ed. Thomas, Springfield, 1963.
35. Morrell, F., Information storage in nerve cells. In: *Information Storage and Neural Control* (W. S. Fields and W. Abbott, Eds.). Thomas, Springfield, 1963: 189-229.
36. Palestini, M., Davidovich, A., and Hernández-Peón, R., Functional significance of centrifugal influences upon the retina. *Acta Neurol. Latinoam.*, 1959, **5**: 113-131.
37. Stern, J. A., Das, K. C., Anderson, J. M., Biddy, R. L., and Surphlis, W., "Conditioned" alpha desynchronization. *Science*, 1961, **134**: 388-389.
38. Sutton, S., Braren, M., Zubin, J., and John, E. R., Evoked-potential correlates of stimulus uncertainty. *Science*, 1965, **150**: 1187-1188.
39. Svaetichin, G., Laufer, M., Mitarai, G., Fatehchand, R., Vallecalle, E., and Villegas, J., Glial control of neuronal networks and receptors. In: *Neurophysiologie und Psychophysik des visuellen Systems* (R. Jung and H. Kornhuber, Eds.). Springer, Berlin, 1961: 445-456.

40. VELLUTI, R., and HERNÁNDEZ-PEÓN, R., Atropine blockade within a cholinergic hypnogenic circuit. Exp. Neurol., 1963, 8: 20-29.

41. VISSER, S. L., Correlations between the contingent alpha blocking, EEG characteristics and clinical diagnosis. EEG Clin. Neurophysiol., 1961, 13: 438-446.

42. WALTER, W. G., COOPER, R., ALDRIDGE, V. J., McCALLUM, W. C., and WINTER, A. L., Contingent negative variation: an electric sign of sensorimotor association and expectancy in the human brain. Nature, 1964, 203: 380-384.

43. WHIPPLE, H. E. (Ed.), Sensory evoked response in man. Ann. N. Y. Acad. Sci., 1964, 112: No. 1.

NEUROPHYSIOLOGY AND LEARNING

I. MEMORY AND THE ORGANIZATION OF ATTENTION

Karl H. Pribram
Stanford University School of Medicine
Palo Alto

II. A "MODEL NEURAL SYSTEM" APPROACH TO THE NEURAL BASIS OF BEHAVIORAL CHANGE

Richard F. Thompson
University of Oregon Medical School
Portland

I. MEMORY AND THE ORGANIZATION OF ATTENTION

Pribram: The full title of my talk should be "Remembering and the Organization of Attention and Intention: The Case History of a Model." There are, of course, other models—other ways of handling the data I shall present —but right now I feel my model to be the best available. To show why, I would like to present a great deal of the data on which this model is built, for many of you have never had the opportunity to see as a whole the material gathered by my colleagues and myself. I shall organize my argument into three questions. Most of the work pertaining to the first question was done some years ago; most of the work related to the last question is now in progress.

First, how can one establish and characterize brain-behavior relationships? Specifically, I was interested in establishing characteristic relationships for those parts of the forebrain which, at the time the studies were initiated, were essentially silent.

Second, what is the psychological meaning of the brain-behavior relationships uncovered?

Third, what is the neurophysiological meaning of these brain-behavior relationships? By this I mean, what is a plausible model that would account for them? This last aspect is, of course, the most interesting, but in order to develop it properly I have to answer the other two questions first.

THE BRAIN-BEHAVIOR RELATIONSHIP

At the time I began this work, around 1946, there were two vast expanses of the brain cortex which were essentially silent to experimental manipulation: the posterior "association" cortex and the frontolimbic systems. We knew of no physiological function to assign to them, and we did not know, though conjectures had been abundant on the basis of clinical and anatomical relationships, what their function in behavior might be. Therefore the first subquestion was, how could we best proceed to desilence these brain areas?

The primary, though not the sole, physiological-anatomical technique used in this early phase of the work was the ablation method, checked histologically. As shown in Figure 18, serial reconstructions of the lesion were always made after sacrifice of the animal, and the depth and relation of thalamus or other structures were outlined whenever possible. Figure 19 shows some examples of reconstructions: a lesion of the hippocampus, showing the sparing (what was not removed at surgery); also shown is the extent of surface lesion.

The two areas I will be most concerned with, the inferotemporal region and the dorsolateral frontal region, are illustrated in Figure 20. With few exceptions, the subjects of the experiment are primates, mostly *Macacus rhesus;* experiments using man will be mentioned as well, but here reconstruction of lesions is of course not feasible.

Combined with cortical removals was an extensive behavioral survey of

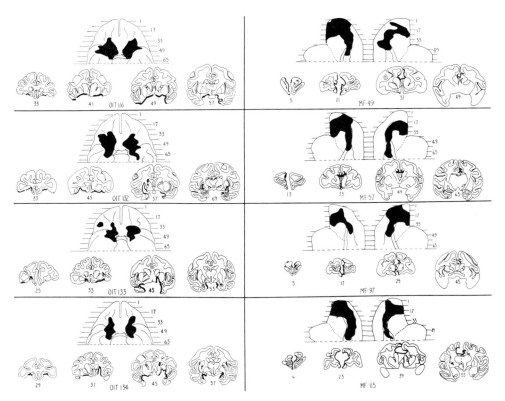

Figure 18. Reconstruction of ablation of the orbitoinsulotemporal (*left*) and medial frontal cingulate (*right*) cortex. (From Pribram, Lim et al., 60.)

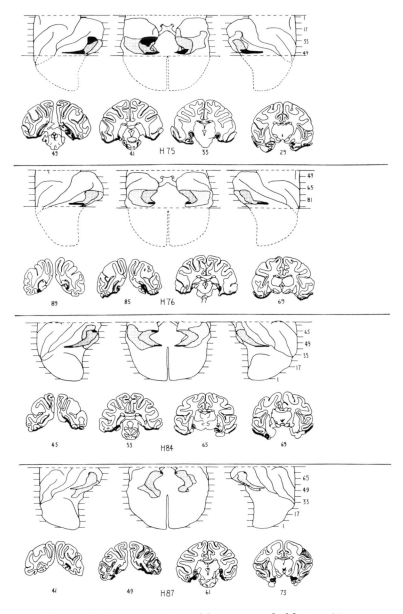

Figure 19. Reconstruction of hippocampal ablation. (From Bagshaw, Kimble & Pribram, 2.)

the subject, both pre- and postoperatively. A variety of behavioral techniques was used. Figure 21 shows a shuttle box in which conditioned avoidance behavior was studied. In Figure 22 we see an operant conditioning situation in which the monkey is taught to lever-press; its pressing rate can be controlled by simple cues and by programming the reinforcement. Figure 23 is an example of the Yerkes box in which monkeys can be taught to make visual choices between two alternatives. Figure 24 demonstrates a multiple-choice procedure which I devised. It is a modification of the Yerkes box; a

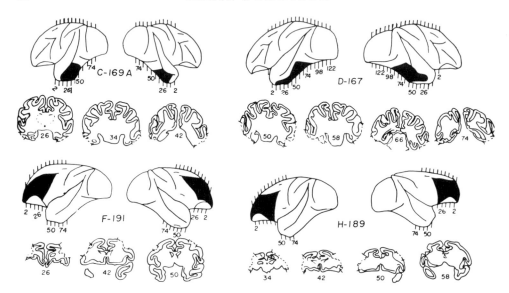

Figure 20. Reconstructions of ablations of the inferotemporal (*above*) and dorsolateral frontal (*below*) cortex. (From Pribram, 50.)

number of cues can be placed over holes in which the rewards are hidden. The position of the cues is randomized from trial to trial.

A further modification (Figure 25) shows our present setup. The multiple choice procedure has been automated and is programmed by a special purpose computer called the DADTA (Discrimination Apparatus for Discrete Trial Analysis) machine (56, 57). This device allows us to perform a great variety of behavioral tasks and saves much effort. In addition, DADTA is a much more powerful tool for the analysis of behavior than we had before. Both animals and children (and even adult humans) like to work the device. There is no experimenter directly involved in the situation, so there is reliability comparable to that obtained with operant equipment. Furthermore, each and every trial (i.e., every panel press) is recorded on punched tape, so that computer analysis of the data can be easily obtained. We can, for instance, program a sequence so the subjects must respond to 1, 3, 5, 7 in that order, before they receive a reward. There are a variety of problems that can be presented (57), and I shall describe some of these.

Figure 21. Shuttle box used for conditioned avoidance experiments. Upon shock from floor or other noxious stimulus, monkey moves from left to right box, eventually learns to respond to CS preceding shock and thus avoid unpleasant stimulus.

Figure 22. An operant conditioning apparatus (Skinner box). Press-lever or other manipulanda together with stimulus cues and reward source shown at back of box.

Just to give an example of the power of this instrument, in the old hand-operated Yerkes box, when a sophisticated animal—one having been trained for several years—is asked to discriminate between the numeral 3 and the numeral 8, it will probably fail to master this in 1000 trials. With the DADTA, a completely naive animal, directly out of the jungle, takes an average of 250 trials, which is five days of training. This is an unexpected dividend.

Grant: Besides Yerkes, Klüver (24) should be given credit for the apparatus.

Pribram: All right, Yerkes, Klüver, then Harlow. There is a current tendency among scientists to attribute a test or device to the latest of its inventors rather than to the earliest. We usually call the crude hand-operated device a "Wisconsin" apparatus.

Grant: I think there is a dramatic difference between Klüver's way of doing it and Yerkes', and it is a very important one. Animals can be readily trained with the Klüver version and not with Yerkes', for example.

Pribram: That is an important technical point. I would also like to point out that the DADTA machine is even better. Let us skip for the moment whose apparatus it is and ask what makes it better. There may be two reasons. One is that it is much more fun to work, with all the clicks and clatter. But probably the most important consideration is that, by changing the position of the cues on each trial, we are rid of any position tendency and find,

Figure 23. Yerkes (Wisconsin General) testing apparatus used to evaluate discrimination and alternation learning and performance. Monkey in cage faces apparatus but is separated from it by opaque screen; on each trial stimulus objects and manipulanda are changed and moved to within its reach on a sliding track and the screen is lifted; animal responds and a new trial begins. Note stimulus objects and manipulanda in lower left and right corners.

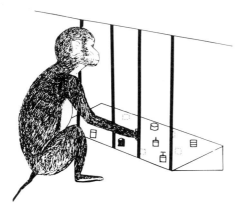

Figure 24. Modification of Yerkes apparatus for multiple-choice testing. (From Pribram, 47.)

therefore, no position habits to confound with the discrimination for which we are testing. Most animals and children will respond to position cues first, and only later will "catch on" that they may be irrelevant. By initially changing position from trial to trial, we immediately alert the subject to the fact that position is irrelevant. That is why the DADTA machine is a more effective tool for teaching discriminations. Another factor may be that in the hand-operated apparatus there is a screen interposed between subject and cues. This screen goes up and down; it is distracting and may interfere with testing. The automated apparatus has no screen; the lights that illuminate the cues just go out. We are designing a new version which will be programmed by a small general purpose computer (PDP-8) which will both operate the display and record the behavior. The technology has advanced sufficiently so that within a year we should be able to type in the particular task that we wish to display to the animal for solution, instead of having to dial it in, as we do now. This will give us still more flexibility in the choice

Figure 25. The automated form of the multiple choice apparatus (Discrimination Apparatus for Discrete Trial Analysis, DADTA). (From Pribram, Gardner et al., 56.)

of tasks. And, of course, with the general purpose computer on line, we will hasten our initial data processing as well.

The experiments to be reported were done with no fewer than four animals per group and, as a rule, the experiments have been replicated. If they have not, I will mention that these experiments stand alone, and have not as yet been checked either by someone working with me at some time or another, or in other laboratories such as Harlow's.

The first question, then, is how to establish and characterize the brain-behavior relationships. To do this, I devised a technique which is called the method of "the intersect of sums" (44). What I did was to take the first 40 animals and list separately those that had a postoperative deficit on a particular problem (such as a visual choice reaction), and those without such deficit. By a deficit is meant either failure to perform the task at criterion in 1000 trials, or to learn it in the number of trials taken to learn the task preoperatively (in other words, no savings). My criterion, arbitrarily chosen, is 90 correct out of 100 consecutive responses; all I have to say in its defense is that it worked. There are of course other criteria—for retention, for instance —and these serve other purposes.

The work summarized in Figure 26 included initially some hippocampal lesions; I felt at the time that I had invaded neighboring structures, and subsequently more precisely placed lesions showed the hippocampus uninvolved in the retention of simple visual discrimination performances. The method of intersect of sums was then applied in this fashion: plots were made of all the lesions that produced deficit (Figure 26A); of all the lesions with no deficit (Figure 26B); the two were superimposed (Figure 26C). The remaining cortex, the inferotemporal region, is the crucial cortical area concerned in visual choice behavior. No other portion of the "silent" cortex is involved. As I mentioned, there were 40 animals in this initial phase of the study. Since then this finding has been replicated many more times. We have now probably close to 1500 monkeys in the total series, a goodly number of which have had the inferotemporal lesion.

Using this method to pinpoint an effect, we next asked the question, what characterizes the brain-behavior relationship? One way of stating the problem is to ask what it is that is localized. Is there a "center" for "biological intelligence"? Is there one for "visual-somatic" space? Is there one for "sensory associations", and so on? We did not ask the question in that form at all. We asked, more simply, what we would find if we extended the "intersect of sums" technique to include other tasks. We discovered that the posterior portion of the silent areas was divisible into regions, each of which served one or another modality. There is modality specificity within this posterior "association" cortex. An example is seen in Table 3. One group of animals was given a parietal lesion; another an inferotemporal lesion. They were tested either for original postoperative learning (Group A) or for postoperative retention of a preoperatively learned task (Group B). The two

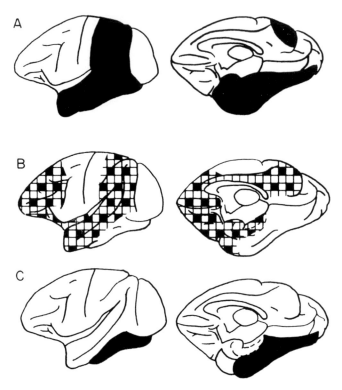

Figure 26. Diagrams of visual choice reaction. A: Sum of the areas of resection of all of the animals grouped as showing deficit; B: sum of the areas of resection of all of the animals grouped as showing no deficit; C: intersect of the area shown in black in A and *not* checkerboarded in B. This intersect represents the area invariably implicated in visual choice behavior in these experiments. (From Pribram, 44.)

TABLE 3

EFFECTS OF INFEROTEMPORAL (IT) AND PARIETAL (P) ABLATIONS ON
VISUAL AND SOMESTHETIC LEARNING AND PERFORMANCE*

		Preop. Learning		Preop. Retention		Postop. Retention		Postop. Learning	
		Discrimination		Discrimination		Discrimination		Discrimination	
		Visual	Somesth.	Visual	Somesth.	Visual	Somesth.	Visual	Somesth.
P	Group A	—	408	—	5	—	637	331	—
	Group B	320	—	0	—	194	—	—	821
IT	Group A	—	410	—	54	—	19	1000f	—
	Group B	518	—	0	—	1000f	—	—	439

* Data modified from Wilson (81).

TABLE 4

Effects of Inferotemporal (IT) and Posterotemporal (PT)
Lesions on Auditory Discrimination*

Animal	Learning and Performance Scores	
	Preop. trials	Postop. trials
IT-249	280	80
IT-282	280	0
IT-288	560	120
PT-248	200	600
PT-278	400	160
PT-289	880	440

* Data from Weiskrantz & Mishkin (80).

groups were trained on both a visual and a somesthetic discrimination task. As can be seen, after the parietal operation there was a difficulty in original learning and retention of the somesthetic discrimination (81). The apparatus used was an infrared device (9) by which the monkeys' performance was observed and televised, converted into visible light for display: the animals were working in darkness, but we could watch their performance on the television screen. Visual discrimination was intact, i.e., the savings criterion was met and original learning fell within the scores of the controls. Conversely, the inferotemporal group performed the somesthetic problem within normal limits, both on learning and retention, but showed complete failure in learning and retaining the visual discrimination (see also Pribram & Barry, 42).

In the auditory mode, the data (80) are not as clearcut. These data have not as yet been replicated, but we are now in the process of doing this experiment again. However, Table 4 shows that inferotemporal lesions, which resulted in a visual discrimination deficit, left auditory discrimination unaffected. Conversely, a posterior temporal lesion, which left visual discrimination intact, produced some deficiency in auditory choices; definitely in one subject, not so clearly in two others. Current evidence places these lesions somewhat too far posteriorly to obtain the main effect. For taste, an anterior temporal locus has been isolated (3, 54) by the similar use of the intersect of sums technique (44).

The question remains as to whether there are any "supramodality" regions in this posterior cortical region. This problem has been worked on a great deal, but as yet most of the results are unpublished. So far there has been no evidence in the monkey that there is a supramodality organization in the posterior "association" cortex (cf. Evarts [16] and Wegener*). In man, the data from Milner's group (35) in Montreal and Teuber's group (78) at MIT suggest that there might be such a thing as a locus for visual-

* Unpublished observations.

somatic spatial organization or for the organization of verbal behavior, irre-spective of mode, but these data are also subject to other interpretations. This is an open subject at the moment which needs much more investigation at both the human and subhuman levels. To summarize, all the evidence points to modality specificity in the posterior "association" cortex.

Now let us turn to the frontolimbic sector and examine the evidence. Fig-ure 27 illustrates the method of the intersect of sums applied to the delayed reaction experiment. The stippled portions in section A represent experi-ments from the literature (28), including one of my own (5), which suggest that there may be a deficit obtained from lesions in these locations; but this turns out to be an artifact of the particular task since there are control ani-mals that have never been operated on at all—four such animals in my expe-rience—which also show a deficit on this task (it is a most boring task, both to administer and to perform). This finding resolves the discrepancies re-garding occasional occurrence of deficit on delayed reaction following pos-terior cortical resections.

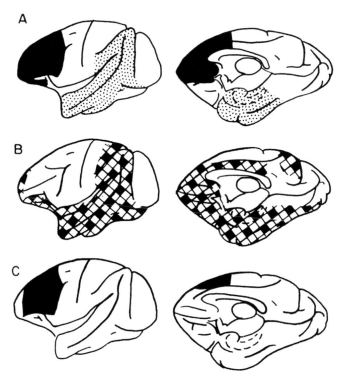

Figure 27. Delayed reaction performance. A: Sum of the areas of resection of all of the animals grouped as showing a deficit; B: sum of the areas of resection of all of the ani-mals grouped as showing no deficit; C: intersect of the area shown in A and that not checkerboarded in B. This intersect represents the area invariably implicated in de-layed reaction performance in these experiments. Resec-tions within the area stippled in A occasionally result in "deficit" as defined here; however, a similar "deficit" ap-pears in nonoperated controls. (From Pribram, 44.)

Another task, delayed alternation, is closely related but not identical to the delayed reaction. Performance of this task is impaired whenever a lesion invades the frontal or limbic cortex. To perform, the subject must simply alternate his response from trial to trial; right, left, right, left, with a screen interposed between trials. For purposes of "localization" procedure, the delayed alternation task appears to be more reliably retained. Nevertheless, as demonstrated here, the results of delayed reaction experiments may still be useful.

Grant: May I raise a question relative to information theory and the variability of the stimulus, particularly with respect to delayed reaction? I know what you mean by its being a rather boring experiment to run, but I assume you were running it with a fixed delay or long delay, or at least in blocks of constant delays. If you vary the delays from trial to trial, I suspect that you might get an entirely different kind of phenomenon, and possibly even a different part of the nervous system would be involved.

Pribram: There are variations of the delayed reaction problem that do make a difference (38, 39, 63), but varying the delay period is not one of them (64). We used a five-second delay, standard correction technique for both tasks. For the delayed response problem we showed a peanut to the animal over one of the food wells, brought down the screen, hid the peanut in the well, and then the screen went up.

Figure 18 illustrates some of the limbic lesions that produce changes in alternation behavior; an orbito-insulo-temporal (OIT) resection is shown. The OIT region includes the amygdala, the anterior portion of the insula, and the posterior orbital portion of the frontal lobe. It receives its projection from the midline, medial macrocellular mediodorsal and medial intralaminar nuclei (32). It can be differentiated as a unit by the method of strychnine neuronography (59, 61). Another such unit is the cingulate, which really comprises a good deal of the medial frontal cortex as well as the cingulate gyrus. This region is the projection sector of the anterior nuclear group of the thalamus (55). These nuclei project not only to the thin strip of cortex above the corpus callosum but more widely to the medial cortex anterior to and under the corpus callosum. Both of these regions have become standard in our repertoire. Finally, lesions of the hippocampal cortex also lead to difficulty with the delayed alternation problem.

When the method of presenting the delayed response and delayed alternation problems is varied, there can be further differentiation between lesion effects (Table 5). Frontal and limbic (OIT), cingulate and hippocampal lesions have different effects on the performance of different variations of the task (60). The effective variation is a change from a left-right to a go-no go procedure. In the alternation situation the animal is reinforced every alternate time and is expected to stay away from the well on the other times: on one trial a peanut is placed in the well, the screen goes up and the animal responds. On the following trial there is no peanut in the well; the animal has to learn to withhold its response. If it does not, the non-reinforced trial is repeated until it does withhold. On the next trial, the peanut is again

TABLE 5

EFFECTS OF LIMBIC ABLATIONS* ON CLASSICAL AND GO-NO GO ALTERNATION

Animal	Classical Alternation							
	Preop. *Learning* to Criterion		Postop. *Relearning* to Criterion		Preop. *Savings* on Retention		Postop. *Savings* on Relearning	
	Days	(Errors)	Days	(Errors)	Days	(Errors)	Days	(Errors)
MFC 49	16	(99)	8	(8)	14	(99)	8	(91)
MFC 57	27	(257)	2	(3)	21	(253)	25	(254)
MFC 97	5	(9)	4	(8)	3	(9)	+1	(1)
MFC 115	10	(24)	2	(19)	−2	(0)	8	(+5)
Average	14.5	(97)	4	(10)	9.0–62%	(90)–(93%)	10.5–72.4%	(88)–(90.7%)
OIT 116	16	(166)	2	(3)	14	(166)	14	(163)
OIT 132	23	(97)	22	(209)	17	(96)	+1	(−112)
OIT 133	13	(18)	4	(25)	11	(18)	9	(−7)
OIT 134	20	(130)	8	(50)	16	(128)	12	(80)
Average	18	(102)	9	(72)	14.5–80.6%	(102)–(100%)	9–50%	(31)–(30.4%)
Total Avg.	16.2	(100)					9.8–60.5%	(59)–(59%)
	Go-No Go Alternation							
MFC 49	13	(533)	4	(27)	2	(471)	9	(526)
MFC 57	20	(886)	14	(245)	16	(860)	6	(641)
MFC 97	23	(745)	12	(726)	21	(741)	11	(19)
MFC 115	14	(340)	4	(55)	12	(337)	10	(285)
Average	17.5	(631)	8.5	(263)	14.2–81.1%	(602)–(95.4%)	9–51.4%	(368)–(58.3%)
OIT 116	11	(496)	6	(192)	9	(491)	5	(304)
OIT 132	15	(816)	10	(380)	12	(813)	5	(436)
OIT 133	11	(713)	10	(1125)	7	(690)	1	(−412)
OIT 134	18	(618)	10	(800)	16	(615)	8	(−182)
Average	13.8	(661)	9	(624)	11–79.7%	(652)–(98.6%)	4.8–34.8%	(36)–(5.4%)
Total Avg.	15.6	(646)					6.9–44.2%	(202)–(31.3%)

MFC: medial-frontal cingulate; OIT: orbitoinferotemporal.
* Data from Pribram, Lim et al. (60).

in the well. This go-no go form of alternation is more severely impaired than the right-left variation of the task when the lesions are limbic (especially OIT). On the other hand, Figure 28 shows that, when the lesions are of frontal cortex, the go-no go variation of the procedure turns out to be much easier for the monkey than the right-left variation (39).

In summary, frontal and limbic lesions produce effects different from those produced by lesions in the posterior cortex. I have not reviewed here the evidence that the frontolimbic defect is not modality specific, but such reviews are in the literature (50, 67). The frontolimbic effect is demonstrated in a class of tasks of the delayed response and delayed alternation type. Further differentiation can be made between frontal and limbic structures by varying the problem from a right-left to a go-no go procedure. Performance in right-left delay tasks is more seriously disturbed by frontal lesions; performance of go-no go delay tasks suffers most from limbic lesions.

Removal of cerebral tissue has not been the only tool in our armamen-

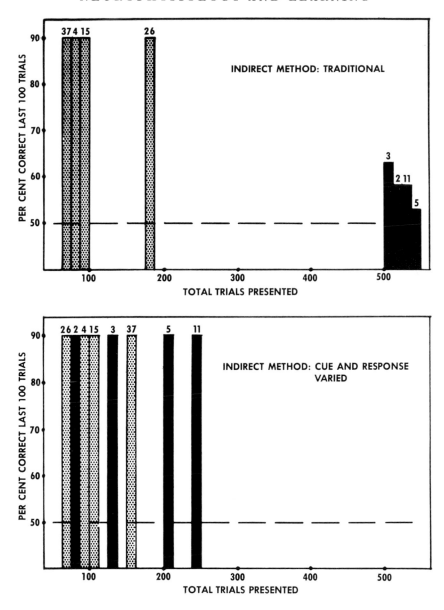

Figure 28. Comparison of the effects of inferotemporal frontal ablations on classical (*above*) and go-no go (*below*) alternation. Each bar represents the performance of one animal (designated by numbers atop bars). Black: frontal ablations; stippled: controls. (From Pribram, 44.)

tarium. Simultaneously, experiments have been carried out in which we placed aluminum hydroxide cream on the cortex or injected it into selected cortical areas (43, 45, 77). Multiple foci of altered electrical activity were thus produced, often leading to actual seizure patterns. The behavioral techniques found useful in the ablation experiments were used in these studies as well.

When we train the animal before the abnormal electrical activity develops (e.g., spikes or spike and slow wave complexes), we find no impairment of visual discrimination behavior as a result of inferotemporal implantation. As seen in Figure 29A, the monkey runs along smoothly at criterion, despite the abnormal electrical activity. As in the case of the ablation experiments, the aluminum hydroxide cream implantations were made in each of the regions we have been discussing. Performance was recorded for many weeks (74, 75, 76). In Figure 29B we have another example—alternation performance after frontal implantation.

On the other hand, if the animals are trained only after the abnormal electrical activity has appeared, a marked change in behavior can be demonstrated (Figure 30): original learning of a particular task is impaired when the electrical activity of the appropriate cortex becomes abnormal. The figure depicts again the visual choice reaction, visual discrimination following EEG abnormality in the inferotemporal cortex. Learning is delayed approximately fivefold. Note that the slope of the curve is not drasti-

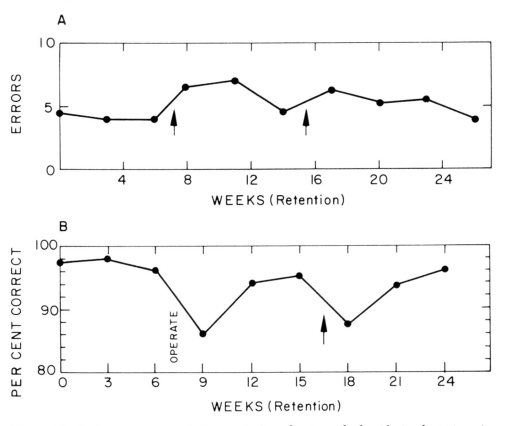

Figure 29. Performance scores before and after aluminum hydroxide implantation. A: Visual discrimination problem and implantation (left arrow) on the inferotemporal cortex; right arrow indicates the onset of electrical seizure patterns. (From Stamm & Pribram, 75.) B. Alternation performance and frontal lobe implantation; arrow shows onset of electrical seizure patterns. (From Stamm & Pribram, 76.)

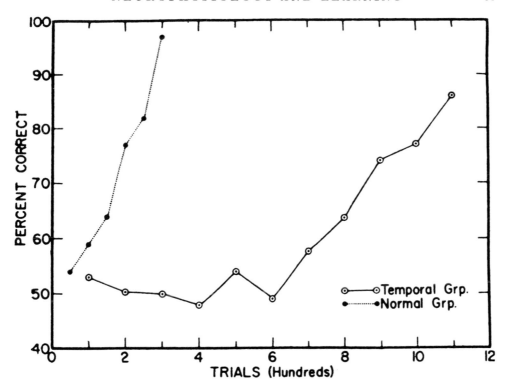

Figure 30. Visual discrimination of a learning curve obtained from a group of monkeys with electrical seizures recorded from inferotemporal implantation sites. (From Stamm & Pribram, 76.)

cally changed; rather, the onset of learning is retarded. This finding may be important to uncovering the mechanism which underlies the disturbance.

Impaired alternation learning is represented in Figure 31. There is no long delay before an inflection point, but alternation learning ordinarily shows no such "single element" attributes even when normal subjects are used, as can be seen from this control sample.

Before going on to even more interesting data, I would like to point out that these last experiments bear directly on something Dr. Galambos mentioned earlier, the problem of distinguishing between performance and the acquisition of that performance. The acquisition of behavior appears to be highly correlated with what we obtain electrically from the brain, but we have not been able to find any such correlation between electrical changes and performance *per se*.

To make the story complete I should mention that a converse experimental result has also been obtained. Using the ablation technique, Lawrence Weiskrantz (79) of Cambridge University followed this paradigm: train the animals on a particular day to criterion on a particular discrimination, let us say A *versus* B. On the following day, test for the retention of A *versus* B,

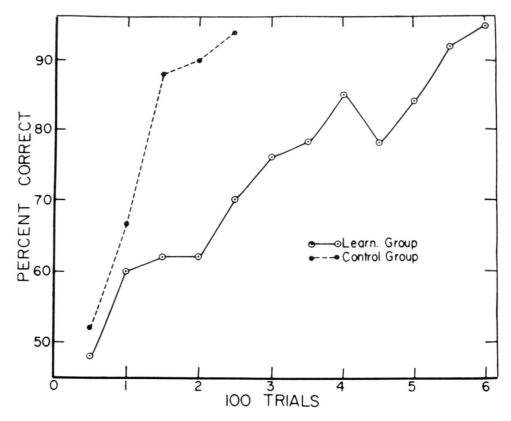

Figure 31. Alternations learning curve recorded from a group of monkeys with frontal
lobe electrical seizures. (From Stamm & Pribram, 75.)

and teach a new discrimination, C *versus* D. On day three test for retention
of C *versus* D, and teach E *versus* F. He did this with many variations, always using easily discriminable cues such as a variety of small objects, and
showed that after ablation of the inferotemporal cortex learning was
unaffected, though remembering suffered severely. In other words, the acquisition of new performance remained unimpaired by the resection; learning rates were identical, summed across days. On the other hand, retention
was markedly impaired; that is, from day to day these animals forgot a
good deal of what they had learned the day before.

In summary, the irritative and the ablative lesions produce different results: the brain's electrical abnormality is correlated with altered acquisition, brain cortex removal with disturbed remembering. I use the word "remembering" here as opposed to "dismembering", in the sense that these
animals must put together again, or retrieve, elements used to solve problems.

Birch: How do you interpret the long period of no change? Is there something happening that is irrelevant to learning?

Pribram: If you can tell me what process is going on to generate the part of a backward learning curve prior to the inflection when learning presumably takes place, I will be glad to tell you what may be going on in these experiments. At the moment, I do not know. (Incidentally, we have plotted many of our visual discrimination results as backwards learning curves and usually obtained a nice sharp rise—though we have not tested for stationarity in most of the experiments.) Figure 31 shows that this same abrupt rise does not appear when alternation behavior is examined.

Brazier: How many days postoperative is zero?

Pribram: Zero is usually at least a month postoperative in these experiments, because the seizure pattern usually does not develop until three weeks to a month after implantation. We wait at least until we have seen the abnormal electrical pattern on two occasions and we record once a week.

Miller: Do such patterns continue once they are established? Is there no change in the electrical activity associated with the beginning of learning?

Pribram: We have tested for only three to six months, and during that time the abnormalities are maintained. I would not say there is no change, but we still see the abnormal activity.

O'Connor: Because of the behavioral manifestation in the operated group, is there any indication of head or eye movements during the delayed augmentation?

Pribram: Not from the lesions I am reporting here. If we make the irritative focus in the motor region, we see Jacksonian motor seizures, and the animals also show tremors both at rest and during intentional movement. But that is another story (58).

The Psychological Significance of the Brain-Behavior Relationships

The psychological significance of the findings described can be concretized somewhat like this: if a deficit in color discrimination is obtained, does it mean that the animal is color blind? Part of the cortex is removed, and the animal now fails a color discrimination; does that in itself mean the animal is color blind? Obviously not. We need other kinds of tasks besides color discrimination to test the limits of the deficient behavior. We turned to brightness differences and to patterns of various sorts, and found all manner of visual tasks to be affected by this particular lesion (36, 38, 39). Figure 32 shows that differences in the physical dimensions of the stimulus, in this case a size, are distinguished less after the lesion (37), but this is not the whole story.

One day, while testing monkeys with such lesions at the Yerkes laboratories in Orange Park, Florida, I sat down to rest from the chore of carrying the monkeys the goodly distance between home cage and laboratory. The monkeys were failing miserably the visual discrimination tasks. It was a hot,

muggy, typical Florida summer afternoon and the air was swarming with
gnats. My monkey reached out and caught a gnat. Without thinking, I also
reached for a gnat: I did not catch it. The monkey reached out again, and
again it caught a gnat and put it in its mouth. I reached out—missed! Finally, the paradox of the situation forced itself on me. I took the beast back to
the testing room, but it was as deficient as ever in making visual choices.

   This observation gave rise to the following experiment, which Ettlinger
(15) accomplished, with the results shown in Figure 33. We hypothesized
that choice was the crucial variable; as long as a monkey does not have to
make a choice, its visual performance should be found intact. Monkeys
were trained in a Ganzfeld made of a translucent light fixture large enough
so that an animal could be physically inserted into it. The monkey could
press a single lever throughout the procedure, but was rewarded only during the period when illumination was markedly increased for several seconds at a time. Soon response frequency became maximum during this
"bright" period. Under such conditions no differences in performance were
obtained between inferotemporally lesioned and control animals. The result

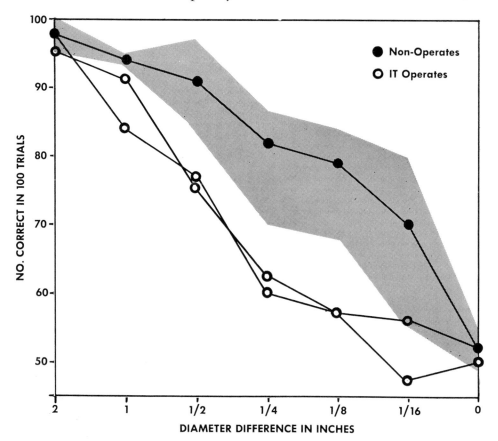

Figure 32. Difference in performance of inferotemporal and control monkeys on a
visual discrimination problem in which size discrimination was varied parametrically.
Shaded area: variability. (From Mishkin & Hall, 37.)

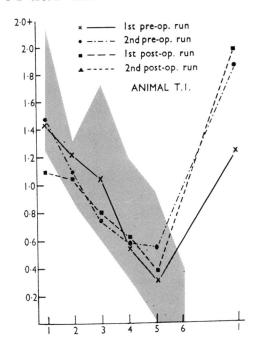

Figure 33. Single manipulandum performance curves of a single animal in a varying brightness situation. *Abscissa:* Geometrically decreasing differences in luminance between positive and negative cues; *ordinate:* log of ratio of response rate to positive and negative cues. Shaded area indicates variability among groups of 4 animals. (From Ettlinger, 15.)

tended to support our feeling that, if an inferotemporally lesioned monkey did not have to make a choice, he would show no deficit in behavior. The animal is not punished for error because that would entail a choice. The lack of punishment is important in making this experiment closer to an "existential" discrimination, which would be ideal. Error is not involved. The monkey can press any time, but has been reinforced only when the "brighter" condition is in effect, and the difference in reward between the conditions is further minimized by the fact that the brighter condition is rewarded on a modified fixed ratio schedule, i.e., not every lever press is rewarded.

Miller: If you reinforced the animal 100 per cent for responding to the correct light and zero for the incorrect response, would it then have a deficit in that same Ganzfeld?

Pribram: In a simultaneous choice experiment, inferotemporally lesioned monkeys fail to respond differentially to differences in brightness (39). Another difference in discrimination is that illumination is general in one case and specific to the object in the other; one is of "ground", the other of "figure". There are also differences in the reinforcement schedule. The following experiment may clarify the problem.

We (62) trained the monkeys on a very simple object discrimination, an ash tray *versus* a tobacco tin. These animals had been trained for two or three years before they were operated on and were therefore sophisticated problem solvers; this, plus ease of task, accounts for the minimal deficit in the simultaneous choice task. When, however, we take the same cues and present them successively (there are two types of successive discriminations: in one the animal has to go either left or right), the monkeys show a deficit when compared with their controls (Figure 34). We know they can differentiate the cues from their performance in the simultaneous situation; yet when a more difficult response is required they have difficulties.

This result further supported the idea that the problem for the operated monkeys was not so much in "seeing" but in usefully differentiating what they saw. It is not only the stimulus condition *per se* but the contexts in which it appears that determine the deficit. Another, more precise, way of stating this is that the deficit ought to vary as a function of the number of alternatives in the situation. This hypothesis was therefore tested directly in another experiment (47). It has not as yet been replicated and so the results must be considered tentative, albeit persuasive. The hope was that an informational measure of the deficit could be obtained. Figure 35 shows that actually something very different appeared when the number of errors was plotted against the number of alternatives.

The square root transformation is of the raw data. Since analysis of variance was used to establish significance, the data had to be normalized first. I want to point out some other complications in the experiment. First, there is the confounding of the number of alternatives in the situation and the order in which they were presented; this is therefore not really a good test of the information measurement model that I had in mind. The experiment

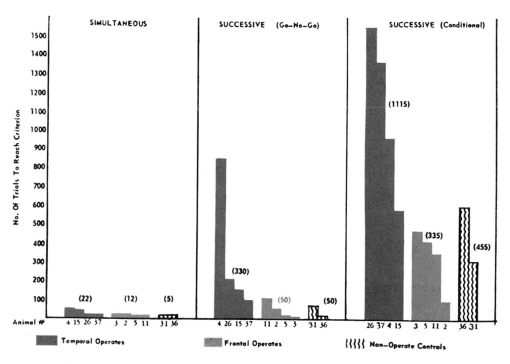

Figure 34. Comparison of learning scores on three types of object discrimination by three groups of monkeys. Note that, though the cues remain the same, changing the demanded response increases the deficit of the inferotemporal groups. (From Pribram & Mishkin, 62.)

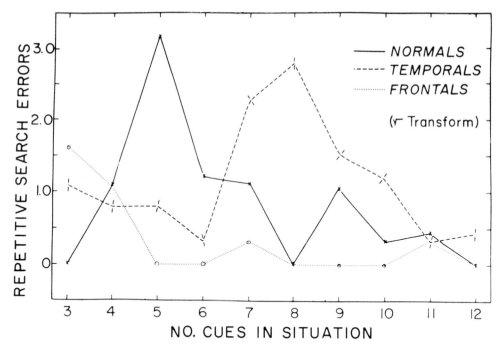

Figure 35. Average number of repetitive errors made in the multiple object experiment during those search trials in each situation when the additional (novel) cue is first added. Four animals per group. (From Pribram, 47.)

could not be done as originally planned because, up to that time, no one had ever tested monkeys on more than three cues at a time. I had to start with two cues and work up. Also, there was no way of matching preferences for cues and so the same cues were used throughout the experiment, balanced in order of presentation among subjects but given in a standard order for each subject. Despite these limitations, a thought-provoking result emerged from the experiment.

If repetitive errors are plotted—i.e., the number of times a monkey searches the same cue, against the number of alternatives in the situation—a hump is found in the curve, a stage of many repetitive errors through which normal animals go; they then recover adequate performance and go on to complete the task with facility. What intrigued me was that during this stage the monkeys with inferotemporal lesions were doing better than the controls. This was a paradox. As the procedure continued, however, and after the controls no longer made so many errors, the inferotemporals began to accumulate an error hump even greater than that shown earlier by the controls. The analysis of variance shows these two curves to be significantly different despite their overlap in the latter half of the graph.

Before I had such an explanation I presented the results of this experiment informally to a group, and Edward Green, a mathematical psychologist, suggested that the position of this hump varied with the number of alternatives sampled by the subject, and that the inferotemporally lesioned monkeys who showed the delayed hump had sampled fewer cues in the early stages of the experiment. Since these cues had to be uncovered, I had a record of actual "sampling" when a particular cue was turned over. It was only necessary to go back through the data to see whether differences in sampling between groups was obtained.

The differences did occur, as can be seen in Figure 36. The monkeys with inferotemporal lesions showed a lowered sampling ratio: they sampled fewer cues during the first half of the experiment. We might characterize their performance as a restriction in their visual field; however, the limitation is not in the visual-spatial field but in the information-processing field, i.e., the number of alternatives they can sample or handle at any one time. This curve shows that most of the variance that accounts for the error humps was obtained when a novel cue was introduced into the situation. The inferotemporally lesioned subjects (as well as the controls) made their runs of repetitive errors on these occasions. (Frontally lesioned subjects invariably chose the novel cue immediately.) During a trial, the monkeys had just one chance to sample a cue; the screen came down between trials. When there were only four or five cues in the situation, the inferotemporally lesioned monkeys found the correct one more rapidly than did the con-

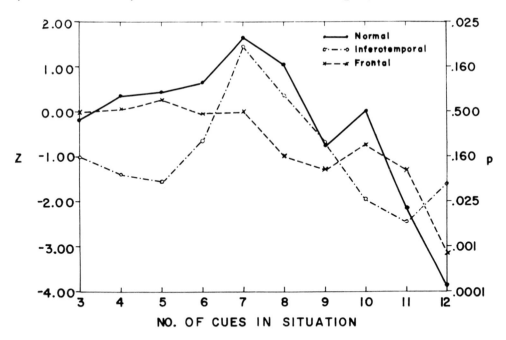

Figure 36. Sampling performance except novel cue. Average percentage of the total number of objects (cues) that are sampled by each of the groups in each of the situations. To sample, a monkey had to move an object until the content or lack of content of the food well was clearly visible to the experimenter. As was predicted (47), during the first half of the experiment the curve representing the sampling ratio of the posteriorly lesioned group differs significantly from the others at the 0.024 level (according to the non-parametric Mann-Whitney U procedure; cf. Mann & Whitney, 31.)

trols, who sampled more of the previously reinforced cues before turning over the novel cue. The correct cue object is always the same until a criterion is met; then a "discrimination reversal" type of procedure takes place until all of the cues have been rewarded. All cues that had previously been reinforced are still present; only the currently correct cue changes. For example, the monkeys go through a whole series of problems for which red is correct. When they reach criterion on red, then reversal is instituted and green becomes correct. After criterion is reached on green, blue is added as the correct cue. To reach criterion they must choose the correct cue on five successive trials.

In summary, the modality-specific defect that results from a posterior "association" system lesion appears to produce an information processing defect best described as a restriction on the number of alternatives searched and sampled—a reversion to chance behavior when compared with a control group whose sampling is guided by the history of prior differential discriminations. In short, the lesioned monkeys fail to remember prior discriminations as well as the controls, and this failure alters the sampling of current cues, i.e., the process of selective attention. I will return to this notion of a memory-based information processing defect when I discuss the model. But first let me present briefly some data on the frontolimbic systems.

For purposes of comparison, Figure 37, A and B, demonstrates that frontally (and limbically) lesioned primates also fail to be influenced by their experience, but in a very different way from the posteriorly lesioned subjects. They appear to be impervious to the consequences of their behavior. Initially, this defect appeared most dramatically as imperviousness to error, i.e., in avoiding shocks (44, 65) and non-reinforcements.

In another experiment (50), the animals were trained in an operant conditioning situation. After several years of training on mixed and multiple schedules, four hours of extinction were run, i.e., the reinforcements (peanuts) were no longer delivered, although everything else in the situation remained the same. Figure 38 shows the results; note that the frontally lesioned animals failed to extinguish in the four-hour period, whereas the control monkeys did. This failure in extinction accounts for poor performance in another task. Figure 39 shows what happens to the number of repetitive errors made in a go-no go alternation: the frontally lesioned animals do make many more repetitive errors. Even though they do not find a peanut, they go right back and keep looking (47).

This result was confirmed and amplified in a study by Wilson (82), who analyzed the occasions for error—did errors follow alternation or nonreinforcement? He devised a situation in which both lids over the food well opened simultaneously, but the monkey could obtain the peanut only if it had opened the baited well. Thus the monkey was given "complete" information in every trial and the usual correction technique could be circumvented. With this apparatus the procedure was presented with four variations:

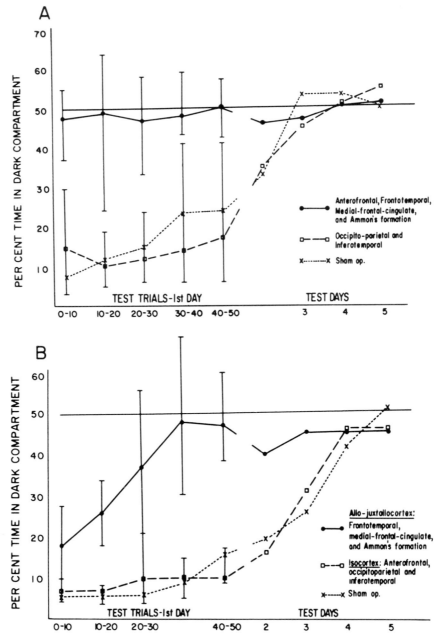

Figure 37. Performance of limbically and nonlimbically ablated monkeys during post-operative extinction of a learned conditioned avoidance response. A: *Pre*operatively learned avoidance; note that limbically and frontally operated monkeys behave alike. B: *Post*operatively learned avoidance; the limbic groups are clearly separated out by this procedure. (From Pribram & Weiskrantz, 65.)

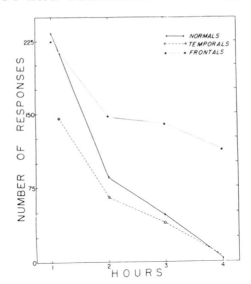

Figure 38. Graph of performance of three groups of monkeys under conditions of extinction in a mixed-schedule operant conditioning situation. Note the slower extinctions of the frontally lesioned monkeys. (From Pribram, 50.)

correction-contingent, correction-noncontingent, noncorrection-contingent, and noncorrection-noncontingent (Table 6). The contingency was whether the position of the peanut depended on the prior correct or incorrect response of the monkey, or whether this position was alternated independently of the monkey's behavior. Wilson then analyzed the relationship between an error and the trial preceding that error. For the normal monkey, the condition of reinforcement and nonreinforcement of the previous trial makes a difference, whereas for the frontally lesioned monkey it does not; alternation affects both normal and frontal subjects about equally; frontal subjects are simply not influenced by rewarding or nonrewarding consequences of their behavior.

This inefficacy of consequences to influence behavior is also demonstrated in the multiple choice experiment just discussed (47). Figure 40

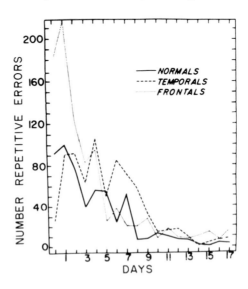

Figure 39. Graph showing the differences in the number of repetitive errors made by groups of monkeys in a go-no go type of delayed reaction experiment. Especially during the initial trials, frontally operated animals repeatedly return to the food well after exposure to the "non-rewarded" predelay cue. Note, however, that this variation of the delay problem is mastered easily by the frontally operated group. (From Pribram, 47.)

TABLE 6

PERFORMANCE OF FRONTALLY ABLATED AND NORMAL MONKEYS*

Percentage of Alternation as a Function of Response and Outcome of Preceding Trial

Subject	Preceding trial			
	A-R	A-NR	NA-R	NA-NR
Normal				
394	53	56	40	45
396	54	53	36	49
398	49	69	27	48
384	61	83	33	72
Total	55	68	34	52
Frontal				
381	49	51	41	43
437	42	46	27	26
361	49	48	38	35
433	43	39	31	32
Total	46	46	33	33

A: alternated; NA: did not alternate; R: was rewarded; NR: was not rewarded.
* Data from Wilson (82).

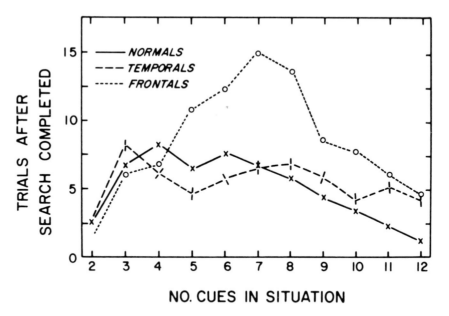

Figure 40. Graph of the average number of trials to criterion taken in the multiple object experiment by each of the groups in each of the situations after search was completed, i.e., after the first correct response. Note the difference between the curves for the controls and for the frontally operated group, a difference which is significant at the 0.05 level by an analysis of variance (F=8.19 for 2 and 6 df) according to McNemar's (33) procedure performed on normalized (by square root transformation) raw scores. (From Pribram, 47.)

TABLE 7

PERFORMANCE OF LOBOTOMIZED AND CONTROL HUMAN SUBJECTS
WHO COMPLETED THE MULTIPLE CHOICE TEST*

	Lobotomized	Controls
Mean total responses	625.9	359.2
Mean average search responses per program on Non-New Cue programs	8.8	5.9
Mean average search responses per program on New Cue programs	6.1	4.2
Mean average post-search responses per program on Non-New Cue programs	24.7	12.9
Mean average post-search responses per program on New Cue programs	3.7	5.9

* Data from Poppen, Pribram & Robinson (41).

shows what happens after the monkeys have found the peanut. The procedure calls for the strategy of return to the same object five consecutive times, i.e., to criterion. The frontally lesioned animals are markedly deficient in accomplishing this task. Again we see that the conditions of reinforcement are relatively ineffective in shaping behavior once the frontal engranular cortex has been removed, so that the monkeys' behavior is relatively random when compared to that of normal subjects (53). Behavior of the frontally lesioned monkeys thus appears to be minimally controlled by its repeatedly experienced, and therefore expected, consequences; the process of intention is impaired.

In case you should object to descriptive labels taken from the subjective realm of discourse (on the basis that they must not be applied to animals), Table 7 shows that the results obtained with monkeys hold for man, in experiments (41) performed with 20 lobotomized patients and their controls. The procedure was made as similar as possible to that used with the primates. And results were remarkably similar.

THE MODEL

These data led me to define (48) the psychological processes impaired by "association" cortex lesions and to suggest the outlines of a model for these processes. To review the definition, the posterior system apparently is involved in the process of selective attention (i.e., search and sampling the environment) while the frontal cortex has to do with the process of intention (i.e., the guiding of behavior by its expected consequences).

Now, at last, the model: the neurophysiology of selective attention and intention. The model is far from being complete or even buttressed by data. Rather, it should be viewed as a progress report and a projection of our current endeavors. Therefore let us first consider some facts, or rather some lack of facts, about the neuroanatomical relationships of the inferotemporal cortex. There is a dearth of neurological evidence to link this cortex to the

known visual system, the geniculostriate system. There are no definitive anatomical inputs specific to the inferotemporal cortex from the visual cortex or
the lateral geniculate nucleus. Of course, connections can be traced via
fibers that synapse twice in the preoccipital region, but such connections
also exist to link the visual cortex to the parietal lobe, the excision of which
does not change visual behavior, as we have seen. In addition, circumsec-
tion of the striate cortex does not impair visual discrimination (8).

Further evidence that these "corticocortical" connections are not the important ones can be seen from the results of the experiment in which I performed a cross-hatch of the inferotemporal cortex, much as Sperry (71) had
done, and found no deficit either in visual learning or in performance (Table
8). On the other hand, undercutting the inferotemporal cortex makes a vast
difference: both learning and performance of visual tasks become preclud-
ed. This suggests that the connections to this cortex essential to visual behavior must come from somewhere below, although large U fibers, dipping
deeply into white matter, are not yet ruled out. However, another possibility can be tested, namely that the essential relations of the posterior association cortex are centrifugal, i.e., efferent (46). There is some anatomical evidence to suggest such a notion: some time ago, I prepared two brains with
inferotemporal resections. These were stained in Dr. Walle Nauta's laboratory by his technique, and showed an efferent tract going down to the region
of the superior colliculus, ending either within its substance or in the surrounding reticular formation. No such fibers could be traced to the lateral
geniculate nucleus. In support of this finding there is a report by Kuypers
(27), who has also traced temporocollicular fibers in monkey.

The idea of an efferent mechanism "gating" or otherwise "partitioning"
the input to the geniculostriate system has a good deal of appeal as an explanation for the process of selective attention. To determine how an effer-

TABLE 8

Effects of Undercutting and Crosshatching Inferotemporal Cortex of
Monkeys on Their Performance in Several Discriminations

	Animal	3 vs. 8	R vs. G	3 vs. 8
Crosshatch	158	380	82	0
	159	180	100	0
	161	580	50	0
	166	130	0	0
Undercut	163	(1014)	100	300
	164	(1030)	200	(500)
	167	704	50	0
	168	(1030)	150	(500)
Normal	160	280	100	0
	162	180	100	0
	165	280	100	0
	170	350	100	0

A   B   C

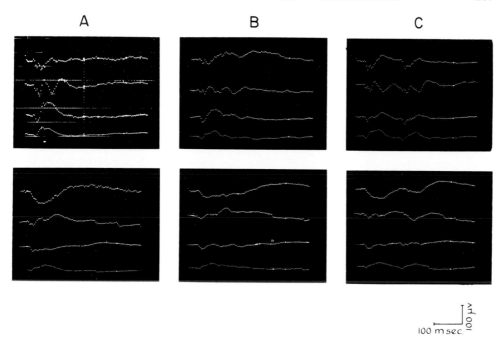

100 m sec.

100 μV

Figure 41. A representative record of the change produced in visual evoked responses by chronic stimulation of the inferotemporal cortex. *Above:* Records taken before stimulation; *below:* records during stimulation. All traces were recorded from the striate (visual) cortex; the top two in each set from posterior, the lower two from anterior striate cortex. The first sets (A) were recorded in response to a single flash, the second (B) to flashes separated by 75 msec., and the third (C) to flashes separated by 150 msec. In addition to the changed recovery, note also the change in wave form of the response upon presentation of even a single flash; this latter change, however, did not appear in all of our subjects. (From Spinelli & Pribram, 72.)

ent mechanism of this sort would work, we did experiments in which, instead of making ablations or implanting an epileptogenic lesion, we chronically and continuously stimulated the brain. These experiments are still in progress and are being accomplished in collaboration with Dr. D. N. Spinelli, a physiologist, who designed the stimulator and the recording equipment we are using (72). The stimulator is sufficiently small so that it can be implanted under the scalp. It puts out a square wave bidirectional pulse, 1 msec. in duration, of about 3 V. The frequency of stimulation is approximately 8-10/sec. The batteries that drive the stimulator are rechargeable.

The records in Figure 41 were made in the awake monkey. Paired flashes were presented and recordings made from electrodes implanted in the occipital cortex. The responses to 50 such paired flashes were accumulated on the Computer for Average Transients. The flash-flash interval is varied from 25-200 msec. The top traces were recorded prior to the onset of stimulation; the lower ones were made after chronic stimulation had been started. Actually, this was the first of our series of experiments to call our attention to the changed recovery phenomenon. Note that there is a general flattening (a finding idiosyncratic to this particular monkey) of the record made with the stimulator on, and that the recovery function is depressed, i.e., recovery is delayed. Figure 42 shows such effects summed across five subjects. I think it reasonable to conclude that chronic stimulation of the inferotemporal cortex produces a very marked delay in recovery of the cells in the visual system to visual stimuli.

A parallel experiment (12) in the auditory system was done in collaboration with Dr. James Dewson. In this study, made in cats, removals of the auditory homologue of the inferotemporal cortex were performed. This homologue is the insular-temporal region in the cat. Dewson has shown that its removal impairs complex auditory discrimination (speech sounds), leaving simple auditory discrimination (pitch, loudness) intact. Removal also alters paired click recovery cycles recorded as far peripherally as the cochlear nucleus. Bilateral ablation markedly shortens the recovery cycle. And, of course, control ablations of the primary auditory projection cortex and elsewhere have no such effect. Thus we have evidence that chronic stimulation of the "association" cortex selectively prolongs, while ablation selectively shortens, the recovery time of cells in the related primary sensory projection system.

These results allow us to specify the model. On the basis of the neurobehavioral and neuroanatomical data, I had previously suggested (48) that the posterior "association" cortex, by way of efferent tracts leading to the brain stem—most likely to the colliculi or surrounding reticular formation (46)—partitions the events that occur in the associated sensory specific system, classifying these events according to one or another scheme. During the

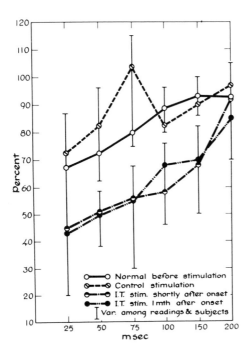

Figure 42. Plot of the recovery functions obtained in five monkeys before and during stimulation of the inferotemporal cortex. (From Spinelli & Pribram, 72.)

course of our joint work, Dr. Spinelli would ask me again and again, "How do you define "partitioning" in neurological terms?" Until we had accomplished these electrophysiological experiments, I had no idea. But once we saw the results, the neurophysiological explanation became evident: partitioning must work somewhat like a multiplexing circuit in electronics. In neurophysiological terms, when recovery time of neurons in the sensory projection system is increased by stimulation of the posterior "association" cortex, fewer cells are available at any given moment to the concurrent input. Each of a series of inputs will thus find a different set of cells in the system available to excitation. There is a good deal of evidence that, in the visual system at least, there is plenty of reserve capacity, i.e., redundancy, so that information transmission is not under ordinary circumstances hampered by such "narrowing" of the channel (1). Ordinarily, a particular input excites a great number of fibers in the channel, insuring replication of information transmission. Just as lateral (or surround) inhibition in the retina has the effect of reducing redundancy (4), so the operation of the "association" cortex enhances the density of information which the channel conveys.

This model has several important implications. First, the nonrecovered cells (the ones that are still occupied by excitation initiated by prior inputs) will act as context- or short-term memory against which the current input is matched. A match-mismatch operation of this sort is demanded by models of the process of recognition and selective attention spelled out on other occasions by Craik (10), Sokolov (69), Bruner (6), MacKay (30), and myself (49, 51, 52). These "occupied" cells thus form the matrix of "uncertainty" that shapes the pattern of potential information, i.e., the "expectancy" which determines the selection of input signals which might or might not occur.

Second, in a system of fixed size, redundancy reduction increases the amount of correlation possible with the set of external inputs to the system (20)—that is, the number of alternatives, the complexity of items, to which an organism can attend is enhanced. This internal alteration in the functional structure of the classical sensory projection system thus allows attention to vary as a function of the spatial resolution which excitations can achieve; i.e., attention can be given to events of greater complexity. The greater the resolution, the sharper the "uncertainty" and, thus, the more likely that any set of inputs will be sampled for information. In the extreme, this sharpening of the appetite for information becomes what the clinical neurologist calls stimulus-binding. Its opposite is agnosia—the blurring of uncertainty due to the simplification of the structure of the channel after damage to the "association" area which leads to an organism's inability to seek information.

Third, this corticofugal model of the functions of the so-called association systems relieves us of the problem of infinite regress—an association area homunculus who synthesizes and abstracts from inputs, only to pass on these abstractions to a still higher homunculus, perhaps the one who makes decisions.

I wish I could, at this time, present an equally rigorous neurophysiological model for the process of intention. But in this area we are a considerably greater distance from a precisely statable model. It is true that the process of reinforcement enhances redundancy (17). And, in part, the operation of the frontolimbic systems tends to balance that of the sensory specific systems. Monkeys with inferotemporal ablations tend to perform better on the alternation tasks which are so disturbed when frontolimbic lesions are made.

The reverse, however, does not hold. The data in Table 9 suggest that the change resulting from frontal ablation is in some respects different from that produced by inferotemporal stimulation. Perhaps this difference lies in the fact that the amount of redundancy *per se* is an insufficient measure of its efficacy (e.g., in minimizing error). The form or pattern of the redundancy is crucial; mere repetition is an ineffective form. Redundancy is thus not a measure of simplicity. Rather, when properly used, redundancy is not solely opposed to information (or uncertainty) but becomes an additional measure of complexity (20). The structure of redundancy, its temporal pattern, is therefore the key to the neurophysiological model of intentional behavior. Its keystone will most likely deal with temporal resolution of events, the temporal structure of behavior. Outlines of this structure have been formulated, but experiments have not as yet been accomplished to detail it sufficiently to allow the model to become actualized in neurological terms (34, 49, 52).

The problem of the homunculus is, of course, an extremely interesting one. Former ways of looking at the input-output relationships of the brain have come up against the problem of an infinite regression (implicit or explicit) of little men inside little men—homunculi associating sensations, abstracting from these associations and passing these abstractions on to the motor systems for action. Somewhere along the line of regress awareness comes in, perhaps in yet another anatomically separable system; and then

TABLE 9

Average Number of Errors Made on Learning of Visual
Discrimination and Alternation

	Laterofrontal n = 8	Control n = 16	Inferotemporal n = 8
Visual Discrimination	175	150	F
Alternation	F	155	90

n: Number of subjects in group.
F: Failure in 1000 trials.

there is awareness of awareness. According to the model presented here, there is no need for such infinite regress. Important functions such as perception and decision are going on within the primary sensory and motor projection systems. Other brain regions such as the posterior sensory-specific associated systems and the frontolimbic systems exert their effects by altering the functional organization of the primary systems. Thus these systems are *not* "association" systems; they simply alter the configurations of input-output relationships processed by the classical systems. In computer language the associated systems function by supplying *subroutines* in a hierarchy of programs, subroutines contained within and not superimposed above the more fundamental processes. In this fashion the infinite abstractive regress is avoided. One could argue that it is replaced by a downward regress of sub- and subsubroutines; to me this type of regress is the more understandable and manipulatable. The posterior association cortex is conceived simply to program, to structure, an input channel, perhaps through action on recurrent inhibitory collaterals within the channel. The effect of such action is to alter the speed of recovery of neurons in the channel once they are excited by inputs. And by means of the operation of such a simple device, information processing, sampling of the environment, and selective attention "automatically" follow.

Another advantage of the model is that the signal itself is not altered; the invariant properties of a signal are unaffected (unless channel capacity is overreached). It is only the channel itself—the channel within which the signal is transmitted—which is altered. Thus the same signal carries more or less information, depending on the "width" of the channel. I am tempted to extrapolate and say that the signal carries different meanings depending on the particular structure or organization of the redundancy of the channel.

Discussion

Magoun: Dr. Pribram's proposal that the association areas of the cortex exert their functions in discriminatory behavior by varying the information-conveying properties of input signals to primary cortical areas, through cortico-reticulo-cortical loops with the central brain stem, seems to me to have a great potential for elucidating the role played by these so-called silent areas of our hemispheres. I thought he built this up in a splendidly sequential fashion. He started with some of the basic features of neuronal physiology, through identification of frequencies of firing as the method by which neurons signal the intensity of excitation, and made reference to the action of facilitation in abbreviating the recovery time of discharging neurons and consequently modifying their interspike intervals, hence their firing frequencies. He went on to relate this to information theory (which explores how neural activity conveys information) in terms of the relations of interspike intervals and the probabilistic aspects of firing frequencies and timing to the features of novelty, monotony, redundancy, association, habituation, or extinction. He then applied these basic concepts to a functional model of higher neural activity, to account for the impairment of perceptual discrimination and acquired performance following lesions in these silent, lateral, frontal, limbic or infratemporal areas, which have never been found to influence significantly the activity of primary sensory or motor cortical systems by way of direct connections.

He next identified the corticifugal projections from these regions to the nonspecific facilitatory or inhibitory corticipetal systems in the central cephalic brain stem, and proposed that, by this route, the silent cortex acquired the capacity for modifying the function of the primary sensory and motor cortical regions serving perceptual and motor skills.

It seems to me that we can find support for this concept from a number of current findings. The collective magnitude of corticifugal projections to the central brain stem appears second only to that from peripheral receptors, and their capacity to modify the discharge properties of subjacent nonspecific systems can be inferred from changes in cortical EEG patterns, as well as by direct observation of changes induced in reticulo-reticular conduction by cortical stimulation.

In addition, as has recently been demonstrated, nonspecific corticipetal influences from the brain stem can either reduce or prolong corticoneuronal recovery time, thus controlling interspike intervals and, hence, the information-conveying properties of these discharging cortical areas. On the input side, for example, Fuster (18), Lindsley (28a, 73), Davis (11), and Dr. Hernández-Peón, as he showed earlier, have all demonstrated improved cortical reception of paired visual, auditory, or tactile signals during attention in human subjects, as well as during behavioral alertness and EEG arousal induced by direct electrical stimulation of the central brain stem in animals.

On the motor side, in both higher animals and man, the initiation of so-called skilled performance or voluntary movement has been found to be associated with the appearance of an arousal pattern of the EEG in the cortical motor area. Moreover, the threshold for evocation of movement by direct stimulation of this cortical area is much lower during alert wakefulness than during drowsiness or sleep. These data seem to fit well with the model presented by Dr. Pribram.

Its elaboration seems to me to provide some of the most insightful and potentially fruitful hypotheses yet to have been proposed concerning the mode of action of these most recently acquired and highly evolved areas of the cerebral cortex, which reach their greatest development in the brain of man. Its formulation seems a brilliant development on the part of a person who has devoted so much of his research career to the study of these cortical regions. I think all of us have been privileged, indeed, to have been able to hear its exposition at this conference.

II. A "MODEL NEURAL SYSTEM" APPROACH TO THE NEURAL BASIS OF BEHAVIORAL CHANGE*

Thompson:[†] Both Dr. Sperry and Dr. Calvin emphasized earlier the importance of analyzing behavioral change at the level of interactions among nerve cells. The research strategies discussed so far in the Conference have generally involved somewhat different levels of analysis. Normal animals are trained, and chemicals are subsequently extracted and analyzed (Dr. Gaito's review), electrical activity is concurrently recorded (Dr. Galambos' review) or, as in Dr. Pribram's extensive and elegant research, lesions are made and the subsequent deficits in performance are measured. All of these approaches are faced with the enormous complexity of organization of the nervous system.

I would like to talk briefly about a somewhat different strategy which is more specifically oriented toward the synaptic interactions among neurons that form the basis of changes in behavior. This approach might be called the analysis of "model neural systems". Instead of dealing with the complexities of the intact nervous system, we first eliminate much of the system and then study the neural processes underlying behavioral changes in the simplified remainder (e.g., spinal cord). The use of neural models is, of course, not without hazards. It is always possible that neither the synaptic mechanisms nor the behavioral changes of the simplified model can be generalized to the intact organism. At the very least the behavioral characteristics of the phenomenon under study ought to be parallel for the model system and the intact animal.

The type of model system analysis I am referring to is well represented by the recent work of Eccles and coworkers on long-term plastic changes in monosynaptic reflexes of the neurally isolated spinal cord (13). As an example, I would like to cite an ingenious study (14), in which nerves for all but a few ankle or toe synergists were cut on one hind limb in chronic spinal cats. The animals were given forced exercise, and the monosynaptic reflex responses were tested for the reduced groups *versus* control side and for an intact group on the operated side *versus* control side. Just as predicted, there was a large increase in monosynaptic responses from stimulation of the reduced muscle nerve relative to the control side, but no asymmetry for synergist groups not operated. Unfortunately, control animals in which the residual muscle groups were carefully protected from all exercise or mechanical stress showed just the same asymmetry of monosynaptic reflexes. The increase in reflex response was at least in part the result of severed nerves, not just of exercise.

In general, such studies have shown a variety of changes in monosynaptic

* The work reported here has been supported in part by Research Grants NB-03494 and B-2161 of the National Institutes of Health.

† Original data presented in this paper were obtained in a joint project with Dr. W. A. Spencer, of the Department of Physiology, New York University of Medicine.

reflexes, but only subsequent to surgical intervention. Normal use alone apparently is not sufficient to produce long-term plastic changes in these reflexes. It would seem that the neuronal system most amenable to synaptic analysis, the spinal monosynaptic reflex, is peculiarly resistant to normal plastic changes.

In searching for model systems useful in the study of learning, it is well to remember Dr. Konorski's suggested term "plasticity", which labels many types of behavioral change resulting from experience (25). While the transected spinal cord may not exhibit classical conditioning or other specific types of learning as they are usually defined, it does show a variety of plastic changes.

I would like to describe briefly a project in which Dr. W. A. Spencer and I have been engaged on the synaptic basis of flexion reflex habituation in the acute spinal cat (cf., 70). Our results to date illustrate some of the advantages and some of the limitations of the "model neural system" approach. Habituation, incidentally, is perhaps the simplest kind of plastic behavioral change. Its general importance has been emphasized in recent studies and writings by Hernández-Peón (22), Pribram (52), Galambos et al. (19) and others, as well as in extensive behavioral literature extending back to the 19th century (cf., 21). While habituation may not be conditioning *per se*, it is certainly a change in behavior as a result of training, and thus by definition an aspect of learning. Sherrington (68), using the acute spinal dog, was perhaps the first to study spinal flexion reflex habituation as such. Prosser & Hunter (66) demonstrated in a very careful study both habituation and dishabituation of flexion reflexes in the chronic spinal rat. In recent times, spinal response habituation has been studied by Hernández-Peón & Brust-Carmona (23), Nesmeianova (40), Kozak et al. (26), and Buchwald et al. (7). In our own experiments we used the unanesthetized decerebrate cat with low thoracic cord section.

The basic experimental design is extremely simple. Amplitude of the response of a flexor muscle to weak skin shocks delivered every few seconds is measured. "Dishabituation" is accomplished by a strong extra stimulus to the leg. During habituation training the muscle response amplitude decreases over a period of minutes to a stable habituation level. If the stimulus is withheld or given only once per minute, the response recovers gradually to control amplitude. A strong dishabituating stimulus given when the response has been habituated produces an immediate increase in response amplitude.

It would seem mandatory for those who study model neural systems to show that the behavioral phenomena of the model resemble those of the intact animal. In searching the behavioral habituation literature, we were able to identify some nine parametric characteristics relating habituation to stimulus and training variables for a wide range of responses and species.

For example, degree of habituation is directly related to frequency of test stimulus, inversely related to intensity of test stimulus, and so on. We were able to show that spinal flexion reflex habituation exhibits the same nine parametric features characteristic of behavioral response habituation, and may thus be considered a legitimate example of habituation. Times for development of spinal reflex habituation and spontaneous recovery range from minutes to an hour or more, depending upon conditions, thus placing them in the normal behavioral time domain.

The roles of several possible mechanisms were tested by the following simple experiments: (a) Electrical stimulation of afferent nerves with monitored neurograms ruled out changes in receptor function and nerve excitability, both for habituation and dishabituation. (b) Ventral root or efferent nerve recordings exhibited the same habituation and dishabituation as did muscle responses, ruling out muscle fatigue and neuromuscular changes. (c) Crucial participation of the gamma loop system was ruled out by section of all ventral roots and/or all dorsal roots, and by administration of Flaxedil: both habituation and dishabituation could still be obtained. (d) Stimulus generalization of habituation occurred to completely separate input nerves, ruling out changes in excitability of input afferent terminals. These experiments show that the essential mechanisms for habituation and dishabituation lie within the spinal cord.

Perhaps our most interesting data came from intracellular recordings of motor neurons participating in the flexion reflex being habituated. These data allowed us to test several hypotheses regarding the central mechanisms underlying habituation and dishabituation. Recordings were obtained using micropipettes filled with potassium chloride, citrate, or sulphate, from flexor spinal motor neurons identified by antidromic activation of muscle nerves.

The basic findings of the microelectrode studies are illustrated in Figure 43. Each response represents a series of approximately ten superimposed tracings recorded from a peroneal motor neuron. The upper lines show polysynaptic PSP's to cutaneous nerve stimulation (superficial peroneal N.) for control tests given once per minute (A), following habituation to a one per 3 sec. stimulus (B), and following recovery at 1/min. stimulation (C). There is a marked and significant decrease of PSP amplitude during habituation, followed by recovery to the control level. Note that not only do the EPSP's habituate, but that the IPSP components also decrease during habituation.

The lower line of tracings (D, E, F) shows interpolated monosynaptic test volleys (stimulation of the deep peroneal N.) given during each of the periods described above. That is, in the control and recovery series (A, and CF) each type of activation (polysynaptic and monosynaptic) was given once per minute, alternating every 30 seconds between the two types. In the habituated series (BF) the monosynaptic test activation was interpolated once a

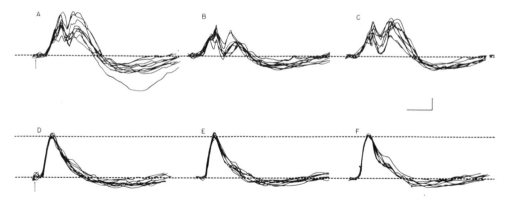

Figure 43. Intracellular responses (K citrate microelectrode) from identified peroneal motor neuron to polysynaptic (A, B, C; superficial peroneal N.) and monosynaptic (D, E, F; deep peroneal N.) activation. A: Control series, stimuli, 1/min.; B: during habituation training, stimuli 1/3 sec.; C: after recovery, stimuli 1/min.; D: monosynaptic tests interpolated 1/min. during control period (same time period as A); E: monosynaptic tests interpolated 1/min. during habituation training (obtained while the polysynaptic response was habituated to the level shown in B); F: monosynaptic tests interpolated 1/min. following recovery (same time period as C). Note decrease of both EPSP and IPSP components of the polysynaptic response (shown in B) after habituation training, but complete absence of any changes in the monosynaptic response. Calibration: 1 mV and 10 msec. (W. A. Spencer and R. F. Thompson, unpublished data.)

minute. There was no change in the monosynaptic EPSP as the polysynaptic PSP decreased. Consequently, there would seem to be no tonic change in the excitability of the motor neuron during habituation.

Interestingly enough, dishabituation by a strong stimulus (we used strong electric shocks or strong pinching of the skin) generally causes a significant increase in the monosynaptic test EPSP, as well as in polysynaptic PSP. There does seem to be a tonic increase in excitability during dishabituation. The influence of the gamma system had been ruled out in the situation, but an interesting point was raised: with the gamma system intact, the duration of the dishabituation effect is greater. The gamma system does seem to play a role in the time course of dishabituation.

Several lines of evidence tend to rule out phasic polysynaptic inhibition as a likely mechanism for habituation. Note in Figure 43 that the IPSP's of the polysynaptic responses decrease rather than increase during habituation. This suggests (but does not prove) that the amount of postsynaptic inhibition on the motor neuron is also "habituating" (i.e., decreasing). Since the postsynaptic responses are polysynaptic, there could be hidden IPSP's in the EPSP portions which might increase during habituation, thus leading to a net decrease in the size of the polysynaptic EPSP. To test this possibility, we obtained polysynaptic PSP's that were predominantly hyperpolarizing (i.e., mostly IPSP's) and reversed the polarity either by injecting chloride ions electrophoretically, or by electrically hyperpolarizing the cell. In both cases the inverted IPSP's *decreased* during habituation. Incidentally,

IPSP's from cells that showed purely hyperpolarizing responses also decreased during habituation. Thus it appears that phasic postsynaptic inhibition on the motor neuron is not the mechanism for habituation.

Finally, the possibility that pre- and postsynaptic inhibitory processes are occurring elsewhere in the system (i.e., in interneurons between input and motor neurons) can be tested with drugs. Strychnine abolishes several known instances of postsynaptic inhibition, and picrotoxin markedly reduces presynaptic inhibition (13). Administration of these drugs, given separately and in combination in doses sufficient to reduce or abolish both pre- and postsynaptic inhibition, has no significant effect on habituation or dishabituation. Consequently, we would suggest that pre- and postsynaptic inhibitory processes are not the neural basis of habituation.

As far as habituation is concerned, all of these data indicate that the decrease in response is the result of reduced input to motor neurons. The decrement must therefore occur in interneurons between input and output. Furthermore, results of the drug studies suggest that pre- and postsynaptic inhibitions are not involved. Our guess, and it is little more than a guess at the moment, is that the neuronal mechanism for habituation may be a polysynaptic analogue of the process of monosynaptic "low frequency depression". The latter appears to be a pre- or subsynaptic process (29), and bears some resemblance to the phenomena of polysynaptic response habituation. Dishabituation appears to be a separate superimposed sensitization process, possibly related to afterdischarge.

I have presented this material in order to illustrate both the advantages and limitations of the "model neural system" approach to the analysis of the synaptic basis of changes in behavior. We have been a great deal more successful in showing what the neural basis of flexion reflex habituation (and, hopefully, behavioral response habituation as well) *is not*, rather than what it *is*. Using some of the analytic tools now available from synaptic physiology, we were able to eliminate a number of possible hypotheses with some degree of confidence. However, we still cannot say what mechanisms do form the neural basis of response habituation.

Successful application of the "model neural system" approach is dependent both upon an understanding of synaptic processes in simplified systems and upon the choice of simplified neural systems that appear to show meaningful behavioral changes. Assuming that the latter requirement can be met, the rapid current progress in the field of synaptic physiology would seem to offer increasing possibilities for the "model neural system" approach to the analysis of neural mechanisms underlying behavior.

Galambos: Do you have measurements of any currents that might be flowing as a result of standing D.C. potentials in the spinal cord? Can the change in amplitude you see actually merely reflect a change with time in the standing potential of the spinal cord?

Thompson: I cannot give you a direct answer, since we did not measure gross D.C. levels of the spinal cord. Our intracellular recordings were D.C., and no slow shifts were seen. The fact that the interpolated monosynaptic EPSP's in Figure 43 did not change would seem to rule out the possibility that shifts in the "standing potential" of the spinal cord are involved.

REFERENCES

1. ATTNEAVE, F., Some informational aspects of visual perception. *Psychol. Rev.*, 1954, **61**: 183-193.
2. BAGSHAW, M. H., KIMBLE, D. P., and PRIBRAM, K. H., The GSR of monkeys during orienting and habituation and after ablation of the amygdala, hippocampus and inferotemporal cortex. *Neuropsychologia*, 1965, **3**: 111-119.
3. BAGSHAW, M. H., and PRIBRAM, K. H., Cortical organization in gustation (*Macaca mulatta*). *J. Neurophysiol.*, 1953, **16**: 499-508.
4. BARLOW, H. B., Possible principles underlying the transformations of sensory messages. In: *Sensory Communication* (W. A. Rosenblith, Ed.). Wiley, New York, 1961: 217-234.
5. BLUM, J. S., CHOW, K. L., and PRIBRAM, K. H., A behavioral analysis of the parieto-temporo-preoccipital cortex. *J. Comp. Neurol.*, 1950, **93**: 53-100.
6. BRUNER, J. S., On perceptual readiness. *Psychol. Rev.*, 1957, **64**: 123-152.
7. BUCHWALD, J. S., HALAS, E. S., and SCHRAMM, S., Progressive changes in unit responses to a repeated stimulus. *Fed. Proc.*, 1964, **23**:
8. CHOW, K. L., Effects of temporal neocortical ablation on visual discrimination learning sets in monkeys. *J. Comp. Physiol. Psychol.*, 1954, **47**: 194-198.
9. COX, R. R., and KRUGER, L., A device for observing animals in darkness. *Am. J. Psychol.*, 1955, **68**: 666-668.
10. CRAIK, K. J. W., *The Nature of Explanation*. Cambridge Univ. Press, London, 1943.
11. DAVIS, H., Enhancement of evoked cortical potentials in humans related to a task requiring a decision. *Science*, 1964, **145**: 182-183.
12. DEWSON, J. H., III, NOBEL, K. W., and PRIBRAM, K. H., Corticofugal influence at cochlear nucleus in the cat. *Brain Res.*, 1966, **2**: 151-159.
13. ECCLES, J. C., *The Physiology of Synapses*. Academic Press, New York, 1964.
14. ECCLES, R. M., KOZAK, W., and WESTERMAN, R. A., Enhancement of spinal monosynaptic reflex responses after denervation of synergic hind-limb muscles. *Exp. Neurol.*, 1962, **6**: 451-464.
15. ETTLINGER, G., Visual discrimination with a single manipulandum following temporal ablations in the monkey. *Quart. J. Exp. Psychol.*, 1959, **11**: 164-174.
16. EVARTS, E. V., Effect of ablation of prestriate cortex on auditory-visual association in monkey. *J. Neurophysiol.*, 1952, **15**: 191-200.
17. FRICK, F. C., and MILLER, G. A., A statistical description of operant conditioning. *Am. J. Psychol.*, 1951, **64**: 20-36.
18. FUSTER, J. M., Effects of stimulation of brain stem on tachistoscopic perception. *Science*, 1958, **127**: 150.
19. GALAMBOS, R., SHEATZ, G., and VERNIER, V. G., Electrophysiological correlates of a conditioned response in cats. *Science*, 1956, **123**: 376-377.

20. Garner, W. R., *Uncertainty and Structure as Psychological Concepts*. Wiley, New York, 1962.

21. Harris, J. D., Habituatory response decrement in the intact organism. *Psychol. Bull.*, 1943, **40**: 385-422.

22. Hernández-Peón, R., Neurophysiological correlates of habituation and other manifestations of plastic inhibition. *EEG Clin. Neurophysiol.*, 1960, Supp. **13**: 101-114.

23. Hernández-Peón, R., and Brust-Carmona, H., Functional role of subcortical structures in habituation and conditioning. In: *Brain Mechanisms and Learning* (A. Fessard, R. W. Gerard and J. Konorski, Eds.). Blackwell, Oxford, 1961: 393-412.

24. Klüver, H., *Behavior Mechanisms in Monkeys*. Univ. of Chicago Press, Chicago, 1933.

25. Konorski, J., *Conditioned Reflexes and Neuron Organization* (S. Garry, Transl.). Cambridge Univ. Press, London, 1948.

26. Kozak, W., Macfarlane, W. V., and Westerman, R., Long-lasting reversible changes in the reflex responses of chronic spinal cats to touch, heat and cold. *Nature*, 1962, **193**: 171-173.

27. Kuypers, H. G. J. M., Discussion (D) in: *Interhemispheric Relations and Cerebral Dominance* (V. B. Mountcastle, Ed.). Johns Hopkins Press, Baltimore, 1962: 114-116.

28. Lashley, K. S., The mechanism of vision: XVIII. Effects of destroying the visual "associative areas" of the monkey. *Genet. Psychol. Monogr.*, 1948, **37**: 107-166.

28a. Lindsley, D. B., The reticular system and perceptual discrimination. In: *Reticular Formation of the Brain* (H. H. Jasper, L. D. Proctor, R. S. Knighton, W. C. Noshay and R. T. Costello, Eds.). Little, Brown; Boston, 1958: 513-534.

29. Lloyd, D. P. C., and Wilson, V. J., Reflex depression in rhythmically active monosynaptic reflex pathways. *J. Gen. Physiol.*, 1957, **40**: 409-426.

30. MacKay, D. M., The epistemological problem for automata: In: *Automata Studies* (C. E. Shannon and J. McCarthy, Eds.). Princeton Univ. Press, Princeton, 1956: 235-251.

31. Mann, H. B., and Whitney, D. R., On a test of whether one of two random variables is stochastically larger than the other. *Ann. Math. Statist.*, 1947, **18**: 50-60.

32. McKegney, F. P., Telencephalic projection of the midline and intralaminar nuclei in the cat. *Yale J. Biol. Med.*, 1958, **30**: 415-428.

33. McNemar, Q., *Psychological Statistics* (2nd ed.). Wiley, New York, 1955.

34. Miller, G. A., Galanter, E., and Pribram, K. H., *Plans and the Structure of Behavior*. Holt, New York, 1960.

35. Milner, B. In: *The Organization of Recall*. (In press)

36. Mishkin, M., Visual discrimination performance following partial ablations of the temporal lobe. II. Ventral surface vs. hippocampus. *J. Comp. Physiol. Psychol.*, 1954, **47**: 187-193.

37. Mishkin, M., and Hall, M., Discrimination along a size continuum following ablation of the inferior temporal convexity in monkeys. *J. Comp. Physiol. Psychol.*, 1955, **48**: 97-101.

38. MISHKIN, M., and PRIBRAM, K. H., Analysis of the effects of frontal lobe damage in monkeys: I. Variations of delayed response. *Am. Psychologist,* 1953, **8**: 405.

39. ———, Analysis of the effects of frontal lesions in monkey: II. Variations of delayed response. *J. Comp. Physiol. Psychol.,* 1956, **49**: 36-40.

40. NESMEIANOVA, T. N., The inhibition of the motor reflex in spinal dogs under conditions of chronic experimentation. *Sechenov Physiol. J.,* 1957, **43**: 281-288.

41. POPPEN, R. L., PRIBRAM, K. H., and ROBINSON, R. S., Effects of frontal lobotomy in man on the performance of a multiple choice task. *Exp. Neurol.,* 1965, **11**: 217-229.

42. PRIBRAM, H. B., and BARRY, J., Further behavioral analysis of parieto-temporo-preoccipital cortex. *J. Neurophysiol.,* 1956, **19**: 99-106.

43. PRIBRAM, K. H., Some aspects of experimental psychosurgery: the effect of scarring frontal cortex on complex behavior. *Surg. Forum,* 1951, **36**: 315-318.

44. ———, Toward a science of neuropsychology (method and data). In: *Current Trends in Psychology and the Behavioral Sciences.* Pittsburgh Univ. Press, Pittsburgh, 1954: 115-142.

45. ———, Lesions of "frontal eye fields" and delayed response of baboons. *J. Neurophysiol.,* 1955, **18**: 105-112.

46. ———, Neocortical function in behavior. In: *Biological and Biochemical Bases of Behavior* (H. F. Harlow and C. N. Woolsey, Eds.). Univ. of Wisconsin Press, Madison, 1958: 151-172.

47. ———, On the neurology of thinking. *Behav. Sci.,* 1959, **4**: 265-287.

48. ———, The intrinsic systems of the forebrain: In: *Handbook of Physiology; Neurophysiology II* (J. Field, H. W. Magoun and V. E. Hall, Eds.). American Physiological Society, Washington, D.C., 1960: 1323-1344.

49. ———, A review of theory in physiological psychology. *Ann. Rev. Psychol.,* 1960, **11**: 1-40.

50. ———, A further experimental analysis of the behavioral deficit that follows injury to the primate frontal cortex. *Exp. Neurol.,* 1961, **3**: 432-466.

51. ———, The new neurology: memory, novelty, thought, and choice: In: *EEG and Behavior* (G. H. Glaser, Ed.). Basic Books, New York, 1963: 149-173.

52. ———, Reinforcement revisited: a structural view. In: *Nebraska Symposium on Motivation* (M. R. Jones, Ed.). Univ. of Nebraska Press, Lincoln, 1963: 113-159.

53. PRIBRAM, K. H., AHUMADA, A., HARTOG, J., and ROOS, L., A progress report on the neurological processes disturbed by frontal lesions in primates. In: *The Frontal Granular Cortex and Behavior* (J. M. Warren and K. Akert, Eds.). McGraw-Hill, New York, 1964: 28-55.

54. PRIBRAM, K. H., and BAGSHAW, M., Further analysis of the temporal lobe syndrome utilizing fronto-temporal ablations. *J. Comp. Neurol.,* 1953, **99**: 347-375.

55. PRIBRAM, K. H., and FULTON, J. F., An experimental critique of the effects of anterior cingulate ablations in monkey. *Brain,* 1954, **77**: 34-44.

56. PRIBRAM, K. H., GARDNER, K. W., PRESSMAN, G. L., and BAGSHAW, M., An

automated discrimination apparatus for discrete trial analysis (DADTA). *Psychol. Rep.*, 1962, **11**: 247-250.

57. ———, Automated analysis of multiple choice behavior. *J. Exp. Anal. Behav.*, 1963, **6**: 123-124.

58. PRIBRAM, K. H., KRUGER, L., ROBINSON, F., and BERMAN, A. J., The effects of precentral lesions on the behavior of monkeys. *Yale J. Biol. Med.*, 1956, **28**: 428-443.

59. PRIBRAM, K. H., LENNOX, M. A., and DUNSMORE, R. H., Some connections of the orbito-fronto-temporal, limbic and hippocampal areas of *Macaca mulatta. J. Neurophysiol.*, 1950, **13**: 127-135.

60. PRIBRAM, K. H., LIM, H., POPPEN, R., and BAGSHAW, M., Limbic lesions and the temporal structure of redundancy. *J. Comp. Physiol. Psychol.*, 1966, **61**: 368-373.

61. PRIBRAM, K. H., and MACLEAN, P. D., Neuronographic analysis of medial and basal cerebral cortex. II. Monkey. *J. Neurophysiol.*, 1953, **16**: 324-340.

62. PRIBRAM, K. H., and MISHKIN, M., Simultaneous and successive visual discrimination by monkeys with inferotemporal lesions. *J. Comp. Physiol. Psychol.*, 1955, **48**: 198-202.

63. ———, Analysis of the effects of frontal lesions in monkey: III. Object alternation. *J. Comp. Physiol. Psychol.*, 1956, **49**: 41-45.

64. PRIBRAM, K. H., MISHKIN, M., ROSVOLD, H. E., and KAPLAN, S. J., Effects on delayed-response performance of lesions of dorsolateral and ventromedial frontal cortex of baboons. *J. Comp. Physiol. Psychol.*, 1952, **45**: 565-575.

65. PRIBRAM, K. H., and WEISKRANTZ, L., A comparison of the effects of medial and lateral cerebral resections on conditioned avoidance behavior of monkeys. *J. Comp. Physiol. Psychol.*, 1957, **50**: 74-80.

66. PROSSER, C. L., and HUNTER, W. S., The extinction of startle responses and spinal reflexes in the white rat. *Am. J. Physiol.*, 1936, **117**: 609-618.

67. ROSVOLD, H. E., and MISHKIN, M., Non-sensory effects of frontal lesions on discrimination learning and performance. In: *Brain Mechanisms and Learning* (J. F. Delafresnaye et al., Eds.). Blackwell, Oxford, 1961: 555-576.

68. SHERRINGTON, C. S., *The Integrative Action of the Nervous System.* Scribner, New York, 1906.

69. SOKOLOV, E. N., Neuronal models and the orienting reflex. In: *The Central Nervous System and Behavior*, Trans. 3rd Conf. (M. A. B. Brazier, Ed.). Josiah Macy, Jr. Foundation, New York, 1960: 187-276.

70. SPENCER, W. A., THOMPSON, R. F., and NEILSON, D. R., Analysis of polysynaptic reflex response decrement in the acute spinal cat. *Physiologist,* 1964, **7**: 262.

71. SPERRY, R. W., Effects of cross-hatching in visual cortex in cats. *J. Comp. Physiol. Psychol.*, 1958.

72. SPINELLI, D. N., and PRIBRAM, K. H., Changes in visual recovery functions produced by temporal lobe stimulation in monkeys. *EEG. Clin. Neurophysiol.*, 1966, **20**: 44-49.

73. SPONG, P., HAIDER, M., and LINDSLEY, D. B., Selective attentiveness and cor-

tical evoked responses to visual and auditory stimuli. *Science*, 1965, **148**: 395-397.

74. STAMM, J. S., and KNIGHT, M., Learning of visual tasks by monkeys with epileptogenic implants in temporal cortex. *J. Comp. Physiol. Psychol.*, 1963, **56**: 254-260.

75. STAMM, J. S., and PRIBRAM, K. H., Effects of epileptogenic lesions in frontal cortex on learning and retention in monkeys. *J. Neurophysiol.*, 1960, **23**: 552-563.

76. ———, Effects of epileptogenic lesions in inferotemporal cortex on learning and retention in monkeys. *J. Comp. Physiol. Psychol.*, 1961, **54**: 614-618.

77. STAMM, J. S., PRIBRAM, K. H., and OBRIST, W., The effect of cortical implants of aluminum hydroxide on remembering and on learning. *EEG Clin. Neurophysiol.*, 1958, **10**: 766.

78. TEUBER, H.-L., Perception. In: *Handbook of Physiology; Neurophysiology III* (J. Field, H. W. Magoun and V. E. Hall, Eds.). American Physiological Society, Washington, D.C., 1960: 1595-1668.

79. WEISKRANTZ, L., Impairment of learning and retention following experimental temporal lobe lesions. In: *Brain Function, Vol. II: RNA and Brain Function; Memory and Learning* (M. A. B. Brazier, Ed.). UCLA Forum Med. Sci. No. 2, Univ. of California Press, Los Angeles, 1964: 203-231.

80. WEISKRANTZ, L., and MISHKIN, M., Effects of temporal and frontal cortical lesions on auditory discrimination in monkeys. *Brain*, 1958, **81**: 406-414.

81. WILSON, M., Effects of circumscribed cortical lesions upon somesthetic and visual discrimination in the monkey. *J. Comp. Physiol. Psychol.*, 1957, **50**: 630-635.

82. WILSON, W. A., JR., Alternation in normal and frontal monkeys as a function of response and outcome of the previous trial. *J. Comp. Physiol. Psychol.*, 1962, **55**: 701-704.

NEW DATA AND IDEAS ON INSTRUMENTAL CONDITIONING

JERZY KONORSKI

Nencki Institute for Experimental Biology
Warsaw, Poland

I propose to discuss the problem of the interrelations of classical and instrumental conditioning. Nowadays there is agreement that classical and instrumental conditioning are different types of phenomena; they have usually been studied separately and therefore their mutual relations are not clear. In the experimental techniques on dogs which Miller and I (10) developed many years ago, classical and instrumental conditioning were closely interwoven, so we had an opportunity to analyze their mutual interdependence and relationship. Work along this line is being continued in our laboratory, and I think that we have some good evidence to substantiate some concepts and ideas which, although not quite new, perhaps need such experimental support. Let me begin by examining the essence of our methodological approach.

Figure 44 shows a typical setup of the Pavlovian conditioned reflex (CR) experiment. The band attached to the dog's leg and two strings leading to the prechamber have been added. By pulling one of the strings the experimenter provokes a passive flexion of the animal's leg. The other string is connected with the system recording the movements of the leg. The figure illustrates our early experimental work (10) and was reproduced by Hilgard & Marquis (5) in their excellent 1940 monograph. Although the technique now in use is much less crude, in essence it is roughly the same.

Figure 45 represents the last stage of the elaboration of a motor instrumental CR by this method. The experimenter compels the dog to perform three passive flexions of the leg one after another; the process lasts approximately ten seconds, long enough to measure conditioned salivation. Then the food (meat powder) is offered. It can be seen that conditioned salivation had already been produced by the passive flexion of the leg. On the right of the figure we see that the animal, after eating the food presented, begins to perform the movement by itself. After each performance food is again presented; the dog eats the portion and moves its leg again and again. In this way the instrumental CR to the experimental environment is established, without any sporadic stimulus.

Figure 46 represents the already established instrumental CR. The animal

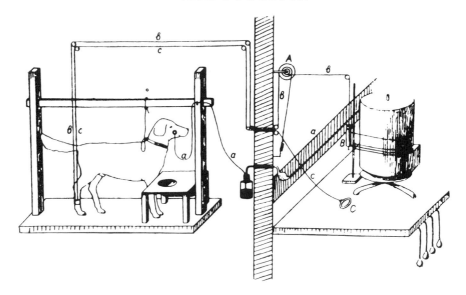

Figure 44. Original setup of our conditioned reflex experiments, showing the arrangement for recording salivation (classical CR). The dog on the stand is in a soundproof experimental chamber, and the experimenter in the prechamber. (From Konorski & Miller, 11.)

performs the movement and obtains food after each performance (IV). At the moment indicated by the arrow we give the animal a much larger portion of food, and consequently the act of eating is protracted. It can be seen that during the consummatory alimentary response the dog does not perform the movement. Of course, the animal can physically do it, but when it is absorbed with eating, the movement is inhibited. After the termination of the act of eating the performance of movements is resumed. When the dog is completely satiated, it will refuse to take food and will not perform the movement. We therefore share the opinion that the instrumental response is driven by drive; hunger drives or controls the trained movement.

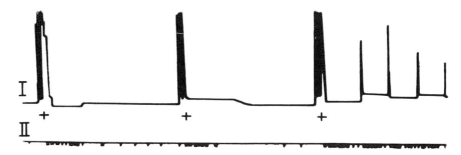

Figure 45. The formation of the instrumental CR by passive flexion of the leg. I: Movements of the leg; crosses indicate passive movements; II: salivation. (From Konorski & Miller, 12.)

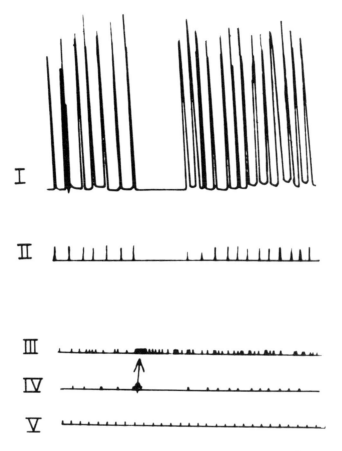

Figure 46. The instrumental CR to the experimental situation. I: Flexions of the leg; II: pressing a bar; III: salivation; IV: presentation of food (arrow denotes increased portion of food); V: time (5 sec.). (From Konorski & Miller, 11.)

The situation is more complicated in Figure 47. As I mentioned previously, during the act of eating (consummatory response), the instrumental movement is inhibited. In this experiment the animal receives classical conditioning before the formation of the instrumental CR, using as classical CS a bell and a metronome (120/min.); during their operation the animal has nothing to do but wait 15 seconds to obtain food. The negative stimulus is a second metronome (60/min.), not reinforced by food. Thereafter the stimulus eventually ceases to evoke salivation (the so-called *differentiation*).

After the animal has been classically conditioned thoroughly, the stimuli are no longer presented and it is trained to perform the movement of the leg to the experimental situation, as seen in channel I; it salivates copiously (channel II)—most of this is, of course, unconditioned salivation. The movement lasts only one second; then the animal receives food. When the bell is again presented for 15 seconds, the performance of the leg move-

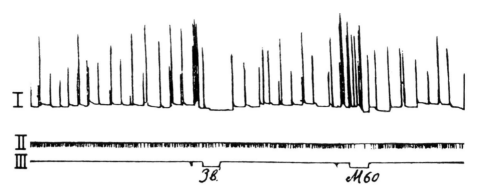

Figure 47. The classical conditioned stimuli applied against the background of instrumental responding. I: Movements of the hind leg; II: salivation; III: conditioned stimuli—first comes the position CS, then the negative CS, each CS preceded by 10 sec. of not presenting food, marked by the dash. (From Konorski & Miller, 12.)

ment is totally inhibited by the CS, just as by the unconditioned alimentary stimulus. The animal looks at the food tray as though hypnotized, waits for food, salivates copiously, but does not perform the movement.

Upon presentation of the negative stimulus (the 60/min. metronome), something very curious occurs (Figure 47, right): the animal keeps performing the trained movement, although salivation is much reduced. This is an important result to keep in mind; for the first time there is persistence of the motor response without salivation. The experiment shows that these two events are not as closely related as one would imagine.

Figure 48 illustrates the extinction of the instrumental CR. From the moment extinction begins (arrow), the animal does not obtain food. It may be observed that the dog performs the movement repeatedly with maximal frequency; the movements are higher than before, and are accompanied by profuse salivation—all of which is of course purely a conditioned response, since the animal does not get food. The movements gradually disappear, as does salivation. But these two processes are not quite parallel, for it can be seen that, when the extinction is far advanced, salivation decreases nearly to zero while the movements are still present. Thus we can say that, although

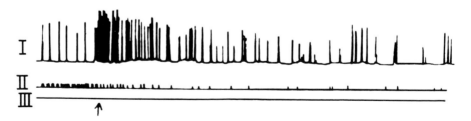

Figure 48. Extinction of the instrumental CR to the experimental situation. I: Movements of the hind leg; II: salivation; III: arrow denotes beginning of extinction. (From Konorski & Miller, 12.)

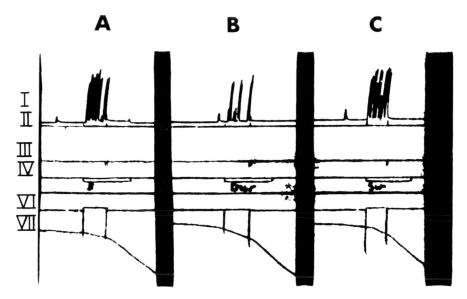

Figure 49. Instrumental CR to the original instrumental CS (A and C) and to the CS transformed from the classical one (B). I: Movements of the leg; II, VI: markers indicate the CS-UCS interval (10 sec.); III: food reinforcement; IV: CS; VII: salivation. (From Konorski & Wyrwicka, 13.)

both the salivary and motor responses do extinguish, they nevertheless do not occur synchronously (12).

The instrumental CR to a sporadic stimulus can also be established when the animal obtains food only after the movement is executed in the presence of this stimulus. The animal, of course, will first perform many movements in the intertrial intervals, but these movements are eventually extinguished, and it will perform the movement only to the given stimulus. While the performance of movements to the CS is always accompanied by more or less copious salivation, the relations between both responses are not simple, for sometimes they run parallel to each other, and sometimes one of them dominates the other. We did many experiments trying to find out why the two responses are not quite parallel, and to determine the conditions under which one or the other is obtained. Most times we were unable to find the causes of these discrepancies.

I would like now to describe another experiment, illustrated in Figure 49, and which was performed by Dr. Wyrwicka and myself (13) in the postwar period. As I mentioned before, when the classical CR is established to a certain stimulus and then the instrumental CR is established either to the experimental situation or to another sporadic stimulus, there is no transfer of the instrumental response to the classical CS. In response to this stimulus the animal will salivate and look at the foodtray, but will not perform the trained movement. We can try to transform the classical into instrumental CR by requiring the dog to perform at least one movement during the ten-second CS-UCS interval in order to obtain food. After some time the animal *will* learn to perform the trained movement to the previously classical CS.

Three different trials are shown in Figure 49. In the first (A) and third (C) trials, the original instrumental conditioned stimuli are given, while in the middle trial (B) the instrumental CS is that transformed from the classical one. It may be seen at once that, while the trained movements are frequent and vigorous in response to the original instrumental CS, they are very poor in response to the transformed CS. So, we see that the stimulus, previously a classical CS, not only fails now to elicit a strong motor response but, on the contrary, has a tendency to inhibit it, although salivation is quite conspicuous. There had been of course, partial extinction of the classical CS before, since the animal did not get food if it did not perform the movement. Initially, the animal performed the movement only after the CS, and then gradually it learned to do so to the CS itself. But the motor response to the transformed CS remained always defective.

In summary, we can say that the relationships between the salivary and the motor responses are rather complex and do not yield themselves easily to proper explanation. Is the drive stronger when the animal just works to obtain food, or when it is quiet, expects food, and salivates copiously? What are the relationships between the two?

I think we can ask two questions in particular, and it seems that both are fundamental to this problem. First, is there a causal relation between the proprioceptive feedback of a movement becoming the classical CS as indicated by salivation, and the instrumentalization of that movement? In other words, does the animal learn to perform this movement because it "knows" that it is a signal for food? The findings presented seem to indicate that this belief, which we held strongly for perhaps 20 years (and I think some people are still holding it), is not true. If it were, the parallelism between the salivary response following the movement and the movement itself should be very close.

Second, if we agree that the instrumental response is caused by the hunger drive, what is the role of this drive in respect to salivation? Again, our results suggest that different factors produce classical and instrumental responses, since these reactions could be almost totally split. To solve the problem, we urgently needed to find certain experimental procedures in which the classical salivary and instrumental motor response would be virtually separated. This type of procedure was developed in collaboration with Dr. Gaylord Ellison (4) of Yale University, who worked for one year in our laboratory.

The first stage of the experiment is simply reinforcement of a stimulus (a buzzer, for example) with food. Of course, after some time the animal begins to salivate to this stimulus. When the classical CR is established, we teach the animal to press a bar situated in front of it and beside the food-tray, each bar pressing being followed by the CS and then by food. Next, we present another stimulus (light). When the animal performs the movement during the operation of this stimulus, the light is extinguished momentarily and the classical CS followed by food is given; when the animal performs the movement in the intervals, nothing happens. In this way the animal learns to perform the movement only to the light. In the fourth stage of the experiment we prolong both conditioned stimuli: the animal is required to make not one but nine movements to the light, and only then is that stimulus turned off and the buzzer turned on. The buzzer is also prolonged, so that the animal obtains food after eight seconds of the stimulus.

The average data of a typical experimental session for each dog are presented in Figure 50. The perpendicular line denotes the moment the buzzer is substituted for the light after the animal has performed its quota of movements. The broken line represents the rate of motor responses, the arrow showing the mean beginning of the operation of the instrumental CS, which depends upon how quickly the animal presses the bar; it is more or less the same for any given dog. The continuous line denotes the rate of the salivary response. The end of the graph indicates the presentation of food. During the operation of the light (left of the perpendicular line) there is a very intense motor response, increasing to the end of the stimulus, and practically no salivation. When the light is turned off and the buzzer is on, the animal immediately stops performing the movements and begins to salivate. It should be stressed that the dog is never discouraged from responding to the buzzer and, if it does perform, the reinforcement comes in due time.

Figure 51 shows typical kymographic records. Let us begin with trial B: during the interval there is no salivation; when the light is presented, the animal presses the bar and still does not salivate; then the buzzer is turned on for nine seconds, and there is copious conditioned salivation, increasing during the end of the CS-UCS interval, and no movements. Trial A shows something interesting: for some reason (this happens in dogs), there is slight salivation in the interval; when the instrumental CS is given, the animal begins to perform the movement and salivation ceases. There is something even more interesting in trial C: the animal begins to perform the movements to the light, but after a few movements it turns to the foodtray, stops its performance, looks at the foodtray for several seconds, salivates, then stops salivating and finishes its quota of movements.

The general behavior of the dogs during the first and second segments is quite different. During the first segment, the animal not only performs the movements but is generally agitated; it vocalizes, is restless and impatient. During the second segment, it becomes absolutely immobile, looks at the foodtray as though hypnotized, and does nothing except salivate and wait for food. Of course, we may interpret this behavior as something artificial, and ask what will happen if the second segment is omitted and food comes just after the performance of the nine movements. The result is seen in Figure 52. After some training of this kind, the stimulus begins to elicit both the salivary and motor responses. The records show some slight antagonism between the two: the performance of movements seems to inhibit salivation, and vice versa. Thus we have returned to our typical experimental procedure, and have obtained the same variegated and somewhat unpredictable results. I think it is necessary to provide some explanation for these findings and to produce a neurophysiological model to account for them.

Figure 53 presents the entire story. We believe that the central alimen-

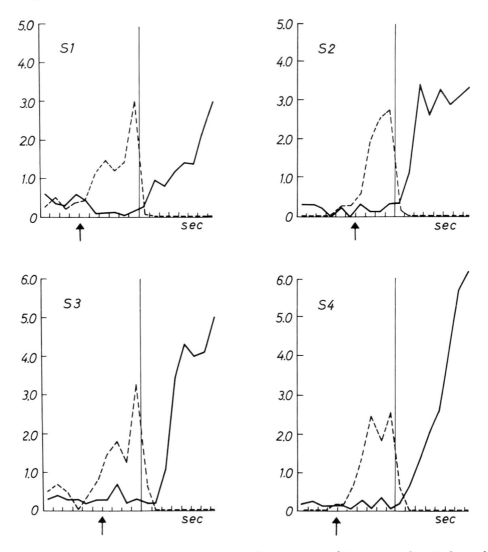

Figure 50. Salivary and motor response to the sequence of instrumental and classical conditioned stimuli. Abscissae: time in seconds; ordinates: rates of drops of saliva or lever pressings per second; arrow: average onset of the instrumental CS; perpendicular line: onset of the classical CS; continuous line: salivation; dashed line: motor responses. (From Ellison & Konorski, 4.)

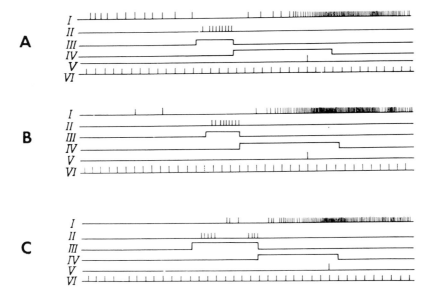

Figure 51. Three typical trials in the sequence of the instrumental and classical conditioned stimuli. I: Salivation; II: bar pressing; III: instrumental CS; IV: classical CS; V: food reinforcement; VI: time in seconds.

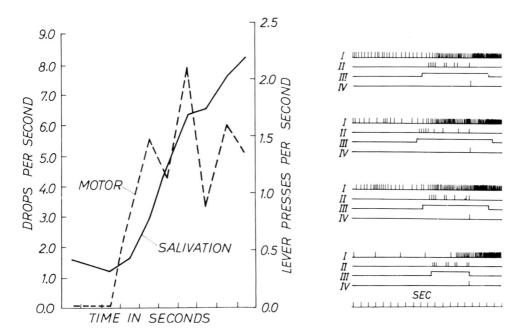

Figure 52. Salivary and motor responses to the instrumental CS after its repeated direct reinforcement by food. *Left:* average data from one session. *Right:* some individual trials (I: salivation; II: bar pressing; III: instrumental CS; IV: food reinforcement.).

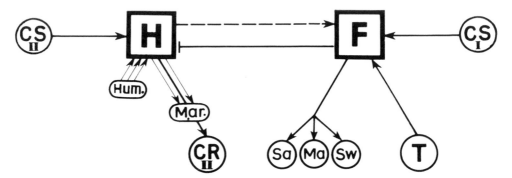

Figure 53. A block model of the relations between the food consummatory system (F) and hunger drive system (H). T: taste stimulus; Sa: salivation; Ma: mastication; Sw: swallowing; Hum: humoral factors; M.ar.: motor arousal; CS_I: classical food CS; CS_{II}: hunger CS, producing instrumental response CR_{II}. Arrows denote excitatory connections; dashed arrows, facilitatory connections; line ended by the perpendicular dash, inhibitory connections.

tary system is composed of two subsystems. (I prefer to use the term "system" rather than "center", which is often used instead of "nucleus", and has some anatomical associations.) One can be called the food or consummatory subsystem, the other is the hunger subsystem. The two are separated both anatomically and physiologically.

The consummatory subsystem is anatomically represented by the thalamo-neocortical part of the brain. The UCS which puts it into operation is of course taste, i.e., food in the mouth. Some of its responses are salivation, mastication, and swallowing. Let us concentrate upon salivation: on the basis of the food UCR, the appropriate CR can be formed; classical CR elicits the same response.

The hunger drive subsystem is represented by the hypothalamic-limbic part of the brain. The stimulus eliciting the hunger reflex is chiefly, but not exclusively, composition of the blood. Unfortunately, physiologists have not given much attention to the hunger reflex, and therefore we know much less about its effects than about those of the food reflex. On the basis of general observations in both animals and humans, we know that one of the effects of the hunger drive is general motor arousal. If some movement is elicited against the background of this motor arousal, and it is reinforced by food, the general motor arousal is channelized, so to speak, and the animal learns to perform this movement as the instrumental CR. Thus there is no chaotic general motor excitement here, but channelized excitement, concentrated chiefly, or perhaps exclusively, upon one movement. Again, if the hunger reflex is accompanied by an external stimulus, it can be classically conditioned: the association between the stimulus and the hunger subsystem will be formed. In that case this hunger CR may be a basis for the formation of an instrumental CR when there is some movement which leads to food.

Now, there are some rather complicated interrelations between these two subsystems. On the one hand, hunger facilitates the food system. When the animal is hungrier it salivates and eats more voraciously, and mastication is more energetic; both the unconditioned and conditioned food reflexes are increased. The opposite relationship is somewhat different, for, according to the results of our experiments (which I know may be debatable), when the animal has food in its mouth, the hunger system is temporarily inhibited; when the act of eating is terminated and the food is swallowed, there is a rebound effect and the hunger system becomes more excited.

In summary, the data from the experiments we usually perform with animals (and I believe this fits man's normal alimentary experience) show that the same stimulus may represent both the food CS and the hunger CS. The more the hunger CR prevails over the food CR, the more agitated the animal will be and the more vigorous the instrumental response. Salivation may be decreased (or it may be normal because the feedback of the movement may be the classical CS). Inversely, the more the food CR prevails over the hunger CR, the more the animal will salivate and the calmer it will be.

Discussion

Pribram: According to some of our data (1), the feeding system may not be exactly as you describe in Figure 53. Removal of the insular region produces degeneration in the midline thalamus, yet feeding behavior is not disrupted, although taste discrimination is markedly impaired.

Konorski: That is an important point. We also did that experiment (30): working with dogs, we removed the anterior composite gyrus, where the taste area is located; after the operation, the sense of taste is in fact abolished, yet the hunger drive is fully preserved. Deprived of the taste control which is indispensable for selection of food, the dog eats everything voraciously.

Pribram: The animal does not eat voraciously; it eats normal quantities. Only when the amygdala and surrounding temporal tissue are removed is food intake increased (24, 25, 29).

Konorski: I mean the dog eats voraciously if it is hungry. On the other hand, if the lateral hypothalamus, i.e., part of the hunger system is removed, the animal can eat food if it is placed deep in the mouth, but it has lost its appetite.

As for my interpretation of the feeding mechanism, I mean chewing, mouthing and swallowing—the motor aspects of the feeding process. To explain it further, I think that the grasping of food by an animal is a simple, natural instrumental reflex. Therefore, when satiated it will not take food, but when food is put into its mouth the whole consummatory response will occur. So we can consider as consummatory response only the response to food in the mouth but not the grasping of food, which belongs instead to the very primitive, not innate but acquired, instrumental responses.

What about us? It is four o'clock. If our meeting lasts much longer, we will feel hungry and uneasy and look at our watches; this is the hunger CR to time. We will not have any instrumental response because the Chairman may be displeased if we try to do so. We will not salivate during the meeting, but as soon as we adjourn we will rush to the dining room; this is our instrumental response, our lever-pressing. When we receive the menu we will begin to salivate; then the classical CS comes in. Frequently we may be *very* hungry beforehand, but when we reach the dining room and know for sure that soon we shall be fed, our hunger may be a bit depressed because of the inhibitory influence of the classical consummatory CS substituting the unconditioned food stimulus.

Miller: I would also like to refer back to Dr. Konorski's model (Figure 53), concentrating on the functional interrelations rather than the anatomy to point out that there is considerable additional evidence supporting some of the functional relationships Dr. Konorski has assumed on the basis of his data. Let us start at the right-hand side of the diagram. He assumes that the stimulation of the consummatory system by taste tends to inhibit the drive system. Evidence that hunger can be reduced by the taste of food and the consummatory act of eating (the effects of these two have not yet been experimentally separated) comes from a variety of experiments in my laboratory and elsewhere (16). Results show that food eaten normally by mouth produces an immediate reduction in hunger which is considerably greater than that produced by injecting the same food directly into the stomach via a chronic fistula (8, 21). Similar evidence is obtained when the reduction of hunger is measured by the decrease in the amount of food subsequently consumed (2), by the reduction in the rate of bar-pressing reinforced by food on a variable-interval schedule, or by the reduction in the amount of quinine required to stop eating (16). Furthermore, saccharine, which tastes sweet but is non-nutritious, produces a reduction in the amount of food subsequently consumed if it is drunk normally by mouth (26), but produces no such reduction if it is injected directly into the stomach (15, 16). These results confirm Dr. Konorski's idea that the activation of the consummatory system has the immediate effect of inhibiting hunger.

Turning to the left-hand side of the diagram, we have observed that, if the hunger system in the lateral hypothalamus is stimulated electrically in the absence of food, the animal becomes excited. Dr. Eric Steinbaum and I (28) have tried recently to determine whether the effects of electrical stimulation in the lateral hypothalamus were strong enough to override the normal weight regulatory mechanisms so that such stimulation could make rats markedly obese. We succeeded in stimulating the rats to overeat so much that they became quite fat. In order to control for the effects of electrical stimulation *per se*, we had a control group that was stimulated for the same period of time in the absence of food. During the course of the experiment we progressively increased the strength of stimulation for both groups, but while the experimental group merely ate more in response to higher stimulation, the control group (stimulated with food absent) exhibited such wild, excited behavior that we were afraid they would tear the electrodes out of their heads; we could not turn up the current as high for the controls as for the experimental group.

These and other observations in similar experiments have convinced us that stimulation of the feeding area leads to motor excitement, and that the opportunity to eat during such stimulation has a calming effect on this general excitement. These are just the kind of functional relationships that Dr. Konorski has described on the basis of his evidence from quite different types of experiments.

So far our results support Dr. Konorski's conclusions. He also contends that the hunger system can be aroused by conditioning. Thus far we have failed to secure experimental evidence for such arousal, either in more natural situations or by the sudden arousal of the hunger system by direct electrical stimulation of the lateral hypothalamus immediately after presentation of a CS (20). Dr. Konorski and I have discussed these experiments and agree that the negative results may be due to the tests being too severe. In order to achieve a compelling demonstration, we used animals which were thoroughly satiated, so that they would not be expected to show any eating in the absence of the UCS of direct stimulation of the hypothalamus, or of the CS associated with it. It is entirely possible that thorough satiation not only involves a reduction in hunger but also a very strong shut-off mechanism evolved to protect the animal from the dangerous effects of distension of the stomach, and of osmotic and other imbalances produced by ingesting too much food too rapidly. Perhaps our procedure aroused such a shut-off mechanism so powerfully that its effects could not be overcome by conditioned arousal.

Immediately after a large dinner I might not be aroused by the description of an especially delicious steak. But let us assume that I am working at my desk; I am neither thoroughly satiated nor really suffering from hunger. Then suppose that someone describes this same steak. I may decide to get up and go to the restaurant and, en route, discuss its especially delectable menu. When I arrive I see a sign that this restaurant is closed on Monday and find that the only other one is several miles away. At that moment I am probably suffering more from hunger than if I had remained at my desk without having been presented with a series of cues previously associated with eating. Perhaps a suitably designed experiment could produce similar results. For example, we might start with animals that were slightly hungry but thirsty enough to prefer drinking to eating, without being so thirsty that they would refuse dry food if water were not present as a competing goal. Would a CS previously associated with electrical stimulation of the lateral hypothalamus cause such rats to leave water and go to food, as would the UCS of electrical stimulation in the lateral hypothalamus (18)?

I have been impressed with the fact that in young children hunger does not behave as though it were solely the direct result of gradual accumulation of food deficit. Rather, it seems to have some of the characteristics of a response that can be aroused by suitable cues, including the positive feedback from some of the responses it elicits, and perhaps even some central sources of feedback. Furthermore, it seems to be capable of being suddenly inhibited by antagonistic responses. For example, a young infant may be sleeping or lying peacefully, and a few minutes later crying vigorously as if in severe distress. The change may be so dramatic that we cannot believe that it was produced by the gradual accumulation of nutritional deficit, so we look for a pin or some other source of sudden pain. But as soon as the child is given a bottle, he starts drinking eagerly and quiets down. When he empties the bottle he may start crying vigorously again, but by the time a new bottle is heated he may be out of the mood and refuse to eat further. Such changes suggest that the hunger system does have some of the characteristics of a response and may be subject to conditioning. [Cf. Miller (17), pp. 262-272.]

Pribram: There is an alternative possibility which would regard the feeding mechanism to be hierarchically, rather than linearly, organized. I would just like to put that possibility on the record, since such a model has been of some concern to me (14, 22, 23).

Miller: You may well be right, but I would have to see a detailed exposition of your alternative hierarchical organization before I would discuss it. If you can present a hierarchical system and make predictions different from those made by my allegedly linear model, I shall be happy to accept whichever model has its predictions confirmed. Certainly, many things are organized hierarchically, and I have nothing in principle against your suggestion, but I do not think we have time now to discuss it adequately.

According to Dr. Konorski's model (Figure 53), I believe it is the inhibition of the drive system by the consummatory system (as represented by the solid line across the bottom of the diagram) that produces the reinforcement of the specific motor response immediately preceding such inhibitions. This is Dr. Konorski's contention, and it would fit in with the drive-reduction hypothesis I have often supported (9).

Without abandoning completely the drive-reduction hypothesis, I have recently put forward an alternative one (19) which assumes that the immediate effect of any reinforcement is to arouse a "go mechanism" that facilitates any response occurring at that moment. The activation of an instrumental response produced by such facilitation is assumed to function exactly like the activation of a classical CR by the UCS. The point I want to make is that it should be now possible to use the kind of electrophysiological techniques described by Dr. Galambos and others to obtain direct evidence relevant to these various hypotheses concerning reinforcement, which I believe to be a central mechanism in learning.

We could begin by doing recordings (ideally, microelectrode recordings) from the hunger system. What happens at the moment when the taste of food is introduced into the mouth? What happens when a CS for eating (and secondary reinforcement) is presented? Do such stimuli produce an immediate decrease in the rate of firing of the hunger system in the lateral hypothalamus, and perhaps an immediate increase in the rate of firing in the satiation system in the ventromedial nucleus? There are techniques available to determine the reality of functional relationships in Dr. Konorski's model; that is one of the advantages of such a model. We can determine, for example, what happens at the moment when the hungry animal gets food in its mouth.

Konorski: As far as I know, there is synchronization of the EEG when the food CR is well established.

Miller: Another suggestion is to record what happens at the moment when a powerful reinforcement is first given. We might observe an animal until we find that a particular movement produced a distinctive burst of activity from a particular electrode; then we might reinforce that activity. Would the immediate effect of the reinforcement be to enhance and prolong that burst of activity, as demanded by my "go mechanism" hypothesis, or would the activity be unaffected or even inhibited? We have just been reminded that, when an habituated stimulus is associated with reinforcement for a number of trials, the effect is to restore the height of the evoked potential and to protect it from further habituation. We would like to know, however, whether the very first reinforcement has any effect on the ongoing evoked potential, or whether the enhancement occurs only on subsequent trials, as if the reinforcement had no immediate effect on the activity but produced only some indirect effect, such as strengthening a connection, which shows up only on a subsequent trial. Such evidence would help us in formulating theories of reinforcement.

Koestler: May I register a heretic protest against this approach? It seems to me that there are two steps. The first is a natural, normal cycle of feeding. Then in the artificial laboratory situation the cycle is interfered with by being chopped up into stimuli and responses, into strivings and consummatory acts. When feeding itself has started, the cycle does not come to a stop, but digestion-expulsion proceeds, and this is not only a response but a stimulus for the restart of the cycle. At any point of the loop, what we call a response might become a stimulus. Thus, salivation is a response, but it initiates mastication. Classical conditioning means that the animal is programmed to expect that food will appear subsequent to certain perceptual signals for food. In operant or instrumental conditioning programs, the animal has to perform some motor action which will produce the food. To change the language, the animal is taught to play games. In one game it learns that a bell means that food will come, so it is time to salivate. In the other game the animal's leg is pulled up, and it learns to repeat the act by itself so that food will be forthcoming. The animal does not salivate before completing the motor action because it has learned that food will come only after it has completed those nine leg movements.

Although we obtain seemingly paradoxical results from the two games with different rules, the animal is behaving consistently. One rule dictates: bell, salivate, and food will come; the second rule demands: move leg, food will come, but salivate only after the leg motions are finished. The time constant is there. So, once we combine these two, the paradox disappears and the animal behaves quite reasonably. I do not think there is any antagonism between salivation and motor response. The antagonism is a semantic construct. The animal will salivate when it expects food. It is not the motor activity which inhibits the salivation; it simply postpones salivation to a later stage.

Miller: I think we have to know some of the historical background to appreciate the beauty of the Ellison-Konorski experiment (4). According to Dr. Konorski's earlier theory (9), it was the fact that the proprioception of moving the leg became the signal for feeding and salivation that caused the movement to be reinforced and learned as an instrumental response. But he has now separated the instrumental movement and the salivation, thereby disproving his earlier theory. Since the leg movement can be completely separated from the salivation, he cannot say that the dog learns to move its leg because the leg movement has become a CS for salivation.

In the United States, Professor Hull and his student, Kenneth Spence, were also impressed with the frequent correlation between instrumental responses and consummatory responses such as salivation (6, 7, 27). Thus, a causal relationship between these two types of events played a central role in their theories, as well as in some of mine. But in these cases the opposite type of causal relationship was assumed; it was supposed that the anticipatory consummatory responses were part of the motivation for the instrumental response, and also that the stimuli produced by the anticipatory responses provided important cues for the instrumental sequences. The Ellison-Konorski experiment (4) challenges this kind of an assumed causal relationship between the conditioned consummatory and the instrumental responses. Although such responses are often intimately mixed together, they can be clearly separated. This demonstration challenges two historically influential hypotheses: the one followed by Dr. Konorski and his students, and the one followed by Hull and his students.

Birch: What happens after the dog has been classically conditioned to a bell-food sequence, and then the experimenter pulls on the string for the first time to lift the animal's leg while the bell is ringing? Is there inhibition of salivation at this point? I expect there is, and this has nothing to do with expectation.

Konorski: There is inhibition of salivation.

Birch: It would also be inhibited if, for instance, the dog were to receive an air puff, or bright lights would shine while the bell is ringing and the animal is salivating. Is it necessary to become involved in a separate hunger drive, a separate feeding drive, and so on? Or are you not saying that there are interferences among afferent inputs which, under given temporal conditions, result in the effective inhibition of one of these inputs? I believe such a hierarchical model can account for all the data presented, without the assumption of the other drives.

Pribram: That is what I had in mind, at least partly. There is a good deal of neurological evidence (3) on the reciprocal relations between a satiety and a feeding mechanism in the hypothalamus, the reciprocality of the medial- and lateral-hypothalamic areas. But it turns out that the lateral area is a group of crossing fiber tracts; this suggests that the systems are hierarchically organized, the satiety mechanism being a neurosensing device (most likely sensitive to the concentration of blood glucose), and the feeding mechanism involving a group of systems ordinarily active unless shut off by activation of the satiety cells. Thus the feeding mechanisms are plural, the satiety mechanism single. Attention to the possibility of hierarchical relationships may suggest explanations for facts which are difficult to handle with the simpler linear model.

I believe Mr. Koestler uses the term "programming" in the same sense I would use it: as something taking place within the nervous system, not as a conscious process or plan being set up by the organism, although nothing precludes the possibility of awareness of such a neural program.

Hilgard: The dog does not know it is being classically or instrumentally conditioned.

Pribram: We have enough physiological evidence to allow us to use such a word as "expectation", to give it operational definitions in both physiological and behavioral terms, and to correlate these definitions with verbal reports from human subjects.

Atkinson: Dr. Konorski, I gather that, after stage four of the training, the animal would begin to salivate if the buzzer was turned on for the ten-second period before the light came on. If the buzzer had already activated salivation, would the probability of eliciting the response to the light be reduced? That seems to be implied by your model at this point.

Konorski: That is the case if the buzzer is presented without light: salivation will be the normal classical CR. It would be interesting to find out what would occur if, following the buzzer, we were to substitute light instead of food.

Atkinson: As an implication of the model, it seems to me that, in extinguishing the operant response, routine extinction would go much more slowly if the CS-1 and CS-2 were paired than if the CS-2 were presented by itself.

Konorski: We have not done that experiment yet.

I would like now to reply to Mr. Koestler's comment and to clarity some misunderstandings. I do not see anything paradoxical in our results. On the contrary, I think ours is the least paradoxical solution, whereas some of our previous results might have been ambiguous. I fully agree that these seem now nearly obvious results; we all know the proverb, "There is nothing more simple than the truth which was found yesterday, and nothing more complicated than the truth which will be found tomorrow." We can ask why the dog salivated when it made the movement—but no matter what the reason was, it did salivate under certain conditions. I did not want to burden my talk with a discussion of all these complex relationships, but I could show records of trials in which the animal salivates copiously if given the CS, and performs the movement only afterwards. In nature these relations appear in all sorts of combinations, and it is very difficult to find their causes. Among others there is, for instance, the problem of whether salivation belongs to the repertory of hunger responses. I think this problem was not solved previously because no one knew whether, among the many effects of hunger itself, there was salivation without contamination by the consummatory response. I am convinced we have the answer, since under our experimental conditions the animal does not salivate although it is experiencing a hunger drive, as shown by its performance of the movement. This indicates that salivation does not belong to the effects of the drive.

If I said there is antagonism between salivation and motor response, I was not entirely correct. As a matter of fact, there is antagonism between some central processes, not between the responses which are their indicators. The instrumental response is an indicator of the hunger drive, and—we now can be sure—salivation is the indicator of the consummatory response.

Mr. Koestler raised a question about the loop in Figure 53. I could not review the whole story, nor was this my intention; the diagram was shown primarily to account for the facts we have discussed. Since all of these facts can be explained by it, we are more or less satisfied with it. I do not think it is the last word, of course, as I am almost certain it can be improved.

There is also the problem of whether the two systems are hierarchical or parallel. To my mind they are parallel. I think that the midbrain-hypothalamic-limbic system is just one hierarchy of hunger and behavior by which the animal seeks food. Then there is a different hierarchy controlling the consummatory response; it is much more neocortical, as it should be, since taste must be very delicate in order to discern what is eatable and what is not. So, we must have a very good neocortical taste analyzer in order to deal with gustatory discrimination, quite independently of hunger.

REFERENCES

1. Bagshaw, M. H., and Pribram, K. H., Cortical organization in gustation (*Macaca mulatta*). *J. Neurophysiol.*, 1953, **16**: 499-508.
2. Berkun, M. M., Kessen, M. L., and Miller, N. E., Hunger-reducing effects of food by stomach fistula versus food by mouth measured by a consummatory response. *J. Comp. Physiol. Psychol.*, 1952, **45**: 550-554.

3. Brazier, M. A. B. (Ed.), *Brain and Behavior, Vol. II: The Internal Environment and Alimentary Behavior*. Am. Inst. Biol. Sci., Washington, D. C., 1963.

4. Ellison, G. D., and Konorski, J., Separation of the salivary and motor responses in instrumental conditioning. *Science*, 1964, **146**: 1071-1072.

5. Hilgard, E. R., and Marquis, D. G., *Conditioning and Learning*. Appleton-Century-Crofts, New York, 1940.

6. Hull, C. L., *Principles of Behavior; An Introduction to Behavior Theory*. Appleton-Century-Crofts, New York, 1943.

7. ———, *A Behavior System; An Introduction to Behavior Theory Concerning the Individual Organism*. Yale Univ. Press, New Haven, 1952.

8. Kohn, M., Satiation of hunger from food injected directly into the stomach versus food ingested by mouth. *J. Comp. Physiol. Psychol.*, 1951, **44**: 412-422.

9. Konorski, J., *Conditioned Reflexes and Neuron Organization* (S. Garry, Transl.). Cambridge Univ. Press, London, 1948.

10. Konorski, J., and Miller, S., Méthode d'examen de l'analysateur moteur par les réactions salivomotrices. *C. R. Soc. Biol.* (Paris), 1930, **104**: 907-910.

11. ———, *Les Principes Fundamentaux de la Theorie Physiologique des Mouvements Acquis*. Ksiaznica Atlas, Warsaw, 1933 (in Polish).

12. ———, Conditioned reflexes of the motor analyser. *Trans. of I. P. Pavlov Physiol. Labor.*, 1936, **6**: 119-232. (In Russian; English summary.)

13. Konorski, J., and Wyrwicka, W., Researches into conditioned reflexes of the second type. 1. Transformation of conditioned reflexes of the first type into conditioned reflexes of the second type. *Acta Biol. Exp.*, 1950, **15**: 193-204.

14. Miller, G. A., Galanter, E., and Pribram, K. H., *Plans and the Structure of Behavior*. Holt, New York, 1960.

15. Miller, N. E., Shortcomings of food consumption as a measure of hunger; results from other behavioral techniques. *Ann. N. Y. Acad. Sci.*, 1955, **63**: 141-143.

16. ———, Experiments on motivation. Studies combining psychological, physiological, and pharmacological techniques. *Science*, 1957, **126**: 1271-1278.

17. ———, Liberalization of basic S-R concepts: extensions to conflict behavior, motivation, and social learning. In: *Psychology: A Study of a Science*, Study 1, Vol. 2 (S. Koch, Ed.). McGraw-Hill, New York, 1959: 196-292.

18. ———, Some motivational effects of brain stimulation and drugs. *Fed. Proc.*, 1960, **19**: 846-854.

19. ———, Some reflections on the law of effect produce a new alternative to drive reduction. In: *Nebraska Symposium on Motivation* (M. R. Jones, Ed.). Univ. of Nebraska Press, Lincoln, 1963: 65-112.

20. ———, Some psychophysiological studies of motivation and of the behavioral effects of illness. *Bull. Brit. Psychol. Soc.*, 1964, **17**: 1-20.

21. Miller, N. E., and Kessen, M. L., Reward effects of food via stomach fistula compared with those of food via mouth. *J. Comp. Physiol. Psychol.*, 1952, **45**: 555-564.

22. Pribram, K. H., A review of theory in physiological psychology. *Ann. Rev. Psychol.*, 1960, **11**: 1-40.

23. Pribram, K. H., Reinforcement revisited: a structural view. In: *Nebraska Symposium on Motivation* (M. R. Jones, Ed.). Univ. of Nebraska Press, Lincoln, 1963: 113-159.

24. Pribram, K. H., and Bagshaw, M., Further analysis of the temporal lobe syndrome utilizing fronto-temporal ablations. *J. Comp. Neurol.,* 1953, **99**: 347-375.

25. Schwartzbaum, J. S., Changes in reinforcing properties of stimuli following ablation of the amygdaloid complex in monkeys. *J. Comp. Physiol. Psychol.,* 1960, **53**: 388-395.

26. Sheffield, F. D., and Roby, T. B., Reward value of a non-nutritive sweet taste. *J. Comp. Physiol. Psychol.,* 1950, **43**: 471-481.

27. Spence, K. W., *Behavior Theory and Conditioning.* Yale Univ. Press, New Haven, 1956.

28. Steinbaum, E. A., and Miller, N. E., Obesity from eating elicited by daily stimulation of hypothalamus. *Am. J. Physiol.,* 1965, **208**: 1-5.

29. Weiskrantz, L., Behavioral changes associated with ablation of the amygdaloid complex in monkeys. *J. Comp. Physiol. Psychol.,* 1956, **49**: 381-391.

30. Żernicki, B., and Santibanez-H., G., The effects of ablations of "alimentary area" of the cerebral cortex on salivary conditioned and unconditioned reflexes in dogs. *Acta Biol. Exp.,* 1961, **21**: 163-176.

CLASSICAL AND INSTRUMENTAL CONDITIONING: DO SINGLE-PROCESS OR TWO-PROCESS THEORIES EXHAUST THE ALTERNATIVES?

ERNEST R. HILGARD
Stanford University
Stanford

My assigned topic is the same as Dr. Konorski's, but in a somewhat different context. I am delighted to be able to follow him because of the clarity of the paradigms he proposed.

Whenever we attempt a neurophysiological explanation of psychological or behavioral relationships, one of our first questions must be, what is there to explain? Recent efforts to work out a taxonomy of learning are directed to this fundamental question, whether at the level of psychological theory or of neurophysiological theory. This is the problem I wish to discuss.

Two-Process Interpretations of Learning

The distinction between two kinds of conditioning, made originally by Professor Konorski and his colleague S. Miller in 1928 (35), has served in one form or another as a convenient classificatory scheme. A number of investigators have found it convenient to use a similar distinction in their theorizing; their classifications, gathered by Kimble (23), are shown in Table 10. I would like to review first some of the history of the two types of conditioning.

Around 1935 I was asked by John A. McGeoch, then editor of the *Psychological Bulletin,* to prepare a summary review (16) on the relationship between the conditioned response and conventional learning experiments. This was done on the assumption that problem boxes, mazes and rote memorization belonged with our conventional learning experiments, and that the conditioned reflex of Pavlov was an important paradigm that might be related to them. Just about that time Skinner (47) proposed his two types of conditioned reflex. Then the question arose as to whether we should count Skinner's operant conditioning as belonging within conditioning or treat it as one of the "other" forms of learning, as being only a simplified Thorndike puzzle-box type of situation.

Dr. Konorski's earlier theories (35) were in a sense similar to my position, for he used the principles of classical conditioning, so to speak, to explain

TABLE 10

Twofold Classifications of Learning Proposed by Different Authors*

Author(s)	Term for Classical Conditioning	Term for Instrumental Conditioning
Thorndike (53)	Associative shifting	Trial-and-error learning
Miller & Konorski (35), Konorski & Miller (26, 27)	Type I	Type II
Skinner (48)	Type S, or Respondent	Type R, or Operant
Schlosberg (43)	Conditioning	Success learning
Hilgard & Marquis (19)	Classical conditioning	Instrumental conditioning
Mowrer (36)	Conditioning	Problem solving

* From Kimble (23).

what happened in instrumental conditioning. Dr. McGeoch and I corresponded extensively on whether to legitimize the two types by using the word "conditioning" for the instrumental type of response, or to hold to the Pavlovian type of experiment. This was of course before the adoption of the terms "classical" and "instrumental". We finally decided that, after all, the Russians had some priority in establishing the terminology. Ivanov-Smolensky (21) and other investigators had done experiments of the instrumental type; at that time Miller & Konorski (35) had called the two varieties "conditioning", so why hesitate? We vacillated because the Russians named everything "conditioning" and "reflex"; for example, Pavlov called instincts "long chains of reflexes" (39). Hence the Russian terminology was not at that time very convincing to American psychologists, since all varieties of learning were called "conditioning". Eventually, we agreed that it would be easier to make the transition to conventional learning experiments if instrumental ones were considered as conditioning. My review (16) in the *Psychological Bulletin*, which appeared in 1937, therefore proposed that these two types of conditioning called there Class I and Class II be recognized.

I was naturally puzzled by the problem of the two classes, whether they involved two process types, as Skinner clearly implied, or whether they were merely two kinds of experimental arrangements. My own preference lay with the notion that the differences were chiefly in experimental arrangement, and I tried to clarify how many behavioral relationships there were in common. One type neglected to measure some processes, and the other type neglected to measure others. Consider the contrast between Pavlov's salivation experiment and Skinner's lever-pressing experiment in which pressing the lever is reinforced by food pellets. In both cases the animals are salivating, and in both cases the animals are operating levers: the levers may be those of the neck and jaws for Pavlov's dogs as they look toward food, nose up the lid of the food pan, or take the food into the mouth —but this instrumental behavior goes on along with the salivation, just as in Skinner's experiment the salivation goes on along with the lever-pressing. In the recorded data, however, Pavlov counted the salivation, ignoring the movements as data, while Skinner counted the movements and ignored the salivation as data. The form of the conditioned response thus depended on the arrangements for measurement; the conditioned response was like the unconditioned response for Pavlov because salivation was measured as the component response to both conditioned and unconditioned stimuli; it was unlike the unconditioned response for Skinner because of the mechanics of the lever: there is no component of lever-pressing available to the animal while eating, except in a derivative sense, i.e., lever actions with paws and mouth in eating which might have something to do with the conditioned lever-pressing. Skinner encouraged this derivative similarity in non-data ways by smearing a little food on the lever to encourage lever-pressing in the first place. In my review I was dogmatic about the relationship between reward and reinforcement, less dogmatic about the functional relationships between the two classes of experiment. With respect to reward and reinforcement (by which I then meant Pavlovian reinforcement), I wrote: "The conclusion appears warranted that *reinforcement behavior classifies as reward behavior and further reconciliation is unnecessary.*" (16, p. 78). I am afraid that this was a rather glib conclusion, but I still believe it holds when the comparison is between Pavlov's food-salivation experiments and Skinner's lever-food-reward experiments.

There are three solutions to the two-type problem: first, to recognize separate processes for each; second, to derive the operation of reward from the principles of classical reinforcement; and third, to consider both types as varieties of reward-punishment learning. I favored the last of these possibilities for, as I have said, this solution made it easier to bridge the gap between experiments called conditioning and other kinds.

The question arose again later on, when Marquis and I were engaged in the preparation of our book *Conditioning and Learning* (19), for Skinner's major work on the behavior of organisms (49) had appeared in the meantime, and we had to decide whose terminology to adopt, whether or not to use Skinner's distinction between "operant" and "respondent" responses. While we were sympathetic to his ideas, we felt that our descriptive terminology should apply to experimental arrangements and not imply a theory (as Skinner's terms clearly did, although in some sense they are alternative). It was quite clear to us, as it must be to anyone who looks closely at the behavior within an experiment, that the measurements as made always abstract from a totality of behavior that is far more complex, and the actual experiment at best only approximates the model it is designed to fit. Thus the Pavlov experiment is no more "pure" stimulus-substitution than the Skinner experiment is "pure" operant, uncomplicated by simple associative learning; yet we all understand the differences in experimental arrangement between the two. That there are at least these two kinds of experimental arrangements is clear enough: the question remains of whether there is a single kind or more than one kind of process underlying them.

Because of our awareness of unsolved theoretical questions, Marquis and I preferred to use the terminology of "classical" and "instrumental" conditioning as a sort of neutral language, referring to the experimental arrangements and leaving open the debate over processes. The terms we introduced have come to be reasonably well understood as referring in general to the Pavlovian arrangements of stimulus-substitution, on the one hand, and to rewarded or operant learning, on the other hand.

We tried to clarify our position by showing how an experiment could be chosen to illustrate certain processes. Then the investigator, committed to this model, would try to force the same explanatory pattern upon other experiments he would probably not have chosen to perform in the first place. Table 11 is a simplified version of the tabulation in *Conditioning and Learning* (19). We felt that the two-process notion did not exhaust the alternatives, so we listed classical conditioning, instrumental conditioning of a particular type, and a third, somewhat more complex type, represented by some of Tolman's experiments (54) rather than by those of the S-R psychologists.

Consider the first two columns in the table. The point is that the experiment is never a pure case of the process it is designed to exhibit, so a second column was added for the "abstracted process". The abstracted process in the Pavlov experiment is the reinforcement of salivation by salivation; that is, the mere occurrence of salivation while the conditioned stimulus is effective should, in principle, establish an association between the CS and the response, and if the animal is already salivating to the CS its salivation is increased, as shown by the excess salivation that follows. This is the principle of *homogeneous reinforcement,* the strengthening of like by like. In the case of instrumental reward we meant the typical food-for-pressing experiment of Skinner, or the hurdle-jumping-to-escape-shock of the early Miller-

TABLE 11

HOW EACH OF THREE EXPLANATORY PRINCIPLES MAY BE PROPOSED AS THE
EXCLUSIVE EXPLANATION OF THREE TYPES OF EXPERIMENT*

Type of Experiment	Abstracted Process	Explanatory Principle as Applicable to Each		
		Substitution	Effect	Expectancy
1. Classical conditioning	Homogeneous reinforcement	*Directly applicable*	Inferred	Inferred
2. Instrumental reward and escape	Heterogeneous reinforcement	Inferred	*Directly applicable*	Inferred
3. Instrumental avoidance; secondary reward	Derived reinforcement ("sign learning")	Inferred	Inferred	*Directly applicable*

* After Hilgard & Marquis (19).

Mowrer experiments. Here the reward (food, safety) is *heterogeneous*, that is, lever-pressing or jumping behavior is strengthened by something quite different, eating or resting. Finally, and here we departed somewhat from the conditioning tradition before or after our book, we recognized Tolman's sign learning as a class requiring perhaps some new principles. This is the case in which behavior is strengthened by the prevention of a noxious stimulus that must in some sense be "anticipated", or by behaving appropriately to some sort of "sign" or "signal" that has a very arbitrary relation to its consequences; because of the possible cognitive or other processes involved as intermediaries, we called the abstracted principle *derived reinforcement*. I must say that Professor Tolman was puzzled by what we did; he was not sure whether to be pleased or offended, although he came to accept our abbreviation of "expectancy" for his more cumbersome sign-Gestalt-expectation.

The abstracted processes (reinforcements) are then in need of explanation. One way to arrive at an explanatory principle is to become attached to a particular kind of experiment, then to rename the findings and call them explanations. Thus it can be seen in Table II that the principle of stimulus substitution (or simple associative learning) is directly applicable in the explanation of homogeneous reinforcement; the "law of effect" of Thorndike (53) (or Hull's drive-reduction) is the principle applicable to heterogenous reinforcement or simple reward learning; and the expectancy principle is directly applicable to derived reinforcement or sign learning. (At this distance in time, much of probability learning would also be fitted here; if the organism acts in accordance with estimated consequences of past probabilities, this may be the equivalent of an expectation.)

Those who hold to stimulus-substitution or simple associative learning as the essential explanatory principle must infer how this principle fits the other arrangements. Perhaps Guthrie's interpretation (14) provides the best illustration of such an attempt: he explained the operation of heterogeneous reinforcement, for example, by assuming that a reward removes the learner from the stimulus situation, so that what he last did in that situation remains conditioned. He thus inferred the effectiveness of reward from the principle of simple associative learning, without any new "law of effect". Hull (19a) represents the second alternative, attempting to dispense with the substitution principle by always looking for some sort of heterogeneous reinforcement (in his terms, reinforcement through drive-reduction). Thus one can work up and down each of the last three columns in Table 11, holding to a common explanatory principle for the various processes.

The alternative, of course, is to accept more principles. As an extreme, one might rest with the diagonals of the table, and assert that there are three major explanatory principles of learning, appropriate to the processes abstracted from these three types of experiment.

This was 1940. That kind of analysis is still pertinent, but in the quarter century that has passed since, a good deal of thought has been given to these matters. The type of thinking represented in the table still seems sound to me, but we may well ask what kind of table we could construct today.

THE NEW TAXONOMY OF LEARNING

The growing interest in this country in the taxonomy of learning is well represented by a recent review edited by Melton (32). Many of its authors are present at this conference; without knowing that Dr. Grant would be commenting on my paper, I had chosen to select some of the material from his chapter (13) in that book. Let us first consider what has happened to the two classes of conditioning.

Classical Conditioning

When Marquis and I treated classical conditioning (19), we left it more or less where we found it, feeling that Pavlov's distinctions between simultaneous, temporal, trace, and delayed conditioning, and so on, referred more to experimental arrangements than to fundamental differences in process. Dr. Grant (13) has now reclassified it, showing that there are various kinds of responses that crop up in classical conditioning experiments, that these follow somewhat different courses during conditioning, and that classical conditioning therefore calls for some distinctions not made by Pavlov. Not only the responses but the experimental operations are different.

On the basis of the experimenter's operations, Dr. Grant proposes four kinds of classical conditioning experiments (Table 12): Pavlovian A is the typical alimentary reflex that Dr. Konorski discussed. Pavlov also had acid-in-the-mouth and morphine experiments (Pavlovian B) which Dr. Grant

TABLE 12
SUBCLASSES OF CLASSICAL CONDITIONING*

1. Pavlovian A conditioning	The typical Pavlov alimentary conditioned reflex. The CS serves a "signal" function; the trial ends with the ingestion of food by the hungry animal.
2. Pavlovian B conditioning	The Pavlovian morphine experiment is illustrative. The complex of salivation, nausea, emesis, elicited by morphine (UCS) comes to be elicited by CS.
3. Anticipatory instructed conditioning	The Ivanov-Smolensky type of experiment in which the UCR is an instructed response, e.g., pressing a rubber bulb when a sound is heard. Then a light (CS) may come to yield the response as a CR.
4. Sensory preconditioning	Two conditioned stimuli (CS_1 and CS_2) are frequently associated. Then a conditioned response established to CS_1 may also be evoked by CS_2.

* After Grant (13).

feels illustrate more closely a situation where there is no similar signaling effect, but rather approaches direct stimulus substitution. From our viewpoint, the pure associative experiment is somewhat clearer in this case than in the signaling experiment in which the food, in a sense, rewards and supplements the salivation; nothing of that adaptive sort happens here, unless we think of salivation as washing the acid out of the mouth, in which case there is a similarity. Anticipatory instructive conditioning, such as pressing bulbs, is introduced as No. 3 in the table. The sensory preconditioning experiment (No. 4 in the table) involves association between conditioned stimuli before they are combined with an unconditioned stimulus.

Dr. Grant's justification for listing these as classical conditioning is their extensive use by Russians who believe they are working within a general Pavlovian orientation. Kimble (24) would accept the first two classes, defined by positive and negative reinforcement, and would add two classes of signalling by the CS: the termination of positive and negative reinforcers, as proposed by Mowrer (38). Kimble believes the Ivanov-Smolensky paradigm (21) to be in fact instrumental conditioning, and the sensory preconditioning to derive from classical conditioning.

I do not wish to take the time here to discuss these points, except to indicate that the simplicity and uniformity of the classical conditioning experiment cannot be taken for granted.

Instrumental Conditioning

When Marquis and I examined various arrangements for instrumental conditioning, we proposed four classes of training: reward, escape, avoidance, and secondary reward. Kimble (23), in revising our book, a task for which we are most grateful to him but in which we had no part, modified our last two types, substituting for them omission training and punishment training. More recently, Grant (13) has extended the list into a very ingenious classification (Table 13), in which he notes that there are three main dichotomies: two types of cue relationship (the cue is present or absent); two types of response (it is either to be made or to be withheld, or inhibited—called positive and negative); and two types of reinforcement (appetitive or aversive, called reward and punishment). Thus there are $2 \times 2 \times 2$ combinations, giving eight kinds of experiments. Some of these are more common than others, but it is possible to conceive of experiments in each of the categories.

To the extent that Dr. Konorski has not considered this entire matrix of experiments in his theory, I feel that the theory might be put under some strain to make the hunger-food comparison fit for all of these responses. In talking here in a brain context without saying anything about the brain, my justification is the same as Dr. Konorski's: we both want to know what it is that we are trying to explain. Dr. Konorski has, of course, done the physiological experiments to carry it further. But what he had to say sets for neu-

TABLE 13

A CLASSIFICATION OF TYPES OF INSTRUMENTAL LEARNING EXPERIMENTS*

Instrumental Types	Cue to Impending Reinforcement	Response	Reinforcement
Reward Training	No	Positive	Reward
Escape Training	No	Positive	Punishment
Avoidance Conditioning	Yes	Positive	Punishment
Discriminated Operant	Yes	Positive	Reward
Omission Training	No	Negative	Reward
Punishment (or Passive Avoidance Conditioning)	No	Negative	Punishment
Discriminated Omission Training	Yes	Negative	Reward
Discriminated Punishment Training	Yes	Negative	Punishment

* After Grant (13).

rophysiology the task of explaining what happens under the circumstances. If it cannot be explained, the goal we sought has not been achieved; we can find perfectly good relationships at a behavioral level, but we will rest easier when we have them at a neurophysiological level as well, and find that they fit.

I do not propose to examine the problems of higher orders of learning, as represented by sequential learning, discrimination learning, the learning of concepts and principles, higher orders of problem solving (e.g., Dr. Gagné's contribution to the Melton review, 12). They pose serious questions to the student of human learning, but we already have enough to puzzle us.

CONTEMPORARY SOLUTIONS TO THE TWO-PROCESS PROBLEM

You might recall that in 1937 I felt (16) that reward in instrumental conditioning and reinforcement in classical conditioning were functionally so much alike that, if the problem of classical conditioning were really solved, the problem of instrumental conditioning would also be solved. A solution came about by indicating that the classical conditioning experiment was really more complicated than the measurements that were made. I did not then say actually that existing explanations of either of the types were satisfactory, and later, with Marquis (19), adopted the view that there were at least three options open: substitution, effect, and expectancy (see Table 11).

Most workers have concerned themselves with only two of these options, i.e., with explanations in terms of simple associative learning (homogeneous reinforcement) or with rewarded learning (law of effect or corresponding principles of heterogeneous reinforcement). The expectancy principle is seldom treated as in any way parallel to the other two; now being classed as a cognitive-type theory, it has often been thought to lie outside of S-R theories, and to be in some sense a more general and unfavored alternative to them.

TABLE 14

POST-HULLIAN INTERPRETATIONS OF REINFORCEMENT*

1. Single-factor theories
   a. Contiguity only (Sheffield, Seward)
   b. Drive reduction only (N.E. Miller)

2. Dual theories
   a. Drive reduction for instrumental acts only (Mowrer)
   b. Drive reduction for classical conditioning only (Spence)

* After Hilgard (18).

In 1956, at the time my *Theories of Learning* was revised (18), I summarized some of the current interpretations (Table 14). There were single-factor theories: Sheffield (45) and Seward (44) were advocating the Guthrian type of theory, and Dr. Miller (34) at times was supporting drive reduction. There were also dual theories such as Mowrer's (36, 37), that accepted drive reduction for instrumental acts only, and Spence's (52), advocating drive reduction for classical conditioning only.

By now of course there are more: I should have to add Estes (9) to the single-factor contiguity theorists, although more would have to be said. Kimble (23, 24) has aligned himself with the two-process interpretation, based on the fact that some responses appear to be conditioned more readily by classical conditioning methods, others by instrumental conditioning methods, and the functional relationships (as in the effects of schedules of reinforcement) differ in the two situations; while he does not hold the view strongly, he still gives it his vote. If we consider the hunger aspect of Dr. Konorski's drive theory, I think we can say it is also of the dual type. It is clear there has not yet been a resolution of the issue.

Is There a Way Out?

I wish to consider four general strategies that may lead us to a resolution of this long-standing problem of the fundamental processes in learning, particularly as reflected in the interpretations of classical and instrumental conditioning experiments: (*a*) solution through further behavioral experimentation, (*b*) the neurophysiological solution, (*c*) the mathematical solution, and (*d*) other reflective solutions.

a. Further Behavioral Experimentation

It might be supposed by now that we have tried nearly everything in the way of direct attacks on learning through experimentation, but of course this is not so. A slight twist, such as that introduced by the Petersons (40) led at once to a raft of new experiments on short-term memory, and other novel arrangements are no doubt possible that will bear on simple associative learning and rewarded or punished learning, even in its simplest forms. We saw one such illustration in Dr. Konorski's work, where the two types of response were separated, showing the circumstances under which the salivary and motor responses overlap, and when they do and do not interfere.

I have nothing to suggest at present in the way of decisive experimentation that is needed, so that, while recognizing that they may bring a resolution, past experience suggests that established theoretical positions in psychology are rarely dramatically changed by new experiments. Consider the abnormal fixation experiments of Maier (29), or the manipulation-curiosity experiments of Harlow and his associates (15), or the insufficient reward experiments of Lawrence & Festinger (28). These put many old theories under strain, but the strain seldom succeeds in breaking them, although a slow erosion doubtlessly occurs. It is almost always possible, for instance, to consider Dr. Konorski's experiments (26, 27) as essentially discriminations between two situations; one could draw a parallel with discrimination, for example, between two very different instrumental responses. My guess is that almost similar patterns would be found for shock avoidance and food response. Skinner has done this kind of experiment with a pigeon pulling up a thread with a foot and pecking with its beak; the interactions of these acts are very complex (50). It might be that Dr. Konorski has separated, not two sharply defined classes, but rather two learning situations, of which there might be many, many more.

So, while we have to continue in this way, I am not very sanguine that anyone's experiments are really going to settle the question. That is, the experiments have to be in relation to speculation rather than just to new empirical data.

b. *The Neurophysiological Solution*

While neurophysiology (and the related findings of electrophysiology and electrochemistry) may give some support to either classical or instrumental conditioning—or to both separately—it is subject to the same danger of abstracting from a totality of events that plagues learning theory.

Classical conditioning might appear to be supported by some neurophysiological experiments, but a proper selection of brain "centers" correlated with response may do nothing but repeat at a different level what was already observed. So, again, I am not too hopeful that the kinds of experiments reported here are going to settle the issue, partly because of the selectivity of the facts. If, for instance, one wants to find brain data related to classical conditioning, it can be done: both Dr. Galambos and Dr. Hernández-Peón have described some. If the behavioral facts are known, some related neural findings can almost surely be found. Thus if a Pavlovian measures only salivation, the resemblance between the conditioned and unconditioned responses is bound to appear: either the observed data will show no conditioning, or there will be conditioned salivation. Now, if instead of measuring salivation one places electrodes in some "salivation center" in the brain, the same will occur: the afferent consequences of the CS will become connected with this "salivation center" just as they overtly became associated with the secretion of saliva. This may help to specify some links in the network of events, but if it is all there is to the experiment we are really little farther along than when we did the conditioning experiment in the first place.

Instrumental conditioning meets with the same kind of problem. Neurophysiology may help to distinguish between components within the central nervous system, as in the ingenious experiments of Deutsch (5), differentiating motivational and reinforcement components. A similar approach has been reported here by Dr. Konorski, working on the hunger centers separately, and by Dr. Pribram, whose experiments separate out the effect of reinforcement. But we already know from behavioral studies that performance changes with drive level, in relative independence of the prior reinforcement schedule; to show that this is demonstrable within the central nervous system as well as in overt behavior gives some additional order to the phenomena, but it may do no more than show a correspondence between brain and behavior, leaving the theoretical quarrels where they were.

What I mean to say is that, as long as there are experiments demonstrating some differences between classical and instrumental conditioning, it is almost certainly possible, by appropriate placing of electrodes, to find corresponding neurophysiological activity. Both classical and instrumental conditioning will therefore remain plausible on neurophysiological grounds.

Our hope in this situation lies in that in our experiments additional happenings are recorded beyond those that are parallel in neurophysiology and behavior. We may abstract from the totality of events, but we abstract somewhat differently at the behavioral and neurophysiological levels; quite the same facts are not always reproduced: we get a little something else, such as electrical responses that persist after extinction when motor response drops out, or vice versa. These small discrepancies, which at first seem inelegancies, may later turn out to be the way to a real advance in knowledge—insofar as there are regularities, and not fully consistent in the two realms of discourse, our thinking will need clarifying. While there is no guarantee that the neurophysiological approach will solve our problem any more readily than the behavioral one, there is hope that independent views of similar problems may in fact bring us closer to the solution.

c. The Mathematical Solution

Mathematical approaches to learning theory (Dr. Simon will tell us more about these later on) have the great advantage of maximum precision in hypothesis testing, well illustrated in the work of Estes (9) and others. Appropriate statistical assumptions allow us to deal with the orderly behavior of aggregates, and the implied finer grain of the events underlying this order is a matter of some speculation. My own feeling is that most of the mathematical theories proposed to date have not been very much concerned with the classical-instrumental distinction; in fact, their equations usually turn out to show that the distinction is somewhat artificial; about the same equation system seems to fit the reinforcement kind of theory as the contiguity theory.

Mathematical theories have given relevance to certain new issues. For example, Estes describes a stimulus-sampling model and a pattern model, but the actual events that are sampled or patterned are not those directly manipulated experimentally. Difficulties arise when the substance of statistical or computer models is translated back into neurophysiology. Thus Miller, Galanter & Pribram (33) describe the difficulties of working things out together:

> One reason for much of the trouble in reaching an agreement about the way the brain works was that two of the authors stubbornly persisted in trying to talk about it in terms appropriate to the dry hardware of modern digital computers, whereas the third was equally persistant in using language appropriate to the wet software that lives inside the skull. After a decade of cybernetics you might think the translation from one of these languages into the other would be fairly simple, but that was not the case. The relation between computers and brains was a battle the authors fought out with one another until the exasperation became unbearable.

My impression, however, is that the distinctions of conventional theory between classical and instrumental conditioning are not of a kind that is apparent in the hypotheses that the mathematics model proponents find useful to test. For example, when Estes (9) tests the relative significance of *magnitude of reinforcement* and *information value of reinforcement,* the distinction, if expressed historically, is more nearly that between S-R drive-reduction theory and a cognitive theory than that between classical and instrumental conditioning. To the extent that Estes finds the informative content of the reinforcement equally important to magnitude of reinforcement, he is (in this respect) furthering a cognitive-type theory. Experimental support comes from various sources, including more recently Egger & Miller (8), who quite independently came out with essentially the same result: that the change in magnitude of reinforcement is very largely an information matter, or at least can be explained as well in terms of information as in terms of magnitude of stimulus. This result shifts the focus of the controversy as between contiguity and effect. The cognitive-type theory, the third approach Marquis and I proposed in 1940 (19), has been more or less overlooked in the major quarrels between single-process and dual-process theories. This type of theory, once thought of as not quite respectable, is gaining more attention through the decision theory and mathematical theories. The whole feedback principle is coherent with cognitive-type thinking.

It is too early to say where all this is leading, but mathematics is a powerful tool, and we may hope that the issues it can deal with are the pertinent ones.

d. Other Reflective Solutions

Finally, I think there are certain types of reflective solutions to our problem that I am not quite prepared to classify. I do not mean to imply that those who design behavioral or neurophysiological experiments, or work with mathematical models, are unreflective. There are, however, some other senses in which free reflection can be brought to bear upon the problems of learning theory; I shall mention three topics or tasks that deserve reflective thought.

The first concerns the *boundary conditions* implied in the design of our experiments. The expression is Spence's, and he uses it in the sense that he must be free to choose his own boundary conditions, and any criticisms of his work must be within his chosen area. While respecting his position—to make our experiments more manageable we must remove ourselves somewhat from everyday experience; this subtraction from the totality is necessary, for science can proceed in no other way—I believe it wise, nevertheless, to stop now and then and ponder such questions as, what are we leaving out? How much have we departed from the ordinary interaction of organism and environment? How forced have our analogies become? The ethologists, for example, have had a wholesome influence upon us just by asking what we are leaving out in our treatment of the animals. Our answers too often have been glib.

As an illustration, take Skinner's concept of shaping of behavior through selective reinforcement (49). This is a very happy way of accounting for novelty of behavior in keeping with a reinforcement theory, and many kinds of laboratory experiments, animal training demonstrations, and clinical experiences give it support. It is a far more appropriate explanation for novelty than Thorndike's principles of multiple response and learning skills through selecting and connecting (53). But one of the facts that is overlooked is that first approximations in novel situations are often very good indeed. These initial adjustments (through matching, copying, imitating) have been ignored in the enthusiastic acceptance of the theory of shaping, and once attention is called to these initial performances, as by Bandura & Walters (1), the omission becomes striking. Imagine trying to teach a child to say "Philadelphia" by shaping his spontaneous emissions through reinforcement! To be sure, we go on to refine his first approximations, as the singing teacher helps his pupil to sing on key; the point is, however, that through some process of imitation the act is often "good enough" the first time. This is the sort of observation we tend to disregard by being carried away by a plausible theory and permitting it to blind us to events outside its borders.

The second topic that calls for some reflection—and this has impressed me throughout this conference—is the distinction between the relative roles of *content* and *process*. Learning theorists are notably process-oriented, using "learning" as a verb rather than a noun. We are less interested in what the learner knows than in how he acquires knowledge, caring very little, in the experimental study of learning, for what the subject is asked to learn: whether chasing a bead around a pursuit rotor, memorizing nonsense syllables, or running a trestle maze—all is learning. Various writers have implied the uniformity of the laws of learning across species. Thus Hull (20) states: "The natural science theory of behavior being developed by the present author and his associates assumes that all behavior of the individuals of a given species and that of all species of mammals, including man, occurs according to the same set of primary laws." The tendency is to pay very little attention to content: the basic process is really present, and we work on any organism with any kind of act.

Yet it has been found repeatedly, right on through our meetings here, that, when an experiment is set up in a slightly different way, content can assume great importance. Dr. Konorski, in his paper at the 17th International Congress of Psychology (25), showed a variety of situations where entirely different discriminations were made in one or another setup; it was not the capacity to tell the difference between tones, or whether these were high or low, but what had to be done with the information that made a great deal of difference. Dr. Pribram has reported here that some types of delayed reaction or alternation were much more difficult than others according to how the numbers were displayed.

Let me illustrate this process-content distinction by the way in which the viewpoint of the learning theorist has carried over into discussions of instinct. So impressed are we by process that we tend to deny instinctive behavior if any learning process can be discovered in its acquisition. Thus, in a widely reproduced paper, Beach (2) refuted the usefulness of the instinct concept by showing that learning processes could be found in most behavior called instinctive. Historically, however, instinct is a content term, not a process term. If our learning theory is of any value we can train by it, but there are many instinctive behaviors we cannot possibly teach. The fact that weaver birds build a particular kind of nest is most important, not that they become more proficient weavers with practice. Let him who denies instinct because "all is learned" try to teach a robin to build an oriole's nest.

I am afraid the learning theorist's attitude may carry over also to the neurophysiologist, who hopes to find the "engram" for a learned habit while having given up on the much more firmly established "engram" for some types of instinctive behavior. Apparently we hope we can catch process, i.e., change, when we are unable to read the fixed neuronal patterns behind species-specific behavior. Anyone who has tried to teach a laboratory salamander to do anything at all, such as to come to the surface of the aquarium at a signal to be fed, must be very much impressed (if he has the curiosity to find out) that the same salamander brain that responds so sluggishly to his laboratory teaching is able to control a complex but flexible migratory pattern that takes the salamander up and down hills to return to the water-hole of its birth. Even the experimental intrusion of blindness does not prevent this return (55); if taken off its path it will explore around and find it. Failure to adapt to our little laboratory situations does not preclude complex behavior repertories. The neurophysiologist interested in "how the brain works", and not in doing something that uses the paradigms set for him by the experimental psychologist, surely cannot consider the control of such behavior outside his area of interest.

The problem of process and content intrudes itself at quite another level. I have mentioned that Kimble is convinced that the differences in what can be learned make classical and instrumental two kinds of learning (23, 24). Verbal behavior in man also represents such a content problem, for speech can be taught to other animals, such as a parrot, but language and the abstractions it makes possible are uniquely man's. A mere process interpretation of learning fails to come to grips with such problems; a little reflection on content brings them immediately to the fore.

The third and final topic that I wish to propose for reflection has to do with the willingness to discard old thought patterns in favor of new ones. It is possible to entertain a new theory without initially believing it, and entertaining a new theory now and then is bound to refresh the theorist, even though he eventually clings to the old.

The inhibiting effect of S-R thinking, largely under the influence of Sherrington and Pavlov, is a case in point. Dewey's trenchant criticism (6) of the reflex arc concept was pre-Sherrington, and it remains as cogent today as it was in the 1890's, Sherrington himself said in 1906 (46) that the reflex was only a convenient abstraction. I spoke up weakly against the S-R concept as long ago as 1948 (17):

> It may be that the stimulus-response language has outlived its usefulness now that the molar psychologies have freed themselves from the necessity of explanation according to physiological mechanisms. Patched up as it is with drives, sets, tensions, secondary reinforcing agents, it is a way of talking carried over from reflex physiology when reflex physiology is no longer the model for psychological study. It would perhaps be a wholesome recognition of the change that has come in psychological thinking to talk about behavior in the presence of certain objects rather than about re-action to stimuli.

I was of course interested to see Miller, Galanter & Pribram (33) carry on with a similar argument in 1960. As they say:

> There is some reason to think that the reflex unit has been vastly overrated and that a good many psychologists would like to get out from under it if they could. The reflex arc may have been useful

in getting psychology started along scientific paths, but the suspicion has been growing in recent years that the reflex idea is too simple, the element too elementary.

I was writing in a Zeitgeist in which psychology had temporarily declared its independence from physiology; they were writing in a time when physiology was reexamining the reflex arc, and coming to declare itself in favor of something with feedback principles built in.

As I pointed out, we really have an input-output psychology, not truly a stimulus-response psychology. Now that we are increasingly concerned with how the "stimulus" gets coded before it enters significantly into discriminations, and measure some decoded output, we are far from sense organs and primary effectors.

Members of the guild of learning experimenters and theorists pay relatively little attention to theories of the cognitive sort, outside the classical and conditioning paradigms. At the same time, however, cognition is gaining ground with child psychologists, psycholinguists, and students of problem-solving and thinking. Though some of those schooled in learning investigation turn to these new topics, they find it hard to break their habit of thinking in terms of familiar conventions, so that even when considering problem-solving and creativity they formulate their problems in the old way (22, 30). A non-member of the guild finds many other directions open, especially via information theory, game theory, ethology, Piaget's genetic epistemology (41), Freud's primary and secondary processes (11), and computer simulation. Some of these other conceptualizations may afford the reflective psychologist and his neurophysiological counterpart a fresh approach to problems seemingly unsolvable in terms of the older formulation.

As I mentioned, Marquis and I (19) in 1940 listed Tolman's expectancy theory (54) as a fair competitor to substitution and effect theories, even in the handling of data from conditioning experiments. I still believe that some such alternative is open, and that it will again have a good hearing in the right hands. It should not be forgotten that Pavlov described the conditioned stimulus as a signal and recognized curiosity as a motive; it takes little forcing to develop a cognitive theory from these starting points. It need not be recognizably a return to the theories of Edward Tolman, no matter whether it comes in cybernetic form, in the Miller-Galanter-Pribram TOTE unit, or in some other form. To answer the question posed in the title of my paper, I do not believe that the usual formulations of classical and instrumental conditioning exhaust the alternatives.

Discussion

Konorski: I would like to make a comment regarding Table 12: I do not think it reasonable to list Ivanov-Smolensky's anticipatory responses among the subclasses of classical conditioning. According to his method (21), the subject is trained, by either passive movement or by instruction, to perform a motor act which is then rewarded, the reward being usually candy for children, and for adults something even more powerful, namely approval ("That's good"); it is a positive social reinforcement. So I would think that this category of responses should be listed under instrumental, not classical, conditioning.

Grant: I would not disagree with you on the matter, but when I prepared that table (13), I had more in mind the false reactions in reaction time experiments. Sometimes the stimulus for the reaction is not given after a ready signal, and yet false reactions are often obtained. Indeed, under some distracting conditions, one can get quite a large number of false reactions. They are not rewarded, particularly; they seem to happen more or less automatically. Marquis & Porter (31) have similar observations.

Hilgard: I am inclined to agree with Dr. Konorski. As I said, I thought this was one of the justifications for including instrumental conditioning; in any case, there is some complexity. Ivanov-Smolensky also used purely instrumental situations with food as the reward. Other subjects were asked to look at pictures, almost exactly as in the Skinner and Ogden Lindsley experiments.

Lipsitt: The Ivanov-Smolensky experiment (21) was such that the conditioned response, when it did occur, was anticipatory to the subject's seeing the stimulus: a piece of food was dropped down a tube; the subject was instructed to squeeze a bulb when he saw the food passing a window in order to divert it to his hand or into a cup. A bell was then introduced at the moment the food was released into the tube. What happened was that the subjects did condition; the basic data for this conditioning were error responses, that is, unrewarded anticipatory responses. To me this seems to be a classical conditioning paradigm: the conditioned response was maladaptive in the sense that it prevented reinforcement, as opposed to the usual instrumental situation, which "effects" reinforcement.

The confusion as to whether the Ivanov-Smolensky conditioning is classical or instrumental is clearly relevant to the taxonomic problems discussed by Dr. Hilgard. While Dr. Konorski would call it an instrumental learning situation, and Dr. Grant apparently classified it as anticipatory instructive conditioning, I believe it is a classical conditioning experiment, and that a more specific S-R type of analysis of the situation is called for, rather than judgment about whether it is classical or instrumental.

Grant: I am in profound sympathy with most of Dr. Hilgard's views; I think we oversimplify so much with the S-R terminology that our thinking often becomes circumscribed, if not stereotyped. Still, I do believe there is quite a bit of life and potential in the old S-R mare yet.

When I tried to classify the conditioning experiments at Dr. Melton's request (13), I went through a period of intense frustration. My wish was to make a content or functional classification and do it sensibly; I found this impossible, due, I believe rather than to my limitations, to the fact that the experiment, the behavior, the content, is much more complicated than psychologists usually admit.

It is of course an advantage to run one's own experiments and talk to the subjects. In observing the same with rats and other animals, the fact is that the experiment is really a minor thing in the animal's life, though it may be a major one in the experimenter's. It is considered (psychologists often do this) with relative clarity in terms of the stimuli and responses involved; in any event, only a very limited number of things is manipulated, a very limited number of responses is observed, and a great amount of what goes on is ignored. It is as if one were to attend a concert with a great interest in the piccolo, entering somewhere in the middle of the performance and leaving after listening to the piccolo player, perhaps noticing him add or skip a couple of notes, then drawing some conclusion about what the composer had in mind. We face essentially the same problem in trying to classify the things the subject does.

So, I was forced in frustration to classify operationally in terms of the experimenter's, rather than the subject's, operation. This is not the best way to go about building a structure of theory; I apologize, but I had no other choice. The operational approach is entirely correct, provided one's operational definitions are applied to the appropriate feature in the subject-experimenter interchange. I was unable to achieve this. So much more could be said; still, in general, I feel very pleased Dr. Pribram said he was delighted now that there are some things in the nervous system related to learning; even though they may not be exactly what we want, there is progress. Occasionally, students in my classes on psychology of learning ask me, "Well, what is it really?" In effect I answer, "It is our faith that there is a change in the nervous system; we do not yet know what it is, but I can say progress is being made."

In my opinion, some of the variables mentioned by Dr. Galambos are more on the performance side, perhaps attention or set, than in the storing of the engram, whatever that may be. But I think our physiological-psychological friends should be somewhat wary of those of us who are more behaviorally oriented: the gifts we bring them, through no ill intention on our part, may perhaps not be as helpful as they might be.

Even in the salamander we deal with a highly evolved nervous system. We try to obtain from our subjects some learning that takes place slowly enough so that progressive changes can be observed. Often we deliberately build changes which are progressive or appear to be, whereas in fact this gradual progressive character of the learning may be perhaps more a function of the complexities introduced by us into the experiment rather than of the individual associations, if we are to talk in S-R terms.

For example, if we do a certain kind of discrimination experiment with the rat, we may find that it learns slowly, while a human subject will learn a similar problem in one or two trials; it is over and done with before we can see it, from the standpoint of having something to study as experimenters. So we give the human subject something that is more of a challenge to his more highly evolved nervous system. It takes him longer to do the task and we get more data, more to think about. We have often made him puzzle out interrelationships in a very complex experiment, so that a lot of work is going on. He can do it, but the simple associative notions of S-R psychology become a minor part of what is going on if the subject has to disentangle interfering responses, separate different kinds of words, etc. The learning task we give him is ecologically valid but, from the standpoint of scientific explanation, we are making some difficulty for ourselves at the behavioral level, and perhaps fantastic difficulties at the physiological level. I think that, if I were studying things from the physiological standpoint, I would try to reduce the behavioral experiments down to the simplest possible forms and try to deal primarily with association.

Pribram: May I disagree heartily? It is not necessarily true that by studying the "simplest" organism or the "simplest" process one learns the most. Sometimes by looking at very complex situations one can somehow see a way through them, and they yield more easily than do apparently simpler situations. And "simple" situations and organisms turn out to have their own multiple levels of complexity if examined closely enough.

The problems that have arisen in behavioral work, in experimental psychology, classical and instrumental conditioning, problems such as those just analyzed so beautifully by Dr. Hilgard with regard to whether an expectancy or a substitution explanation is most effective, often—not always but often—are resolved by going to the neurological level of discourse. This different way of looking at the data can tell us which of the two alternative behavioral theories or subtheories is the more useful, or whether, indeed, they are really different. It may well be that both ways are indistinguishable once we have the neurological facts; the argument may disappear at the other level. So, I do not think it is right to say that we can find *any* old thing in the brain depending on what the model is. Given several alternative models of the data gathered at the behavioral level, we can sometimes choose between them on the basis of neurological data. For instance, I feel (42) that the contiguity and the expectancy positions with regard to reinforcement become indistinguishable once we know the physiological facts about the process of habituation (so effectively worked out and presented at this conference by Dr. Thompson, and on a former occasion by Sokolov, 51).

Grant: I do not think we are actually in disagreement, for we are talking about different things. The organism will not hold still for us very well, although we would like it to do so. For example, in verbal learning and retention, we become aware of the protean, active, dynamic character of this process. Take simple nonsense syllables, which patient Herman Ebbinghaus (7) developed in order to get away from familiarities with the language. We discover that one of the difficulties in retention of verbal material, even with nonsense syllables, arises out of letter sequence, a structure of the language with which the subject is so familiar (56). We find, for example, that he has a very hard time learning unfamiliar nonsense syllables (usually ones where the digrams and trigrams of the syllable are very unusual in the English language) but he retains them rather well because there is no interference between the initial learning and the subsequent retention tests; once the competing letter sequence problems have been solved, the unfamiliar trigrams are retained; retention is readily demonstrated. However, if he is given familiar nonsense syllables (where the letter sequences are quite common to the English language), he learns them easily but his retention is very low. In the process of learning this particular set of high association value nonsense syllables he had to suppress, probably quite actively, many of his language habits, just as in the other case, but in the retention interval there is apparently trouble from two sources: a recovery of the language sequence habits, suppressed during learning, which are now so closely similar to what he has newly learned; and loss of the differentiation between what he just learned and his normal language habits. Also, during the retention interval he reads, uses the letters, and these bring back a good deal of interference and disrupt the retention of the particular learning he had done.

The point, in general, is that, although we tend in our own thinking (perhaps from the simplicity of our language or the simple-mindedness of psychologists) to view these as sort of static processes, laying down engrams, etc., the old gestalt psychologists were not completely wrong in referring to dynamic traces and the like. They were disinclined to analyze the traces in anything like a subtle fashion. So I worry about certain kinds of learning experiments leading to easily found simple changes in the nervous system when the nervous system is a very active performer in the retention interval.

Miller: Much has been said about the taxonomic classifications of classical *versus* instrumental conditioning. The question that really interests me is whether these two types of conditioning obey functionally different laws. In many respects they are strikingly similar. A few differences are, however, beginning to emerge. One of these is in the effects of partial reinforcement, that is, not reinforcing every response. This procedure appears to increase the resistance of instrumental responses to extinction and decrease that of classical conditioned responses (23).

Although this difference has appeared in a number of experiments, I am not absolutely sure that the real variable involved is the difference between classical and instrumental conditioning. For example, it could be that all of the classical conditioned responses tested to date have been relatively quick and effortless, while the instrumental responses have been more prolonged and effortful. Perhaps the different effects of partial reinforcement are a function of this difference rather than of the distinction between classical and instrumental conditioning. I have done at least one experiment on the instrumental response of bar-pressing in which I failed to get any effect of partial reinforcement. I have not yet published the results because I wanted to do more work and be absolutely sure; perhaps other exceptions to the apparent rule have not been published for the same reason.

Recently, Allen Wagner (57) at Yale seems to be uncovering another functional difference in the effects of a variable on resistance to extinction. He is finding that under certain circumstances a larger reward increases the resistance of a classical conditioned response to extinction, but decreases the resistance of an instrumental response. Again, it is conceivable that some other dimension, such as effortfulness, is the crucial variable. In any event, it is clear that we should look for functionally different laws. If the laws are the same in every respect, the difference between classical and instrumental conditioning is not very important; to the degree that the laws are different, this distinction is important.

Konorski: If the notions which I have presented are true, at least at first approximation, I would be happier to speak now not about classical and instrumental but about consummatory conditioned reflexes and drive conditioned reflexes.

First, I think it is important to add that exactly the same rules which can be applied to the alimentary conditioned reflexes (classical and instrumental) can also be applied to avoidance reflexes. With avoidance, the situation is quite the same, namely the reduction of fear drive caused by the cessation of the fear CS leads to the consolidation of the instrumental CR. Then we can discriminate between consummatory defensive CR and fear CR. For instance, there is an interesting experiment (10) in which a good avoidance CR is established without going through the stage of the escape CR; this occurs when the animal performs some movement to the CS in order to avoid the noxious stimulus, e.g., the introduction of acid into the mouth. When the noxious stimulus itself is again applied, protracting its duration, one might predict strong transfer, i.e., the animal would be expected to perform an even more vigorous CR to the UCS than to the CS. But this is not the case: to the introduction of the acid into the mouth the animal displays a strong consummatory response consisting of mouthing movements rejecting the acid, but shows no tendency to perform the instrumental act. The instrumental act to the UCS is performed only when the training goes through the stage of escaping, i.e., when the noxious stimulus lasts until the animal performs the movement. Then the presentation of the UCS evokes the fear response of its continuation, and the animal escapes it. So we have here a similar relationship between the fear and acid reflex and the hunger and food reflex.

I think one more step should be taken: all the theories discussed by Dr. Hilgard could be reduced to one contiguity principle. In classical conditioning there is a contiguity between two exteroceptive stimuli which are associated by repeated pairing; in instrumental conditioning, drive becomes associated with the kinesthesis of that movement which accompanies the drive reduction, preventing its retroactive inhibition.

Birch: How do you account for the development of instrumental conditioning in animals that are unable to perform the movement? Many years ago Bitterman and I (3, 4) discussed one of the difficulties in the theories based upon drive reduction notions and action notions, pointing out that there is a number of experiments in which, for example, the motor nerves to a limb are crushed and the animal is simultaneously shocked with a light presentation; once regeneration occurs, the animal acquires the avoidance behavior, independently of its not having done it before. What is being reduced?

Konorski: There is a mistake there. All these experiments are concerned not with avoidance conditioning but with classical conditioning.

Birch: I do not think there is a difference.

Konorski: Oh, a very clear difference.

Birch: I think this is in the mind of the experimenter, but not in the phenomenon, and not in the neurology.

Konorski: I do not know how to argue with that.

Birch: You must tell me how this animal acquires avoidance response.

Konorski: When we deal with classical conditioning we have to deal with contiguity of stimuli, this contiguity being totally misunderstood in the S-R theory. After all, the S-R schedule represents only the first and the last links in the series of events, and does not take into account the central nervous processes mediating the stimulus and response. What really occurs is that the CS becomes associated with the pain stimulus, and this association is independent of whether the ventral roots are crushed or not.

Birch: This is precisely what we argued at the time.

Konorski: The animal will not be able to perform the movement if the ventral roots are crushed or if it is immobilized or curarized. If the movement is feasible, it will be performed because of the connection, not of the S and R, but of the central representation of the conditioned and the noxious stimuli. This is a well-known notion of SS conditioning. With instrumental conditioning the situation is different and more complicated, for we do not know the role of the proprioceptive feedback and whether it may be substituted by the central feedback.

Birch: What you are saying then, in effect, is that you agree with me and others that the basic process in association is sensory integration?

Konorski: Yes, I fully agree with that.

Birch: We are in agreement at that level. As for the mechanism of directed action in the sense of developing an additional instrumental response, I would argue that I would prefer to see it on a parsimonious basis, and I would account for it in terms of further sensory integrations rather than evoke a new mechanism.

REFERENCES

1. BANDURA, A., and WALTERS, R. H., *Social Learning and Personality Development*. Holt, Rinehart & Winston, New York, 1963.
2. BEACH, F. A., The descent of instinct. *Psychol. Rev.*, 1955, **62**: 401-410.
3. BIRCH, H. G., and BITTERMAN, M. E., Reinforcement and learning: the process of sensory integration. *Psychol. Rev.*, 1949, **56**: 292-308.
4. ———, Sensory integration and cognitive theory. *Psychol. Rev.*, 1951, **58**: 355-361.
5. DEUTSCH, J. A., Behavioral measurement of the neural refractory period and its application to intracranial self-stimulation. *J. Comp. Physiol. Psychol.*, 1964, **58**: 1-9.
6. DEWEY, J., The reflex arc concept in psychology. *Psychol. Rev.*, 1896, **3**: 357-370.
7. EBBINGHAUS, H., *Memory; A Contribution to Experimental Psychology* (H. A. Ruger and C. R. Bussenius, Transl.). Teachers College, Columbia Univ., New York, 1913.
8. EGGER, M. D., and MILLER, N. E., When is a reward reinforcing? An experimental study of the information hypothesis. *J. Comp. Physiol. Psychol.*, 1963, **56**: 132-137.
9. ESTES, W. K., Probability learning. In: *Categories of Human Learning* (A. W. Melton, Ed.). Academic Press, New York, 1964: 89-128.
10. FONBERG, E., Transfer of the conditioned avoidance reaction to the unconditioned noxious stimuli. *Acta Biol. Exp.*, 1962, **22**: 251-258.
11. FREUD, S., Formulations regarding the two principles in mental functioning. In: *Collected Papers*, Vol. IV (J. Riviere, Transl.). Hogarth, London, 1956: 13-21.
12. GAGNÉ, R. M., Problem solving. In: *Categories of Human Learning* (A. W. Melton, Ed.). Academic Press, New York, 1964: 293-317.
13. GRANT, D. A., Classical and operant conditioning. In: *Categories of Human Learning* (A. W. Melton, Ed.). Academic Press, New York, 1964: 1-31.
14. GUTHRIE, E. R., *The Psychology of Learning*. Harper, New York, 1935.
15. HARLOW, H. F., and MCCLEARN, G. E., Object discrimination learned by monkeys on the basis of manipulation motives. *J. Comp. Physiol. Psychol.*, 1954, **47**: 73-76.
16. HILGARD, E. R., The relationship between the conditioned response and conventional learning experiments. *Psychol. Bull.*, 1937, **34**: 61-102.
17. ———, *Theories of Learning*, 1st ed. Appleton-Century-Crofts, New York, 1948.
18. ———, *Theories of Learning*, 2nd ed. Appleton-Century-Crofts, New York, 1956.
19a. HULL, C. L., *Principles of Behavior; An Introduction to Behavior Theory*. Century-Crofts, New York, 1940.
19a. HULL, C. L., *Principles of Behavior; An Introduction to Behavior Theory*. Appleton-Century-Crofts, New York, 1943.
20. ———, The place of innate individual and species differences in a natural-science theory of behavior. *Psychol. Rev.*, 1945, **52**: 55-60.

21. IVANOV-SMOLENSKY, A. G., On the methods of examining the conditioned food reflexes in children and in mental disorders. *Brain*, 1927, **50**: 138-141.

22. KENDLER, H. H., The concept of the concept. In: *Categories of Human Learning* (A. W. Melton, Ed.). Academic Press, New York, 1964: 211-236.

23. KIMBLE, G. A. (Rev.), *Hilgard and Marquis' Conditioning and Learning*, 2nd ed. Appleton-Century-Crofts, New York, 1961.

24. ———, Categories of learning and the problem of definition: comments on Professor Grant's paper. In: *Categories of Human Learning* (A. W. Melton, Ed.). Academic Press, New York, 1964: 32-45.

25. KONORSKI, J., On the mechanism of instrumental conditioning. In: *Proceedings of the XVIIth International Congress of Psychology* (Washington, D. C.). North Holland, Amsterdam, 1963: 45-59.

26. KONORSKI, J., and MILLER, S., On two types of conditioned reflex. *J. Gen. Psychol.*, 1937, **16**: 264-272.

27. ———, Further remarks on two types of conditioned reflex. *J. Gen. Psychol.*, 1937, **17**: 405-407.

28. LAWRENCE, D. H., and FESTINGER, L., *Deterrents and Reinforcement; the Psychology of Insufficient Reward.* Stanford Univ. Press, Stanford, 1962.

29. MAIER, N. R. F., *Frustration; the Study of Behavior Without a Goal.* McGraw-Hill, New York, 1949.

30. MALTZMAN, I., On the training of originality. *Psychol. Rev.*, 1960, **67**: 229-242.

31. MARQUIS, D. G., and PORTER, J. M., JR., Differential characteristics of conditioned eyelid responses established by reflex and voluntary reinforcement. *J. Exp. Psychol.*, 1939, **24**: 347-365.

32. MELTON, A. W. (Ed.), *Categories of Human Learning.* Academic Press, New York, 1964.

33. MILLER, G. A., GALANTER, E., and PRIBRAM, K. H., *Plans and the Structure of Behavior.* Holt, New York, 1960.

34. MILLER, N. E., Comments on multiple-process conceptions of learning. *Psychol. Rev.*, 1951, **58**: 375-381.

35. MILLER, S., and KONORSKI, J., Sur une forme particulière des réflexes conditionnels. *C. R. Soc. Biol. (Paris)*, 1928, **99**: 1155-1157.

36. MOWRER, O. H., On the dual nature of learning—a reinterpretation of "conditioning" and "problem-solving". *Harv. Educ. Rev.*, 1947, **17**: 102-148.

37. ———, Two-factor learning theory: summary and comment. *Psychol. Rev.*, 1951, **58**: 350-354.

38. ———, *Learning Theory and Behavior.* Wiley, New York, 1960.

39. PAVLOV, I. P., *Conditioned Reflexes; an Investigation of the Physiological Activity of the Cerebral Cortex* (G. V. Andrep, Transl. and Ed.). Oxford Univ. Press, London, 1927.

40. PETERSON, L. R., and PETERSON, M. J., Short-term retention of individual verbal items. *J. Exp. Psychol.*, 1959, **58**: 193-198.

41. PIAGET, J., *Introduction à l'Épistémologie Génétique.* Presses Univ. France, Paris, 1950.

42. PRIBRAM, K. H., Reinforcement revisited: a structural view. In: *Nebraska Symposium on Motivation* (M. R. Jones, Ed.). Univ. of Nebraska Press, Lincoln, 1963: 113-159.

43. Schlosberg, H., The relationship between success and the laws of conditioning. *Psychol. Rev.*, 1937, **44**: 379-394.

44. Seward, J. P. Introduction to a theory of motivation in learning. *Psychol. Rev.*, 1952, **59**: 405-413.

45. Sheffield, F. D., The contiguity principle in learning theory. *Psychol. Rev.*, 1951, **58**: 362-367.

46. Sherrington, C. S., *The Integrative Action of the Nervous System.* Scribner, New York, 1906.

47. Skinner, B. F., Two types of conditioned reflex and a pseudo type. *J. Gen. Psychol.*, 1935, **12**: 66-77.

48. ———, Two types of conditioned reflex: a reply to Konorski and Miller. *J. Gen. Psychol.*, 1937, **16**: 272-279.

49. ———, *The Behavior of Organisms. An Experimental Analysis.* Appleton-Century-Crofts, New York, 1938.

50. ———, Are theories of learning necessary? *Psychol. Rev.*, 1950, **57**: 193-216.

51. Sokolov, E. N., Neuronal models and the orienting reflex. In: *The Central Nervous System and Behavior*, Trans. 3rd Conf. (M. A. B. Brazier, Ed.). Josiah Macy, Jr. Foundation, New York, 1960: 187-276.

52. Spence, K. W., *Behavior Theory and Conditioning.* Yale Univ. Press, New Haven, 1956.

53. Thorndike, E. L., *Animal Intelligence; Experimental Studies in Animals.* Macmillan, New York, 1911.

54. Tolman, E. C., *Purposive Behavior in Animals and Men.* Century, New York, 1932.

55. Twitty, V. C., Migration and speciation in newts. *Science*, 1959, **130**: 1735-1743.

56. Underwood, B. J., and Schulz, R. W., *Meaningfulness and Verbal Learning.* Lippincott, Chicago, 1960.

57. Wagner, A. R., Siegel, S., Thomas, E., and Ellison, G. D., Reinforcement history and the extinction of a conditioned salivary response. *J. Comp. Physiol. Psychol.*, 1964, **58**: 354-358.

MATHEMATICAL MODELS AND ARTIFICIAL INTELLIGENCE

HERBERT A. SIMON[°]
Carnegie-Mellon University
Pittsburgh

In the general area we are surveying in these sessions, we all seem to be confronted with the same problem, and our solutions are various. On the one hand, some who cleave tightly to the protoplasm have perhaps some difficulty in defining what the protoplasm has to do with learning, but know they are dealing with the brain. There are others who are quite sure they are dealing with learning but quite unsure of what it has to do with the brain. I am clearly in the second category. I will not presume in my remarks to say what my theory has to do with the brain. If any of the neurophysiologists present can find aid or comfort in what I might say, I will be grateful. I would like first to draw a map of the territory, and then spend most of my time on one small country on that map.

People who employ formal models and/or computers in the study of behavior or psychology use various dichotomies to indicate subareas within that general province. As my first dichotomy I shall set up "artificial intelligence" and "cognitive simulation". I cannot give a formal definition of intelligence; within the trade, the term "artificial intelligence" is mostly used by those interested in seeing what computers can do, in making computers solve problems—play chess, prove theorems, do "cybernetic" things, as the Russians use that term. Many do this as a way of exploring the organization of complex processes, independently of how such processes are organized or accomplished in human beings; they are only secondarily, if at all, interested in what humans can do. Those concerned with cognitive simulation are not, *per se*, interested in what a computer can do, but rather (and this I suppose to be the relevant interest of this group) in using the computer as an aid, a tool to help understand and find out what a human being can do or does do in certain kinds of cognitive activities. My remarks will deal with cognitive simulation and not with artificial intelligence, which makes the title assigned to me somewhat of a misnomer.

The second dichotomy concerns the other half of the title, "mathematical

[°] The work reported here was supported in part by a grant from the Carnegie Corporation, and in part by Research Grant MH-07722 from the National Institutes of Health. Almost all of the work has been carried out in collaboration with Allen Newell. Specific debts to numerous other colleagues are acknowledged by references in the text.

models". Important work is being done in psychology making use of what I shall call classical mathematics—probability theory, difference or differential equations, and numbers. Other models that are not mathematical in that classical sense are still formal in the sense that the theories are stated precisely enough to be phrased in computer languages but they are, generally and sometimes totally, non-numerical in character. These are usually called "information processing models". I shall try to illustrate quite specifically what I mean by that, for I shall be talking about them and not about mathematical models, which I suspect will be the subject of Dr. Atkinson's remarks later on, and which he is better qualified than I to discuss.

The third dichotomy, arising from psychological work that makes use of some sort of computer simulation, is between what I would call brain models and information processing models. There have been attempts to simulate on the computer the behavior of a network of nerves interconnected in certain ways (the network's elements having certain of the properties of neurons, and the connections having some of the properties of synapses). The best known simulation of this kind, by Rochester, Holland, Haibt & Duda (26), embodies Milner's (20) revision of the cell-assembly theory. Likewise, some of the pattern recognition models—I am thinking of Frank Rosenblatt's perceptron (28)—are intended to reflect certain of the properties, or hypothetical properties, of nerve nets, retinas, or a combination of both.

In contrast with these, the information processing models are much more aggregative in form. They do not deal with neurons at all. While they are theories of the central nervous system, I think they are best described as theories of the *organization* of the central nervous system that do not reach the physiological level in describing what is going on in that system—which would call for a detailed characterization of elements such as neurons. In view of all that has already been said about organization and levels at this conference, I do not think I need to apologize for, or even to explain at length, an approach that purports to theorize about complex cognitive behavior without attempting to say anything very specific about protoplasm or neurons. It is not intended to be directly biological. Newell and I (24, 31) have discussed elsewhere the methodological justification for an information processing approach.

There have been many analogous approaches in other fields of knowledge, the simplest being perhaps the Mendelian genetic theory. The Mendelian factor was a construct that explained observed phenotypes by postulating certain underlying genotypes. Today the Mendelian factor is in turn being explained by the biochemistry of chromosomes and genes, but one can go quite a long way in genetics without such biochemical explanations. Genetic theory will explain many things about crossbreeding without requiring any understanding of how the mechanisms are realized in a biological system. A similar analogy could be drawn with chemistry—explanations first at the level of the periodic table and valences which later received their own explanation in terms of atoms. Such an intermediate level theory is my theme here, and that is what I mean when I say I do not know whether there is any interest or aid and comfort for neurophysiologists in this kind of theorizing. It may well be that the constructs in the theory are at such an aggregative level that physiologists will see no way of making contact with them; this is a question I shall examine after we see what the theory does state.

Let me review briefly a particular information processing theory that has been more strictly formulated as a set of computer programs in a computer-programming language (6, 23, 30), describing first a particular version of the theory in general terms, then the kind of data gathered to test the theory, and reaching finally the question of what relevance, if any, this might have for those interested in the brain as a biological structure. In postulating the theory, I will start by describing the system that we are going to try to use to explain complex cognitive behavior.*

First, we postulate that there is a *memory*, that this memory is capable of storing *symbols* (i.e., discriminate patterns), and that it is capable of storing *structures* of symbols—structures of a very particular kind we will call "lists". By a list, we simply mean an ordered set of symbols such that, given one symbol, we can always speak of the next one in the list. This is equivalent to assuming we have an operation which, for any given symbol in immediate memory, brings the next symbol in its list into immediate memory. We can have lists of symbols which are themselves lists, and thus build up hierarchical structures. The relation of "next", might sound more familiar to psychologists if I called it "association", but we are going to postulate very specific properties of lists, which may or may not correspond to the properties usually attributed to associations.

Second, the system has a *sorting mechanism* capable of discriminating symbols. Again, the theory does not postulate how this mechanism operates biologically; it is assumed to be capable of discriminating symbols and structures of symbols or parts of such structures.

Third, we postulate a set of *elementary processes* for operating on symbols. Such processes allow the system to input a symbol into memory, to copy a symbol or symbol structure, and to output a symbol. Perhaps there are processes for erasing symbols. Fourth and fifth, we postulate two other mechanisms I shall discuss further: an *interpretive mechanism*, basically a mechanism that takes symbols as its inputs and, as a function of these symbols, either causes things to happen in the central memory or, through efferent channels, causes the outputs to bring about overt behaviors. Finally, we postulate *learning mechanisms*, i.e., those that are capable of modifying both symbol structures and the sorting mechanism.

The interpretive mechanism—to use computer language for a moment—is

* For a fuller account, see Newell and Simon (23, 31).

a system which will take a symbol structure, treat it as a program, and execute that program; it will do something. Let me cite an example (30). A human subject is given a sequence of letters, say ABMCDM, and asked what the next letter is. Most subjects of reasonable intelligence will answer "E", and will be able to go on with the sequence indefinitely. This sequence, after it has been input and while being held in memory, is an example of a list of symbols of the sort that we postulate can be stored in memory (Postulate 1). When it is input, presumably the shapes are recognized as familiar English letters, and discriminated on this basis by the sorting mechanism (Postulate 2). Now we ask how the subject produces another letter in the sequence. The theory postulates that the subject, on the basis of some processing of the input list (Postulate 3) will arrive at the conclusion that he can generate the next member of the series with the help of the English alphabet stored as a list in his memory. The interpreter (Postulate 4) would be the mechanism that goes down the stored English alphabet in memory, finds that in the storage the letter "E" is stored next to "D", and produces the "E" as the correct answer to the problem.

Thus, what I call the interpretive mechanism is one that would execute a program of scanning inputs and find some regularities, as well as, in the example I just gave (under control of the pattern it had discovered), execute the program of going down and finding the next letter in the alphabet and outputting that letter. If it is performing this task, somewhere in the scheme there must be subroutines that look for such patterns, finding them sometimes and sometimes not. What I have given here is a set of labels for the main components in what might be called the general-purpose part of this program that is implicated in the performance of almost any kind of cognitive task. In addition, there will be stored in memory, as lists of symbols or structures of such lists, all sorts of programs that will serve to give this system various kinds of special capacities, such as the capacity to detect patterns, to play chess, etc.

The term "interpretive" is borrowed from computer language. The interpreter comes as close as any part of the system to being the "homunculus": it is the active part in control that determines what is going to be done next. It corresponds to the control and sequencing parts of standard computers. I am, in fact, distinguishing it from a compiler.* I would prefer to avoid such technicalities here.

The actual program that embodies these assumptions, that lives underneath these labels, is actually a fairly complex computer program. As a matter of fact, there is no single program extant at the present time that has incorporated all the mechanisms I have mentioned. What I have described is a composite of approximately three programs† which could be put together

---

* In computing, a program that translates instructions written in a higher-level language into machine-language instructions so that the translated program can be executed subsequently by the computer is called a *compiler*. A program that carries out such a translation, not prior to the execution of the program but during its execution, is called an *interpreter* (24).

† Described by Feigenbaum (6), Newell & Simon (23) and Simon & Kotovsky (30). See p. 181.

even within the present size of computers. I have presented a fairly elaborate set of postulates about the content of this program; a set, as I have indicated elsewhere (31), that might be compared in complexity with the set
of reaction pathways postulated in theories of the photosynthetic reactions.
These postulates cannot be written down in three lines like Newton's Laws;
their general description takes ten book pages and their accurate specification is a program of several thousand instructions.

The basis for postulating such an elaborate information system is that,
with the right postulates, a mechanism of this kind can account at least approximately for certain broad classes of complex cognitive behavior. By
"account for" we mean, first of all, that by actually writing the computer programs which embody these mechanisms, and using the programs to perform
tasks, we can show that the mechanisms are *sufficient* to produce the complex cognitive behavior in question. It has been shown (31) that computer
programs containing this and no other kind of complexity, having only processes that can actually be executed and organized in this way, can play
chess, can discover proofs for theorems and can take the Thurstone Series
Completion Test and answer correctly at least the simpler items.

In any area of science there are certain observable phenomena we are interested in explaining. Findings about dogs lifting their feet and salivating
were considered in Dr. Hilgard's presentation; some constructs were introduced, and some postulates were made about them. From these constructs
and postulates certain predictions were derived about the behavior that
would take place if the system in question satisfied the constructs and the
postulates. In this way are theories tested. Of course, we do not claim that
the particular theory which explains our data is uniquely capable of doing
it. All we know is that up to this time the theory has had a certain success in
predicting, and it has done well or badly in some areas. This is what we expect of a theory.

Discussion

Zigler: Is it possible to have a program employing two divergent processes that, operating simultaneously, find the same answer? One thing we do
know about intelligence is that, in the course of its development over time,
a given end product is attained by quite different processes. I just wondered
if this fact of development could be simulated with the program. In the
ABMCDM sequence, a child might come to "E" in a way different from an
adult. There are many documented instances of this sort.

Simon: At any given moment a program such as I have described would
come to the answer, if it came to it at all, in a particular way; it would have
stored in memory (we could actually go into memory and find out what it
had stored there) a particular pattern—an abstraction, if you like—of the letter sequence it was using to generate the extrapolation. (Cf. Simon & Kotovsky, 30.) A number of patterns could generate that particular sequence:
for example, if we divide the sequence ABMCDM into triads, we can see

that the symbol of each triad is next in the alphabet to the first; the third symbol is "M"; the fourth one is next to the second one. Or: the first symbol in each triad is the next to the next of the first one in the previous triad, and the second one is next to the next of the second one in the previous triad. It would be rather difficult in this particular case to know which of these patterns an individual had in mind unless he were asked how he would generate the next member, which he might or might not be able to describe. Or we could use his verbal behavior as another piece of evidence.

It is certainly possible that two different programs, both of them capable of this task, could be performing in slightly different ways. In fact, it would not be difficult, through minor variations of the program, to move it from one of these modes of behavior to the other.

Zigler: There is a very basic issue here, as far as the developmentalists are concerned. When you say that you have simulated intelligence, we would like to know whose intelligence or what level of intelligence. A major problem in developmental psychology has been the deduction or construction of some kind of progression to handle the change in intellectual process over time. We would like to see someone produce a model that handles the change itself, rather than some end process. We know your final theory cannot handle the cognitive process or simulate intelligence at every level; it has to be wrong at every level except the one for which it would be right.

Simon: Suppose we take a "snapshot", so to speak, of a particular human being at some point in his life, and try to characterize him. Presumably he has stored in his brain, in one form or another, certain general-purpose machinery which changes slowly or remains fairly stable, at least over a short period of time. He also has all sorts of special-purpose equipment, which we call his knowledge or particular skills, much of which changes fairly drastically and fairly rapidly over a relatively short period of time through learning experiences.

Eventually we would like to start out with a system that has some of the general-purpose characteristics of a child, let us say, and that will, through experience and interaction with its environment, continually modify itself until it has not only perhaps changed some of its general capabilities but also has acquired many of the specific capabilities that an adult acquires through such learning experiences. This is quite a task, and I think it should be approached in several steps. I know of no one who thinks he can come even close to it at the present time.

An approach would be to start out by simulating an adult or a class of adults all having the same level and type of competence, with the notion that a better understanding of the structure of the processing system of such adults would in itself suggest what has to be developed. That is, an understanding of the structure of an adult mentality (the nature of the information, skills and programs that have to be stored, for example, to enable an adult to play chess or to discover patterns) would be, in itself, an important source of information and clues as to what must be involved in the learning processes that led to this ability.

A second and quite different strategy would be to experiment with programs that modify the system itself, including its relatively general parts; that is, we might experiment directly with the structure of the learning program with the thought that, if we could do a reasonable job of simulating its important parts, we could, so to speak, grow our own adult.

Both approaches have been used in some of the research on information processing systems; several of these systems are intermediate between the two approaches. A program (EPAM) which embodies a subset of these mechanisms and has had a fair amount of empirical testing by now, is directed at the learning question (6, 9, 10, 29). It was designed to explain or account for the way in which human beings learn nonsense syllables in the psychological laboratory by the paired-associate and serial-anticipation methods. It turns out, now that this program is in existence, that it is capable of performing quite a number of other kinds of learning tasks, including some that use other stimuli than syllables as the learning material. Without going into much detail on its program content, I would like to review the kinds of questions that EPAM purports to answer and has had some success in answering, and compare and contrast these with the kinds of questions that have been asked and answered in the psychological laboratory about the same learning tasks.

A problem that has been studied extensively in nonsense-syllable learning is why and how meaningful material is learned much more rapidly in paired-associate learning (35) than meaningless material, or high-meaningful material much more rapidly than material of low meaningfulness. In the EPAM simulation, that question would be translated by asking what kind of a representation we could give for meaningfulness or anything similar in the psychological situation. A hypothesis might be that high-meaningful material can be represented by lists of symbols that already had been made familiar to the system. By this we mean that they had previously been given to the system, that the sorting mechanism had already been allowed to practice on them and to learn them in some fashion or another (29). Low-meaningful material would then be that which had not been exposed to the system—lists that were new to it, that it had never previously tried to discriminate or practice on. In fact, we can use standard lists of syllables from psychological experiments and simply give prior familiarization training on those particular letters or syllables regarded as having high familiarity or high meaningfulness—if nonsense-syllable specialists will allow me to use the two words together.

Grant: Does your familiarization training use a type of stored program, problem-solving approach?

Simon: The computer has in storage a program that includes the kinds of elements I previously enumerated, including a sorting mechanism. We simply present a set of symbols to it and say, in effect, "Sort them". If we look inside the computer we will discover that, under these instructions, it will begin to grow in memory what amounts to a tree structure, where the branches of the tree come to represent different symbols in the set with which we are familiarizing it.

Donchin: Do you permit degrees of difference, or is your distinction between identity and difference?

Simon: The system matches on identity at the lowest level of elementary symbols. Since structures can be made up of such elementary symbols, there can be many degrees of difference in the compound structures. In fact, we can then run experiments which involve similarity of symbols and use the same criteria of similarity used in the verbal learning experiments with human subjects using the same symbols.

Rothkopf: Within your system, is the stored program part of the account of the learning process?

Simon: Yes, and one of its components is the sorting mechanism.

Rothkopf: This is interesting because you previously stated that these computer programs account for learned phenomena in the same way any other scientific theories do. I can certainly see that you can produce outputs similar to those which any given learning experiment would produce. How do you verify the inputs of your reference experiment? How do you make sure that your system does not have more elaborate inputs than those with which the human being has to operate, and that it has, as it now is fashionable to say, the same heuristics?

Simon: We postulate the critical characteristics of the inputs, not at the retina certainly, but a few levels back of the retina. The processing scheme demands that these inputs have the characteristic of being made up of elementary discriminable patterns of some kind which can themselves be organized by the asymmetrical association called the "next" association into lists of such patterns and higher-order lists (10).

Rothkopf: You have to explain in your theory how, from a particular set of inputs, you arrive at a particular set of outputs. I can see how you can determine with little doubt that the outputs required by your theory correspond to those which you observe. However, it is not clear to me how you decide that the kind of inputs you have to provide your machine are the same as those with which a living organism has to work. This point is crucial because, if your machine is equipped with more elaborate heuristics than man, the machine's ability to simulate human outputs will not be very convincing.

Simon: I am not sure I understand the question, but let us suppose we are trying to predict the outcome of an experiment, which Underwood (33) happens to have run, on similarity among nonsense syllables. In order to get syllables of high similarity, Underwood constructed his stimuli by building syllables with certain letters in common. In other words, strings of patterns that have some elementary subpatterns in common.

Now we construct a computer input (29) in which each syllable is represented by a string of subpatterns ("letters") and in which the same subpatterns ("letters") are used in the construction of different syllables. Just as Underwood's subjects read lists of syllables in which some letters occur repeatedly in different contexts, so the computer receives as its input strings of patterns in which the same subpatterns occur repeatedly. There is the same concept of identity in dealing with these two situations.

Lipsitt: Would it be correct to assume that, in order to get an output that simulates human functioning, assumptions would have to be built in about the way in which we know human beings behave?

Simon: Any theory must do that. As an example, from Newton's three laws of motion and certain initial conditions, some predictions can be deduced mathematically. If done correctly, to deduce something mathematically means all the conclusions were contained logically in the premises. The information-processing theory suffers from the same limitation, namely that all a computer will do when we set it spinning is what we programmed it to do—what we really programmed it to do, not necessarily what we thought we programmed it to do. This is exactly equivalent to saying the conclusions of any theory are implicit in the premises. The interesting and important word is *implicit.*

Rothkopf: You have already made the important assumption that stimuli for human beings have letters as functional component elements, and that these provide a reasonable measure of similarity.

Simon: That is already hypothesized and, of course, the hypothesis ought to have some testable consequences if we are to believe it. I would like to indicate the sort of predictions we make with such a system.

If we compared paired-associate lists of high similarity (i.e., where almost any pair of symbols has at least two letters in common) with lists of low similarity, considering the similarity of just the stimulus syllables in the system, how much more rapidly would the subject learn the lists with stimulus syllables of low similarity than with those of high similarity? The system does make a prediction (its exact specification would need a few other qualifications): theoretically, it ought to be about 40 per cent faster (29). What would happen if the high and low similarity conditions were imposed on the response symbols rather than on the stimulus symbols? The theory says degree of similarity will then make virtually no difference in speed of learning. These are rather strong predictions. In fact, they do not depend in any sensitive way on the parameters of the program; they come out quite directly from the method of encoding the stimuli.

Likewise, in my previous example of familiarization, let us compare the number of trials the system would require to learn paired-associate lists of

low familiarity (i.e., lists of syllables to which it had not been exposed before) as against the number of trials it would take to learn lists of high familiarity (i.e., where the sorting mechanism on the individual syllables was
run often prior to the paired-associate trials). The theory—that is, the program—says that it takes about three times as long to learn the syllable pairs
of low familiarity as it does to learn pairs of high familiarity, and that this
3:1 ratio is an upper bound, as much of an advantage as familiarization can
give (29).

These are rather strong quantitative predictions. Testing them by running our own experiments or by searching in the literature for the many experiments conducted on these variables shows that the theory makes out
rather well. Experiments such as those reported by Underwood & Schulz
(35, Chapter 3), indicate that there is an upper bound to the magnitude of
the effects of familiarization and meaningfulness in nonsense syllables, and
that this is in the 2.5-3:1 range.

Grant: I am afraid I am very concrete-minded. This familiarization process with the machine still bothers me. Is it a program such as we would
write if we wanted the machine to learn to play tick-tack-toe with people so
that it would test each outcome of success or failure and store its experience
in competing with other people?

Simon: No, it is the same program the parts of which I listed earlier, plus
the instruction, "Sort each syllable as you come to it". The sorting mechanism
does not simply take anything presented to it and dispose of it one way or
another. In the process of inputting, it compares what it gets with what has
already been stored, discovers if it is confusing things—or at least *sometimes*
discovers if it is confusing things—which are in fact different and, as a result, it gradually increases its discriminations.

The mechanism also uses its knowledge of results. As it sorts objects, it
not only keeps the absolute minimum information needed to sort them, but
a small amount of redundant information. If another object then comes
along and is, so to speak sorted to the same bin, the redundant information
is available for determining whether or not the two objects sorted to the bin
are identical. If they are not, the sorting net is proliferated and some additional redundant information is kept. For example, if the system saw only
one identical twin at a time, sooner or later it would learn to distinguish
them even though the twins were never present together.

Pribram: What is the relationship between the stored program and the
permanent memory of the computer in hardware terms?

Simon: Almost none, in the sense that one has to have a general purpose
computer; but any general purpose computer, by being given an IPL interpreter, can be made to execute this program (16, 24).

Pribram: In other words, the program is essentially a short-term rather
than a permanent memory store in the sense that it is manipulatable, finite
and so on. Am I correct?

Simon: If we look at it as a piece of hardware, it is easy enough to clean out the memory of a computer. In fact, however, some of these program mechanisms behave as though they were human long-term memory. That is the role played by the sorting mechanism in the EPAM system, whereas the mechanism that detects the pattern in the ABMCDM example behaves like short-term memory.

The short-term memory is distributed around in various places. For example, when the system is sorting a new syllable it has not previously seen, it has to hold the syllable in memory while it is sorting. That would be part of the short-term memory. We do not have in the system a good detailed representation of short-term memory.

The part of the sorting mechanism that remembers, so to speak, things it has seen before, is long-term memory. It is a matching sort of affair, and stores a certain amount of redundant information (i.e., more information than it actually needs for sorting the objects it sees) as a basis for determining when it has seen new objects.

Koestler: Dr. Pribram is reluctant to ask the obvious question. If similarity is the criterion of recognition, then the linking together in the interpretative mechanism would have to include language tricks in the lists. That is the question, is it not?

Pribram: It is very closely related to the point. I am beginning to wonder whether much of this is not sort of an intermediary memory process which is neither short-term nor long-term memory, but something else that lies halfway inbetween, that seems to have more capacity than very short-term store yet has the sort of organization you mention.

Simon: I guess all I can say is that the particular mechanism handling the particular tasks I have described was designed to behave like those aspects of human memory which are particularly involved in nonsense-syllable learning tasks, and seems to do so to a gratifying extent.

Let us first recognize that one of the problems in building a theory today is in deciding how many memories there are and their relations to each other. Let us be careful, in talking about immediate, short- or long-term memory, to treat these as hypotheses and not as accepted statements of fact. At present there are represented in the program only two kinds of memory, short- and long-term; immediate memory—in the sense of "the magical number seven" (19)—is only represented in its grossest aspects. I do not know how short the term of "short-term" memory really is.

Rothkopf: You had a program to handle similarity data. Was the same program or a different one used to handle the material on meaningfulness?

Simon: The same program was used, but with different syllable inputs.

Rothkopf: Suppose you had two pairs of syllables that stood in the same relationship to each other with respect to similarity. You might have QVM and QPM, and also the syllables BIT and BAT. The second pair happens to spell out meaningful words. We know from some paired-associate experiments that people do not tend to confuse within these two pairs in the same way. How would you go about accommodating this kind of finding?

Simon: If, before running the paired-associate trials, the system is given the syllables BIT and BAT among the high-meaningful ones to be used in the experiment, and is permitted a substantial number of familiarization trials with them (simply giving it these syllables individually and not as pairs, and giving the instruction to sort them), when the syllables are put in lists as paired associates we will find that EPAM will memorize those pairs approximately three times as fast as it will memorize pairs that have not been given the familiarization training.

Rothkopf: Would those meaningful syllables then also show a ratio of 40 per cent more difficulty for syllables having two letters in common?

Simon: No. I should have specified, perhaps, that the finding about similarity concerns syllables of low meaningfulness (cf. Table 3, columns 5 and 6 in Simon & Feigenbaum, 29). The 40 per cent effect of similarity will disappear with high familiarity, just as it does in the human data: human subjects will not learn high-similarity syllables more slowly if the meaningfulness is high, nor will EPAM (cf., Table 3, columns 1 to 4, *op. cit.*),

Donchin: How do you determine what is a sufficient number of presentations?

Simon: The phenomenon is nonlinear. By "sufficient number of times" I mean that there would be no variation in results if we ran it ten more times. The interesting thing about the human data is that there appears to be, from the numerous reported experiments (35), an upper bound on the amount of facilitation of learning that can be obtained by using syllables of high meaningfulness and/or familiarity; the ratio 3:1 appears again and again in the literature.

Grant: Why does your machine not learn the whole list in one trial?

Simon: Why should it? There is no instruction in the program which says "Take the list that is given to you and store it in your memory". It has to receive such an instruction in order to learn in one trial. The hardware is perfectly capable of doing that; computers are better fixators than human beings. We are trying to construct a program that will, in fact, behave the way the human being does, so the processes we put in are not those that simply store a thing away the first time it has seen it.

Koestler: Can the machine store more easily than a human being? The human being has so many possibilities, memorizing jingles and other tricks of finding inner relationships.

Simon: That is hypothetical. All I said is that there is a computer program, EPAM, which is precisely specified. With it I can specify some operations which I call familiarization trials, and I use these. My theory is that this organization of processes accounts for the easier learning of high-meaningful lists and low-similarity lists. The way in which I test my theory is to see whether quantitatively it predicts the right amount of facilitation—and it does.

Pribram: Perhaps Mr. Koestler means that programmers ordinarily use simple repetition to get redundancy into a system, whereas in ordinary affairs we have more effective ways of producing redundancy.

Simon: I do not know what we use. I only know I have a set of processes which are formally specified and perfectly rigorous. If you believe this theory, then you will predict a maximum of 3:1 facilitation. This prediction is borne out in experiments in which people compare syllables of very high meaningfulness with those of lowest meaningfulness. Perhaps you have a better explanation; I can only say that I have obtained a prediction from my theory which happens to conform with the data.

Jensen: There is the question of whether the 3:1 ratio can be predicted from Mr. Koestler's idea or from yours, Dr. Pribram.

Pribram: I do not think either Mr. Koestler or I are talking about nonsense syllables; we are talking about ordinary language.

Simon: With jingles we have units larger than individual words; in fact, the ratio can be larger than 3:1. I do not think it really is a simple matter.*

Rothkopf: We might be spending too much time discussing the principles involved in this type of approach to theory. Perhaps you could tell us just how much of meaningful learning your particular program can account for. What kind of experiments does it accommodate?

Simon: If that is agreeable, let me try. I think this discussion of the nonsense-syllable learning is useful in giving an indication of the kind of prediction such a theory purports to make. What the entire theory represents is, as I said, essentially a composite of three separate programs: EPAM (6); something called the General Problem Solver (GPS) (23); and something called the Series Pattern Generator (SPG) (30). They use basically subsets of the common set of processes I have described. If it were worth the trouble—and it would be a fair amount of trouble—the programs could be put together so they could all function in the computer at one time and, in fact, use common parts. A large part of the behavior they explain would be called problem-solving behavior rather than learning behavior. I do not know where one leaves off and the other begins. It partly depends on what we call short-term memory and long-term memory.

The areas in which these programs have been compared in detail with human data are: first, EPAM in the area of nonsense-syllable learning; second, GPS in areas of problem-solving at a complexity level of the discovery of proofs for geometry theorems (although that is not an actual task for which the GPS program has been used) or the missionary-and-cannibal puzzle; third, SPG in tasks such as the Thurstone Series Completion Test and others of the same general kind.

When GPS was constructed we did not have in mind the missionary-and-cannibal problem; this was suggested to us by somebody who wanted to

---

* See Hovland's data (13, Table 2). The maximum facilitation of unrelated but meaningful English words over nonsense syllables is about 3:1. But with *related* words, i.e., continuous prose, there are still larger familiar units at the level of phrases, hence additional facilitation, perhaps by another factor of 3:1.

make a television show, and we thought it was reasonable to ask GPS to solve it. Some interesting things can be discovered from watching human beings work out this problem. First, it would not be difficult to do an exhaustive search of the tree of alternatives, for there are only a few possible legal moves; that is proposition No. 1. Proposition No. 2: human beings frequently take half an hour or more to solve the problem, yet systematic trial of all legal moves could give the answer in about five minutes. Proposition No. 3: human beings do not encounter difficulties just anywhere in that problem, but at the specific point where, to solve it, they have to bring two people back across in the boat. If the GPS is really simulating human behavior, we would demand that it try all possible legal moves; we would expect it further to have difficulties and make some false moves at the point where two people had to be brought back across the river. This is exactly what it does, and this is the reason for supposing that what it does bears some relationship to what human beings do in solving the same problem. In fact, it predicts the locus of the difficulty in that problem. This really is prediction, since GPS was not designed to handle this particular problem.

Rothkopf: Some years ago, Hunt (14) reported an experiment with a factorial design, in which he varied the meaningfulness of both the stimulus and response terms. Have you attempted to account for anything of this kind?

Simon: I do not know Hunt's experiments. We have, in fact, replicated some of the main experiments on similarity and familiarity, including those of Underwood (33), Bruce (2), and Chenzoff (5). In all cases we obtained results which agreed (29) quite well with the published experimental results, without tinkering with the parameters in the program. As a matter of fact, I do not know what parameter we could tinker with that would change these particular results; their insensitivity to the program parameters is the reason we are interested in these experiments. EPAM has made two other predictions and anticipated one or two things which have since appeared in the literature. In application to serial lists rather than paired-associate lists, the theory correctly predicted the quantitative shape of the bowed serial position curve (11). It is well known that the shape, over a wide range of situations, is invariant, independent of ease or difficulty of syllables, if properly plotted in terms of percentage of total errors made on each syllable. I am referring to the McCrary-Hunter result (18). EPAM made a correct quantitative prediction of the shape of this curve. Basic to the theory is the prediction that, if we take nonsense syllables of low familiarity or meaningfulness, the time for learning per syllable (time, not trials) should be virtually constant under a wide range of conditions, including drum speed, intertrial interval, etc. This could have been shown to be true by data in the literature; recently, Bugelski (3) ran some experiments that show that this constancy holds approximately.

If the EPAM theory had been running soon enough, it would also have predicted some of the results of the Rock experiment (27). In fact, it makes some definite statements about one-trial learning: it says that in order to demonstrate one-trial learning, response syllables of high rather than low familiarity should be used. I think this agrees with Underwood & Keppel's summary (34) of the circumstances under which one-trial learning does or does not take place. All of these results are predicted by the set of mechanisms I have proposed.

Feshbach: Suppose in one case there is a marked discrepancy. Are there any rules which would enable you to modify the program parameters in such a way that it would not interfere with all the other predictions that have been successful in the past?

Simon: The right way to play this game is to find a set of experimental situations in which the system can be placed, such that, if the parameters are tampered with to match one of the experimental situations, the behavior of the system will almost certainly be different in others. In this way we put enough constraints on the freedom of system. In describing predictions, I tried to limit myself to phenomena where I would not know how to tamper with the mechanism in order to fit the data. In a couple of months I might have changed, say, that 40 per cent to 90 or 20 per cent, but fundamentally these results are not artifacts of parameters.

Jensen: But are they not actually the natural outcome of the structure of the problem? We have *trigrams,* and the fact that there are three letters surely has something to do with the outcome.

Simon: It does, indeed. Since I believe the theory, I also believe that is why, in human data, the 3:1 advantage also appears. If that is so, we should not look for anything more profound in the human data, many of which are artifacts of the way in which we construct our experimental task environments.

Zigler: I find this theory very elegant and impressive. The fact that it does not do everything that we would like it to do is beside the point. Its formal features are appealing to me; it is the only one I know of that meets the two formal requirements of theories: each construct is defined, and the relationship between each and every other construct is specified. I am very curious about how you managed to build such a good theory. Did you use the data of past experiments, or did you actually study the processes employed by people when learning such a list, or did you combine the two?

Simon: Before we become too enthusiastic about the theory, I could probably spend an equal amount of time telling what is wrong with it. The method by which this theory was constructed was no different from any other: first you assimilate what you know about the phenomena (a good question to ask yourself is, what is the simplest kind of thing that would behave this way?). Then you begin to program your data, only to discover that you have not specified nearly enough mechanisms to make such a scheme work. In fact, all sorts of things may remain undefined. This forces you to begin to define them. To do so, you search the literature for any hints as to how things work, or you introspect or look for cues anywhere you can. There is nothing idiosyncratic about the way such a theory is built.

One of the virtues of this approach for describing complex systems is the fact that you can write it down in formal language and can cumulate things without losing track of where you are, so to speak. You can, in fact, build up fairly complex interacting mechanisms in which you can predict rigorously the consequences of the interactions. With this technique, it is not a case of adding something because it is needed over here, and forgetting its effect over there: the computer, sooner or later, will not allow you to forget the interactions. If this technique has any power, the power lies in the computer language itself, in the fact that complex systems can be cumulated in such languages, piece by piece. You do not have to think about the whole thing at once; you can think about it step by step, and the computer tells you what the consequences of the interactions are.

I hoped to give a taste of theories of this kind, of the kinds of predictions they do make. I cannot forego one other example of a prediction because, as your questions indicate, one of the peculiarities of this type of theory is that it allows all sorts of rather direct postulates to be made about the structure of the stimulus and to by-pass many of the problems encountered in stimulus scaling.

You will notice there was no need to construct a scale of similarity in the nonsense-syllable experiment; we simply introduced input syllables that had certain parts of their patterns in common. We define similarity operationally the same way we do in the human experiment. As an example of what we mean by the direct representation of the structure, consider a series completion problem: DEFGEFGHFGHI. To help the subject, we might divide the symbols in threes: DEF GEF GHF GHI. We ask him what the next symbol is, and this is not immediately obvious. But if the sequence is written in another way, DEFG EFGH FGHI, I think it is immediately obvious what the next letter should be. In fact, both are the same sequence, but grouping by fours makes it easier to discover the pattern than grouping by threes.

Having observed such a problem, we can now try to make some predictions about how to construct sequences that will be difficult or easy for humans. What is the relationship of this to the theory I was describing earlier? The particular theory we have—the one I called the Series Pattern Generator (30)—says that in solving such a sequence people first try to find the periodicity of the sequence. After that, they try to find the pattern.

We have given this problem to human subjects in two conditions: one with the sequence printed out on paper, and one in which they saw the letters one by one in succession. We discovered the second way made this particular problem very much easier than the first. Of course, the reason (according to our theory) is that, if the subjects are given the problem all at once, they search for the repetitions of identical symbols, and in this example the symbol identities suggest a division into triads. If they see the whole sequence at once, they divide it into triads and run into trouble; if they divide it into fours, they find the pattern easily. This kind of interaction from the theory to human subjects in new experiments suggests improvements in the theory when it fails to predict.

Let me make a concluding remark that brings us back to physiology. I think that among the ways in which the task of the psychophysiologist may be viewed is to postulate a system in terms of elements on the level of molecules or neurons such that, if the system did have the postulated properties, then a human brain embodying such a system and installed properly in the human body would deal with the missionary-and-cannibal problem or learn nonsense symbols in the way human beings do.

Another approach that neuropsychologists might take is to consider how things having the properties of large molecules and neurons and systems of these, can be used to store patterns and lists of patterns; that is, to find the counterpart in protoplasm of what I have been calling a list or a structure of symbols, or of what I have been calling the sorting mechanism. If we could explain how protoplasm did these relatively simple things—they will not seem very simple to somebody working with molecules—then the kind of information processing theories that I have been talking about can carry us the rest of the way, because they tell us that anything that can do these simple things can, in fact, also carry out complex cognitive behavior.

We can derive some optimism about this more modest neurophysiological task from knowing that there exist some physical systems that can perform such complex tasks—to wit, computers properly programmed. This should at least give us some hope that the biological mechanisms for doing these things need be no more than perhaps a couple of orders of magnitude more complex than the physical mechanisms that now do them. I say it gives us some hope, not that we have any connections yet with the physiological level. Perhaps it will be easier, in theory building, to take some such intermediate level of theory and try to build toward the middle from the end.

Guilford: Do you ever input some irrelevant information along with the relevant?

Simon: Most of the work to date has been fairly limited on the side of the worldliness or prior experience of the simulated person. One reason why we have used tasks such as discovering Thurstone's series, logic, or missionaries-and-cannibals rather than tasks drawn from life is that, to simulate a person solving problems drawn from life, we would have to put in memory a great deal more experience at the outset.

Within the narrow realm in which this experimentation has been carried out, we have done some work along the lines you suggest (8, pp. 129-133). For example, in the theorem-proving programs, one form of learning that is rather easy to include in the simulation is the storing of theorems whose proofs are discovered in such a way that they can later be used as premises in subsequent proofs. In some of our early experimentation we found that the power of the system to prove theorems could be enhanced by storing some of the previous results, but that the function was not monotonic: as the system had more and more knowledge of previous theorems, its power of proving subsequent theorems increased, but then leveled off or even decreased. The reason was simply that the system wasted too much time exploring around in its mass of knowledge trying to find something relevant. There are other forms of learning which could presumably overcome this effect. We had no way then of increasing the discrimination of the system as it accumulated more experience but if, at the same time, it had had some EPAM-like learning (which would have increased its discrimination by classifying theorems in a progressively finer way), it could have learned to look for just the appropriate theorems. Lacking such discrimination learning, the system showed the effects of pedantry.

Lipsitt: Would it be correct for us to conclude from what you have said that you have here a very elaborate and very efficient hypothetico-deductive, theoretical system into which you feed assumptions, and the deductions you get from the system are no better than your assumptions, and it is in your assumptions that your program is tied to reality?

Simon: The assumptions are the program.

Lipsitt: Yes. Then with respect to developmental phenomena, insofar as we have developmental information and this information can be fed into your program, you may be able to give us some deductions or predictions.

Simon: But please do not underestimate what you call the "feeding in". Let me make clear that constructing such programs or modifying them to encompass new ranges of task is, of course, a major job. It is research in theory. There is no guarantee of success. I think the examples we have seen here are sufficient to show this.

In principle, it would be interesting, as one of the next steps, to grow one of these programs from a pup rather than to introduce it to the world in a more or less adult stage with respect to task skills. We have some research going on in this direction. For example, a doctoral thesis (36) now in progress involves a program that reads the instructions—instead of "reads" I should say "extracts", "looks at"—on a battery of intelligence tests (like the Thurstone Serial Symbolic Test) which includes symbolic material, not word meanings. It looks at examples of such questions, determines what the problem is, programs itself to answer the question, and then answers it. This is a step in the direction of having a system develop its own program.

We have another project under way (37) to determine what would be required for such a system to learn to play games, not by giving it a program for the legal rules of the game, but by giving it a description of the game in declarative language, and perhaps some examples of correct play.

Feshbach: The problem has to be put in computer language. Is the translation invariant? Is there only one way of asking a problem, or are there several, so that the computer might give a different response if the question is not properly stated?

Simon: As GPS stands today, I think a fair answer would be that there is one way to give the problem but, from experience with other programs, I think that is a fairly superficial characteristic of this one.

Robert Lindsay (17) at the University of Texas has done a good deal of work on programs that accept natural language inputs, declarative inputs. With such a program, what happened might depend on the order in which the declarative sentences are given and exactly what they said; however, just as in ordinary language, the program is relatively insensitive to the specific order in which declarative sentences are used. It is not foolproof. It would be easy to introduce this characteristic of Lindsay's program into GPS, but this has not been done at the present time.

O'Connor: Can you comment on the kind of decay function we all have in our memory?

Simon: At present, the programs I have described do not contain any reasonable theory of forgetting.

Miller: At the Princeton Conference, Feigenbaum (7) described a phenomenon which seemed analogous to the forgetting occurring in human learning. This was particularly interesting because it was not put directly into the program as any fading of memory traces, but appeared as a by-product of confusion produced by new learning. Much, if not all, of human forgetting appears to be the result of such interference.

Simon: That is correct. EPAM will show some forgetting, essentially as a result of generalization, and will show some oscillation in learning (9). We think it has learned something, then it gets another syllable and it turns out that it did not. My statement was that I did not think the program contained a reasonable set of forgetting mechanisms. I do not believe this one mechanism accounts for all of the data on retention and forgetting, even of nonsense syllables.

O'Connor: When you specify that the system is to compare two symbols, do you specify that it just compare and dismiss them?

Simon: During familiarization trials a large part of the information disappears. The system may keep it around—I say "May" because, in fact, what it does is highly contingent on all the circumstances, such as what happened to it before, and so on. Each time it looks at a syllable not already completely familiar, it may keep around a little more information about the syllable than it had before, particularly if, on trying to discriminate, it finds some information which seems to contradict information it thought it had. I wish I could put that in a more concrete way.

Incidentally, there are descriptions of most of the programs I have mentioned (except SPG) in a book recently edited by Feigenbaum & Feldman, called *Computers and Thought* (8). GPS and EPAM are described there, as

well as a number of other programs I have not reviewed. There is one publication now on the series generator by Kotovsky and myself (30).

O'Connor: So far you are talking about intelligence. Is there anything to
be said about backwardness?

Simon: Nothing that could not be accounted for as the absence of intelligence. There are many problems this program will not solve.

Grant: If the computer does not have enough memory capacity and we
want, say, to program it for tick-tack-toe, and we cut out one needed bank,
it will not always settle on a satisfactory "stat" to beat us; it will oscillate,
being pretty good for a while, and then it will slip.

Simon: It will slip if we have an incomplete strategy for tick-tack-toe, because of insufficient storage or for other reasons.

Grant: That is one form of backwardness.

Gagné: Is that not an example of backwardness which you gave, in the
sense that this particular program had limitations as to how many proofs it
could handle? Once it reached a certain point, it was worse off than before.

Simon: The program exhibits lots of "backwardness", if by this you mean
all sorts of reasons why it does not work perfectly. These programs are intended to simulate people; they are not designed to do things perfectly. For
example, the version of the series generator Kotovsky and I described (30)
was given a battery of 15 tests that came from a standard intelligence test
(probably one of Dr. Guilford's), which we had also tried out on people. We
found people who could do 3 of the 15, and others who did all 15. The particular program we tested happened to do 7, if I recall correctly.

Grant: Dr. O'Connor's suggestion is interesting in the sense that, if you
build defects into your program, it will of course not learn on a trial; and you
actually have some choice as to how you do that.

Simon: That is correct. Of course, we could play the brain localization
game here if we really wanted to go far afield. I have been very conserva-
tive. Perhaps I might have picked up some of Dr. Pribram's material and
said, "Obviously EPAM is located in the parietal lobe back here and the series generator is in the frontal". Then we could design experiments on the
effects of removing one of them. If we begin to take these theories seriously,
then they provide a means for deciding what kinds of tasks are "similar", in
the sense that destruction of the same brain mechanisms should simultaneously disable the victim from performing them. That makes it sound
much simpler than it is, for almost any task we can think of turns out to use
most parts of the entire program; that is what is wrong with simple localization experiments, too. But at least the theory would give us some clues as to
what kind of test batteries ought to be affected in similar ways in aphasias.

Pribram: These are what we might call the "Hilgard precautions".

Zigler: What Dr. Grant has said and Dr. O'Connor suggested should be
emphasized. The possibilities are indeed rich. We cannot use these empirical data to explain backwardness, but what we can do is to start with Dr.

Simon's program and the several suggestions found in the literature on mental retardation. As I understand his theory, several of the results pertain directly to processes (or theoretical constructs) in his system. The hypothesized defect could be built in at various points in the system to see if the product simulates the findings from retardates. If it does, validation of the theory would be advanced.

Simon: I do not have a considered judgment as to whether it is presently worthwhile considering this kind of research on brain damage. It will obviously be the right direction to go at some time.

Atkinson: From my viewpoint, the most striking feature of Dr. Simon's remarks was that there were certain universal constants that characterize EPAM. This a very desirable state of affairs for testing a theory; it characterizes most theories in physics. In Dr. Simon's example, of familiarization training never yielding better than a 3:1 ratio in terms of learning time, it was surprising to me that the 3:1 ratio is a fundamental feature of EPAM and that it is a constraint that necessarily follows from the type of branching scheme and list structure assumed. I was really struck by the fact that he viewed the 3:1 ratio as being fundamental. In fact, if I recall the statement correctly, he said that he could not think of another way of formulating EPAM that would not lead to the 3:1 prediction.

Simon: The 3:1 ratio derives from our desire to avoid elaborate representations of letters or syllables, or of anything else. We simply want to have the capacity to discriminate elementary patterns, whatever they may be. The way we construct more elaborate patterns is by having short strings of elementary ones; if we want still more elaborate ones, we construct short strings of the second-level patterns. Two facts produce the 3:1 ratio: first, that the stimulus consists of three-letter strings—if we had seven-letter nonsense syllables, the ratio would not be 3:1, that is why that ratio does not apply to jingles. Second, we want a recursive structure, so that we can sort at any level of complexity, and anything can become a familiarized unit (10). Once it has become a familiarized unit, it can serve as a unit in a larger structure. I do not know how to obtain another ratio with three-letter syllables without giving up the recursive structure which seems to me important and fundamental to the system.

MATHEMATICAL MODELS FOR VERBAL LEARNING

Atkinson: At this point I think there would be some value in my presenting an alternative approach to a theory of verbal learning which is formulated as a mathematical model rather than as a set of instructions in a computer program. It will give us a chance to compare these two theoretical approaches on a number of dimensions: specifically, the range of applicability of the two approaches, the nature of the axiom systems, the types of theoretical predictions possible, and the procedures for testing and revising the theories. At a conceptual level I think my approach is very similar to that of Dr. Simon's; however, the way we choose to translate these broad conceptual statements into precise theoretical assumptions is quite different.

Before I describe a specific model for verbal learning, it will be useful to distinguish several levels of theoretical predictions. Certainly, most of the predictions generated by a model presuppose parameter estimates. Typically, part of the data is used to perform the estimation and then the model is used to predict the remainder of the data. Several levels of prediction can be distinguished according to how far the model predicts beyond the data used for estimation. For simplicity, let us assume that learning is described by the following equation:

$$q_n = \alpha^{n-1}$$

where q_n denotes the probability of an error in trial n. Successive points on the theoretical learning curve can be generated by substituting estimated numerical values of α and values of n into the equation.

If α were estimated from the very learning curve data we seek to predict, a very modest type of prediction, i.e., curve fitting, would be accomplished. This operation does qualify as prediction because a model will not necessarily provide satisfactory curve fits. It may well turn out to be impossible to describe the data with a given function by any choice of parameter values. Thus, if a reasonable description of the data is achieved, one must concede that the results provide some support for the model.

The next higher level of prediction involves an element of over-determinism. A parameter is said to be over-determined if its value can be estimated from a given set of data in two or more independent ways. Related to this notion of over-determinism is the use of a parameter estimate obtained from part of the data to predict some other independent aspect of the data. For example, if α in the equation above were estimated from the total error data, the value obtained could then be substituted in the equation to predict the learning curve. This would be genuine prediction, for the total error data do not determine the learning curve. If the predictions are accurate we have indeed gone a step beyond curve fitting.

A still more venturesome level of prediction involves invariance in the parameters over an array of experimental situations. That is, we would like to evaluate the parameters of the model in one experimental situation and then use these estimates to generate completely *a priori* predictions of behavior in other situations. Successful examples of prediction at this level are not as yet numerous in psychology; still, as I will indicate later, there are some. This type of prediction is always a difficult feat: its achievement requires not only an adequate model but also a detailed understanding of the variables involved in a number of different situations. In this regard it seems reasonable to assume that values of some of these behavioral parameters will ultimately be determined by physiological or biophysical experiments, but in my opinion there is little hope of arriving at this stage in the foreseeable future.

The levels of theoretical prediction that I have described form a hierarchy against which the significance of a model can be measured, and should be kept in mind as I describe a particular mathematical model for verbal learning. The experimental problem I shall examine is very similar to the one described by Dr. Simon, namely paired-associate learning. In the particular experiment I have in mind, the subject is informed in advance of the responses he may use. He is then shown the stimuli one at a time in some random order, and is asked to guess which of the responses has been designated as the correct answer for that particular stimulus. After the response is made, the subject is told the correct answer and then the next stimulus is presented. After the entire list of stimulus items has been presented, the experimenter rearranges the items in a new random order and again presents the list to the subject. As each item is shown to him, the subject attempts to anticipate the correct response, following which he is reinforced—i.e., informed of the right answer.

An example of one such paired-associate study is an experiment by Atkinson & Crothers (1), in which the stimulus items were 18 Greek letters and the responses were three nonsense syllables, RIX, FUB, and GED. Each response was paired with six stimuli, so that the three responses were used equally often as the correct answers. On the first trial the proportion of successes (correct anticipations) was very close to the value of 0.33 to be expected if the subject simply chose one of the responses at random as each stimulus was presented. The curve rises exponentially and gradually approaches an asymptotic value of 1, i.e., eventually only correct anticipations occur.

One of the first theoretical attempts to account for data of this sort assumed that the effect of each reinforcement was to add an increment to the strength of the association between the stimulus and the correct response. Suppose that the probability of a correct anticipation on trial n, which will be denoted $\Pr(c_n)$, is taken as an estimate of the associative strength on trial n. The probability of an error on trial n, $\Pr(e_n)$, is an indication of how much remains to be learned. The basic assumption made in the "incremental" theory is that the effect of the reinforcement on trial n is to increase the probability of a correct response by an amount which is a constant proportion θ of the amount remaining to be learned, i.e.,

$$\Pr(c_{n+1}) = \Pr(c_n) + \theta \Pr(e_n). \qquad [1a]$$

Thus, every time a subject is told the correct answer to a stimulus item, there is an increase in the probability that the correct answer will be given when the item is presented again. Note that this increase does not depend upon whether the answer given is correct or incorrect. Using the fact that $\Pr(e_n) = 1 - \Pr(c_n)$, equation [1a] may be written as

$$\Pr(c_{n+1}) = (1 - \theta)\Pr(c_n) + \theta. \qquad [1b]$$

In this form it is easy to see that the probability of a correct response on trial $n + 1$ is assumed to be a linear function of the probability on the preceding trial; hence, this is frequently called a *linear* model. The properties of such a model have been extensively investigated. In particular, it can be shown that $\Pr(c_n)$ may be written as a function of the parameter θ and g (the guessing probability on trial 1, which will be the reciprocal of the number or responses), namely

$$\Pr(c_n) = 1 - (1 - g)(1 - \theta)^{n-1} \qquad [2]$$

The theoretical curve for this situation was obtained from equation [2] with $\theta = 0.42$, and it agrees very closely with the observed values. It is important to realize that the learning process for each individual item in the list is represented by equation [2]. That is, if the probability of a correct response for a given stimulus item could be measured by some hypothetical "probability meter", the course of learning would resemble measurements from an analogue device such as a variable resistor operating in such a way that on trial 1 the probability measurement would be equal to the guessing rate g, and on each succeeding trial the probability value would gradually move upward by some amount, as if the knob of the resistor were being turned in the same direction on each trial by an exponentially decreasing amount.

There have been objections to this type of representation of the learning process on several grounds. Some psychologists, for example, have argued that, while very simple organisms might behave in this fashion, higher animals, especially when confronted with more complex problems, show learning of an all-or-none sort. It is not my intention to go into the history of the controversy concerning the relative merits of continuous and discontinuous characterizations of the learning process; I want rather to consider a model that is like the all-or-none process, and then look at the kinds of differential predictions made by the various models.

Following the analogy between the linear model and a variable resistor, the all-or-none model may be represented by a two-position switch which operates as follows. Initially the switch is in the "unlearned" position and reponses are made at random from the available response set. After each reinforcement the switch is turned from the "unlearned" to the "learned" position with probability a, whereas with probability $1 - a$ the switch remains in the "unlearned" position. Once the switch has been turned to the "learned" position it remains there, and the correct response is always given. More specifically, the model may be formulated as a two-state Markov process in which an item is assumed to be in the unlearned state U at the start of the experiment. When the subject is informed of the correct response to be associated with an item, then with probability a learning occurs and there is a transition to the learned state L, whereas with probability $1 - a$ the item remains in state U. If an item is in state U, then the probability of a correct response is g, the guessing probability. Once an item is learned, however, there will be no subsequent errors. These assumptions are incorporated in the matrix below, which specifies the transition probabilities between the two states U and L from trial n to trial n + 1, and the response vector which gives the probability of a correct response in each of the states:

$$\begin{array}{ccc} L_{n+1} & U_{n+1} & Pr(\text{Success}) \\ \begin{matrix} L_n \\ U_n \end{matrix} \begin{bmatrix} 1 & 0 \\ a & 1-a \end{bmatrix} & & \begin{bmatrix} 1 \\ g \end{bmatrix} \end{array} \qquad [3]$$

The probability of a correct response on trial n, $Pr(c_n)$, for the all-or-none model is readily derived by considering the probability of an error on trial n: in order for an error to occur on trial n, an item must remain in state U for n — 1 trials, this with probability $(1 - a)^{n-1}$, and an incorrect guess must be made when this item is presented on trial n, this with probability $1 - g$. Thus, $Pr(e_n)$ is $(1 - g)(1 - a)^{n-1}$, and so

$$Pr(c_n) = 1 - Pr(e_n) = 1 - (1 - g)(1 - a)^{n-1}. \qquad [4]$$

It is evident that when an identification is made between θ and a, the two models, though based on very different premises about the underlying learning process, predict the same mean learning curve. As an example of a statistic that does differentiate the models, consider for a particular stimulus-response pair the conditional probability of an error on trial n + 1 given an error on trial n, i.e., $Pr(e_{n+1}|e_n)$. In the linear model the probability of an error on trial n + 1 does not depend upon whether the preceding response was right or wrong, and so

$$Pr(e_{n+1} \mid e_n) = Pr(e_{n+1}) = (1 - g)(1 - \theta)^n. \qquad [5]$$

Thus, for this model, the conditional probability of an error is an exponentially decreasing function of the trial number.

For the all-or-none model, however, the fact that an error occurs on trial n furnishes an important piece of information, viz., the item must have been in the unlearned state at the beginning of trial n, since no errors can occur once the item becomes learned. In order for an error to occur on trial n + 1, learning must *not* have occurred following the reinforcement on trial n (probability $1 - a$), and an incorrect response must be made on trial n + 1 (probability $1 - g$); therefore

$$Pr(e_{n+1} \mid e_n) = (1 - g)(1 - a). \qquad [6]$$

Thus the linear model predicts that over trials $Pr(e_{n+1}|e_n)$ will decrease exponentially, whereas the all-or-none model predicts that this probability will remain constant. Although the conditional probability does tend to decrease over trials, these data (1) are more in agreement with the constancy prediction of the all-or-none model than with the decrease predicted by the linear model based on the same parameter value used to fit the mean learning curve. Nevertheless, a noticeable decline over trials in these data has been found to characterize many paired-associate studies, and when appropriate statistical tests are applied, this decline has proven to differ significantly from the constancy predicted by the all-or-none model.

Consequently, consideration has been given to ways in which the basic models described above may be modified so as to yield a more adequate account of paired-associated learning. I shall not attempt to deal with all the variations that have been proposed, but rather describe an extension of the all-or-none model developed by Edward Crothers of the University of Colorado, Robert Calfee of the University of Wisconsin, and myself.[*] The inability of simpler models to account for all the details of the data indicates that one or more important psychological processes have been disregarded. For example, in paired-associate learning it has been shown that considerable forgetting may result because the subject is trying to learn a number of stimulus-response pairs simultaneously.

One way in which forgetting may affect the learning of paired associates is suggested in the following analysis. Suppose we consider the course of learning for a single item i from a list. The item is presented to the subject, and following his response he is told the correct answer. Now, if item i is presented again immediately, it is very likely that the correct answer will be given. However, if other items from the list are interpolated between the two presentations of item i, the subject will be less likely to answer correctly on the second one: the interpolated items are said to interfere with the retention of item i or, more commonly, the subject forgets the association to item i. In general, as the number of interpolated items between the nth and $(n+1)$st presentation of item i is increased, the amount of forgetting increases.

The two complementary processes—learning due to reinforcement and forgetting due to interference—are both incorporated in the model I shall now describe. Each item in a list may be assumed to be in one of three states: an unlearned state (U) in which the subject guesses at random from the set of response alternatives, a short-term memory state (S), and a long-term memory state (L). The subject will always give a correct response to an item in the short-term state but it is possible for an item in state S to be forgotten, i.e., to return to state U. Once an item moves to state L it is completely learned, in the sense that it will remain in state L and the correct response will always be given on subsequent presentations of the item.

The associative effect of a reinforcement is described by matrix A below:

$$A = \begin{array}{c} \\ L \\ S \\ U \end{array} \begin{array}{ccc} L & S & U \\ \left[\begin{array}{ccc} 1 & 0 & 0 \\ a & 1-a & 0 \\ a & 1-a & 0 \end{array}\right] \end{array} \qquad [7]$$

This matrix gives the probabilities of transitions between states for an item immediately after reinforcement. Thus, if an item is in the unlearned state and the subject is told the correct answer, then with probability a the item is learned (i.e., it moves to state L), whereas with probability $1 - a$ it moves to state S. Thus, immediately following a reinforcement, an item will be either

[*] For a detailed treatment see Atkinson & Crothers (1) and Calfee & Atkinson (4).

in long-term or short-term memory, and if the item is immediately presented again, the subject will give the correct response.

The effect of an interpolated unlearned stimulus-response pair on the
learning state of a particular item is described by matrix F,

$$F = \begin{array}{c} \\ L \\ S \\ U \end{array} \begin{array}{ccc} L & S & U \\ \left[\begin{array}{ccc} 1 & 0 & 0 \\ 0 & 1-f & f \\ 0 & 0 & 1 \end{array} \right] \end{array} \qquad [8]$$

If an item is in short-term memory and an unlearned stimulus-response pair
is presented, then the interference produced by the unlearned pair results
in forgetting of the item (i.e., transition to state U) with probability f,
whereas with probability $1 - f$ the item remains in short-term memory. If an
item is in long-term memory, the interference has no effect, and if an item is
in the unlearned state then, again, the interference will have no effect.

The matrix describing the transitions between states from trial n to trial
$n + 1$ for a given item, which will be denoted T_n, is found by taking the
product of A and the Z_nth power of F, where Z_n is the number of unlearned
pairs which intervene between the nth and $(n + 1)$st presentations of the
particular item. The association matrix A represents the nth reinforced
presentation of the item, and the forgetting matrix F is applied Z_n times,
once for each of the intervening unlearned pairs. The matrix multiplication
yields

$$T_n = \begin{array}{c} \\ L_n \\ S_n \\ U_n \end{array} \begin{array}{ccc} L_{n+1} & S_{n+1} & U_{n+1} \\ \left[\begin{array}{ccc} 1 & 0 & 0 \\ a & (1-a)(1-F_n) & (1-a)F_n \\ a & (1-a)(1-F_n) & (1-a)F_n \end{array} \right] \end{array} \qquad [9]$$

where $F_n = 1 - (1 - f)^{z_n}$.

Unfortunately, there is no way of extracting from the data the exact value
of Z_n, the number of interpolated pairs which are not in state L. If an incorrect response is given to an intervening stimulus-response pair, the pair
must be in the unlearned state; if the response is correct, the pair may be
in either long-term or short-term memory, or it may even be that the intervening pair is in the unlearned state and the correct response occurred by
chance. Since the exact value of Z_n cannot be determined, as an *approximation* we can use the expected number of unlearned items intervening between the nth and the $(n + 1)$st presentation of an item. Suppose that there
are $X + 1$ items in the list being learned. On the average, X items will be
interpolated between any two consecutive presentations of a particular
item. Since the items are arranged in random order, the average position
of a particular item will be in the middle of a trial. Thus, for half the interpolated items (those which precede item *i* on trial n), the probability of
being either in state U or state S will be $(1 - a)^{n-1}$. Similarly, for the other

half of the interpolated items (those which precede item i on trial $n + 1$), the probability that learning has not taken place is $(1 - a)^n$. Combining these results, the expected number of unlearned items intervening between the nth and $(n + 1)$st presentation of item i will be $X(1 - a/2)(1 - a)^{n-1}$, and it is this value which will be used as an approximation to Z_n in equation [9].

Keeping in mind that F_n is a function of Z_n, the mean learning curve may be obtained by noting that, for an error to occur on trial $n + 1$, an item must have failed to move to the L state on n preceding trials, which has probability $(1 - a)^n$; also, the item must change from state S to state U between the nth and $(n + 1)$st presentations, which occurs with probability F_n; finally, while in state U, an incorrect guess must be made with probability $1 - g$. Hence:

$$\Pr(c_{n+1}) = 1 - (1 - g)(1 - a)^n F_n. \tag{10}$$

For fixed values of a and f, as the length of the list is increased (i.e., as X becomes larger) F_n increases, and therefore $\Pr(c_{n+1})$ will decrease. In other words, the model predicts that the longer lists will be more difficult to learn, which is of course in agreement with empirical findings.

The probability of an error conditional on an error $\Pr(e_{n+1}|e_n)$, is also found by noting that, if an error occurs on trial n, the item must have been in the unlearned state. Thus the probability of an error on the next trial is

$$\Pr(e_{n+1} \mid e_n) = (1 - g)(1 - a)F_n \tag{11}$$

since learning must fail, with probability $1 - a$, to result in transition to state L, forgetting must occur with probability F_n, and an incorrect guess must be made. Since F_n decreases over trials, $\Pr(e_{n+1}|e_n)$ will also decrease over trials.

Lack of time prevents me from exploring other implications of this model. For example, in paired-associate experiments one is not only interested in predicting the sequence of correct and incorrect responses, but also in giving an account of response time, i.e., the time between the presentation of the stimulus item and the emitted response. Response times tend to be quite reliable and display very orderly changes over the course of an experiment. There is a natural way of extending the model I have described to account for response time measures.

Because the amount of forgetting is a function of the trial number, this last model will be referred to as the Trial-Dependent-Forgetting (TDF) model. I shall now summarize some data from a paired-associate study (4) in which list length was varied, and apply each of our models to evaluate their relative merit.

The subjects for the experiment were three groups of 25 college students, each of whom learned a single paired-associate list. The stimulus member of each pair consisted of a two-digit number, and the response member was one of three nonsense syllables (RIX, FUB or GED). A set of 21 stimulus items was chosen on the basis of low inter-item association value, and for Groups 9, 15 and 21, the experimental list consisted of a selection of 9, 15 or 21 items, respectively, from this set. For Group 21, the entire set of stimulus items was used, whereas for the other groups a different subset was randomly selected for each subject. Each of the three response alternatives was correct equally often for each subject. The list was learned to a criterion of two consecutive errorless trials or ten trials, whichever was shorter. The experimental list, arranged in a random order, was presented to the subject, and for each item the subject was required to choose one of the three responses, following which he was informed of the correct answer. After the entire list had been presented in this fashion, the second trial then proceeded without interruption in the same manner, with the items arranged in a new random order.

The mean learning curves for the three groups were found to be ordered according to list length; i.e., as the number of items in the list is increased, there is a concomitant decrease in the mean proportion of successes on trial n. The curves for $\Pr(e_{n+1}|e_n)$ are also ordered by list length, and there is a decrease in the conditional probability over trials for each of three groups.

In order to determine the quantitative accuracy of the various models described, it is necessary to obtain parameter estimates. There are a number of alternative procedures for estimation; the one I shall use involves chi-square minimization on specific response sequences. This method yields parameter estimates having certain desirable properties and also provides a goodness-of-fit test. The derivation of the theoretical expressions for these is very lengthy, and the interested reader is referred to the Atkinson & Crothers paper (1) for further details.

In the case of the all-or-none and linear models, estimates of the parameters a and θ were found which minimized for each group. This minimization is not readily performed by analytic means, and so a high-speed computer was programmed to find parameter estimates by a search procedure on the parameter space. Since the TDF model is formulated in a fashion that takes list length into account, values of a and f were found for this model that jointly minimized the χ^2 function for all three groups. Parameter estimates obtained by the minimization procedure were obtained, as well as the minimum χ^2 values for each of the models over all groups. The linear model is definitely inferior to the all-or-none model, and the TDF model does a better job than either of the other two, although for this model one less parameter was estimated from the data.

In spite of the fact that the TDF model provides a more adequate account of the data than the other models, there is some cause to be dissatisfied with the formulation. For one thing, the overall χ^2 value is about 163, which (with 88 degrees of freedom) far exceeds the 0.001 level of significance. More importantly, there is evidence that the association parameter, a, is not independent of list length. It will be recalled that parameter estimation for the TDF model was carried out under the assumption that the parameters a and f are invariant over list lengths. The appropriateness of this

assumption was evaluated by finding the best estimate of the two parameters separately for each experimental group. Good agreement was found
among the three estimates of the forgetting parameter f (the estimates were
0.25, 0.25 and 0.21 for groups 9, 15 and 21, respectively). However, the
separate estimates of the association parameter a were ordered according to
the number of items in the list; for groups 9, 15 and 21, the estimates were
0.20, 0.17, and 0.14.

Consequently, consideration was given to modifications of the TDF model
which would give a more adequate account of the data and also yield parameter values that would be relatively invariant over the list length variable.
In the association phase of the model as originally formulated (equation
[7]), it was assumed that the probability of moving to long-term memory
was the same whether an item was in the unlearned or the short-term state;
in both instances the transition probability was a. In the revised TDF model
which will now be described, it will be assumed that the effect of a reinforced presentation of an item will depend on the state of the item at the
time of reinforcement. If the item has been forgotten and is in state U, then
there is a transition to long-term memory with probability b, whereas with
probability $1 - b$ the item goes to short-term memory. If an item is in state
S (i.e., it has not been learned but neither has it been forgotten since the
last reinforced presentation), then with probability a the item is learned
and moves to long-term memory, whereas with probability $1 - a$ it remains
in state S. Thus matrix A (equation [7]) is replaced by matrix A':

$$A' = \begin{array}{c} \\ L \\ S \\ U \end{array} \begin{array}{ccc} L & S & U \\ \left[\begin{array}{ccc} 1 & 0 & 0 \\ a & 1-a & 0 \\ b & 1-b & 0 \end{array} \right] \end{array} \qquad [12]$$

In all other respects the revised model is unchanged from the original formulation and, in particular, the expected value of Z_n will be used as an approximation to Z_n in deriving statistics. That is, suppose that $Pr(L_n)$ is the probability of an item being in long-term memory on trial n which, for the revised
TDF model, is a function of a, b, f and X. Then the expected number of
unlearned stimulus-response pairs between the nth and $(n+1)$st presentations of an item will be

$$X\{1 - \tfrac{1}{2}[Pr(L_n) + Pr(L_{n+1})]\} \qquad [13]$$

The minimum χ^2 estimation procedure was used to obtain estimates of a,
b and f for the three experimental groups jointly. The introduction of the
parameter b in the revised TDF model reduced the overall χ^2 value of the
original TDF model by more than 25 per cent, from 163 to 119, which
represents a considerable improvement. Moreover, when estimates of the
parameters a, b and f were obtained separately for each of the experimental
groups, it was found that the three estimates of f were quite consistent with
one another, and that the variations in a and b were unrelated to list length.

It is of interest to note that the probability that an item is learned is more than three times larger if the item is in short-term memory than if it is in the unlearned state; i.e., the estimate of the parameter a is 0.37 while b is 0.11. This relation between a and b suggests an explanation for the dependency between the association parameter in the original TDF model and the length of the paired-associate list. The effect of increasing list length in these models is to make it more likely for an item to be in state U. In the original model, where a and b are assumed to be equal, the estimate of the associative effect of a reinforcement will be some weighted average of a and b, which I will call $\bar{a}$. In the case of a list with very few stimulus-response pairs, the probability that an item is in state S is larger than when there are many pairs since, as the number of pairs becomes larger, more forgetting will occur and hence an item is more likely to be in state U. Thus the relative contribution of the parameter a to the average $\bar{a}$ will decrease as list length increases, and as list length becomes very large, $\bar{a}$ will approach b. Since a is greater than b, the finding that a decreases with increasing list length in the original TDF model would be expected.

The mean learning curves predicted by the revised model for each of the three list lengths show good agreement between the data and the theoretical curves. The model was also used to predict curves for $\Pr(e_{n+1}|e_n)$; the data points are fairly variable, but in general the theoretical curves fit reasonably well (4).

Another implication of this theoretical approach is with regard to problems of optimization, in which the object is to apply normative techniques to a given learning model in order to specify the conditions leading to optimal performance. For example, if one has a model that gives a good account of paired-associate learning over a wide range of experimental situations, it is natural to inquire about the implications of the model for determining optimal procedures of "instruction". If the stimulus presentation, response, and reinforcement histories are known through trial n, then it should be possible to use the model to describe what item to present on trial $n + 1$ in order to maximize the amount of material that will be learned by the end of the experimental session. Stated otherwise, the logical structure of the learning model will specify how the stimuli should be selected from trial to trial in order to minimize or maximize some terminal goal set for the student. Such developments have obvious implications for education; in principle, for any learning model we should be able to set up a related decision structure which takes as input certain information from preceding trials and decides what instructional material should be presented next. Some research on this topic has already been done for models of the types I have considered here; much of this research employs iterative techniques resembling dynamic programming as its optimization method. This work, though primitive and oversimplified to date, has been very exciting to me because of its implications for instructional procedures involving computer-based teaching systems.

Without pursuing this example further, I hope I have given a fairly clear picture of my view of the theoretical enterprise in psychology. There is one last point, however; if we examine the various χ^2's I have mentioned and select the one associated with the best fit, a value of 119 is obtained with 87 degrees of freedom. This value of χ^2 is significant at the 0.05 level; therefore, on the basis of statistical considerations, the model would be rejected. The sensible retort to this statement is the point I have been trying to emphasize throughout: we always assume that any model can be rejected on statistical grounds if enough observations are made; the goal is not to reject or accept a given model at some predetermined level of significance, but rather to make comparisons among models and ask how well the model performs relative to other models. Simply stated, a model will not be rejected on purely statistical grounds but only when there are other models that consistently do a better job of prediction.

I think that the work I have described is on a far more modest scale than the theoretical program outlined by Dr. Simon. I am sure some will feel that its range of applicability is far too limited, but I would not be dismayed by such a remark. Ten years ago one certainly could not have come close to giving the type of quantitative account of learning that I have described here, and if progress keeps pace over the next decade I think we will be very close to a theory of learning with the same sort of "feel" about it that theories of physics have.

I have characterized the model in terms of three states, but within the general theoretical framework more states could be added, and undoubtedly such an elaboration would increase the predictive accuracy of the model. In the same sense that Dr. Simon's theoretical structure yields a 3:1 ratio, so would the present theory yield a set of predictions relatively independent of the number of underlying states. Thus, in terms of this theoretical work I would not want to argue that the neurophysiologist should base his experimental investigations on a three-state conceptualization of the learning process. I would, however, recommend to neurophysiologists that they would be better off working with behavioral situations where the psychologist had already provided a reasonably accurate theoretical description, i.e., where models have been developed whose parameter values are relatively invariant over a wide range of experimental manipulations. For these situations, the neurophysiologists can investigate relationships between neurological events and parameter values of the psychological theory, rather than less refined behavioral measures.

In this regard, let me add one more remark. There is a developmental feature of this theoretical work that is intriguing and I think will be quite suggestive to the child psychologist. As I characterized the model, there were two learning parameters, *a* and *b*, and a forgetting parameter, *f*. What happens to these parameters as a function of age? Dr. Duncan Hansen at Stanford University has run a number of paired-associate studies, comparable to those I have just reported, with five- and ten-year-old children. The intriguing feature of his data is that upon application of the TDF model the parameters *a* and *b* tend to be constant over age groups. To be sure, older children learn more rapidly, but in terms of the model the improvement is due to changes in *f*, namely the value of *f* decreases with age. Thus the model is arguing that younger children have difficulty in mastering paired-associate tasks, not because their learning parameters *a* and *b* differ from those of older children, but because more forgetting is occurring from trial to trial. This result agrees with my own observations of my daughter's behavior, and I hope soon to be able to report some more definitive work regarding such a developmental effect.

Miller: If the items are made more similar to each other, is the forgetting parameter changed?

Atkinson: Extensions of the model to situations involving stimulus similarity is a natural next step, but as yet I have not done any systematic work on the problem.

Within the general theoretical framework I have outlined here, one should be able to treat a broad class of verbal learning studies, including much of the recent research on short-term memory and related phenomena. But, again, the theoretical framework is not precise enough to define a specific model for every new experimental situation; instead it generates a class of models. The job of the experimentalist is to determine which member of the class of models is most adequate, so that this information can be used to update the general theoretical structure, which tends to be loosely defined.

Hilgard: Dr. Simon, do you feel that your theory is finer grained than Dr. Atkinson's?

Simon: On a number of things such as number of errors it is not at all easy to distinguish among the models with respect to the statistics that can be calculated from them. I believe the sensitivity of behavior of this type of model with change in parameter is discussed in the Atkinson & Crothers paper (1).

Both Dr. Atkinson and I have done some thinking about calculating for EPAM statistics similar to those done for the stochastic learning theories (not the statistics on the reaction times, which are not considered in our theory at all). My general conclusion is that it is going to be hard to choose between the two models in this respect. As for the stochastic learning theories, however, I do not see how experiments on similarity of familiarity can be run without introducing new parameters.

Atkinson: Wrapped up in my three parameters *a, b* and *f* are undoubtedly a number of processes of the type that Dr. Simon has incorporated in EPAM. It is my hope (and scientific bias) that much of this theoretical detail can be ignored for especially defined experimental situations, and be represented by a few parameter values. It will later be necessary to present a theory to account for the particular parameter values observed; for now I consider my current theoretical goals to be difficult enough to achieve.

Simon: There is no way of representing similarity directly with stochastic theories; similarity has to be described in terms of some parameter of Dr. Atkinson's system. There is no direct characterization here of the stimulus situation.

Hilgard: It seems there would have to be some resolution of that kind of problem before the model could be useful for neurophysiologists. I think it is a step in the right direction.

Atkinson: Actually, the sorting and listing processes described by Dr. Simon are very much like the mechanisms I have in mind when I speculate about the long-term and short-term states of memory. However, until I see some way of testing these notions experimentally I will probably keep my formal theorizing at a more concrete level.

Rothkopf: May I lodge a meek protest? Before we ask the neurophysiologist to account for the relationships described by either computer or mathematical models, we should consider that these are models of small splinters of the natural domain involved. They represent small areas of variations of behavior in learning, or even in verbal learning.

Because I spend most of my time in the laboratory, I am impressed with the complexity of human behavior and how difficult it is to isolate experimentally robust, general variables. The tender variables with which many of these models are concerned control relatively little compared to those which determine whether an experimental subject is paying attention to the relevant stimuli or even whether he is keeping his eyes open.

Simon: I do not want to make a case here, but I think the statements you just made are somewhat extravagant. First, these theories deal with a significant range of classical experiments about learning in psychology.

Rothkopf: These experiments have not taken psychology very far.

Simon: If we are going to formalize psychological theory, we should first agree on a starting line. Second, although nonsense syllables have been paid much attention at this conference, there has been at least as much testing of this kind of theorizing with respect to human problem solving, and the theories are not idiosyncratic to the problem situation; the General Problem Solver is quite general in the sense that the program itself is independent of the specification of the task environment. Third, it is not correct to say that the sorts of theories I was describing neglect such phenomena as attention. As a matter of fact, if we look at the serial position curve prediction I made earlier, and at the reason for this prediction, we see it arises from some very specific assumptions about the management of attention in that program (11). It suggests, again, some ways in which the subject could be made to modify his serial position curve—which is well known can be done.

Rothkopf: I cannot seriously argue about how much of a splinter you are breaking off. None of these theories states clearly what the theorizing is about. The size of the splinter handled by your models cannot really be determined until we decide what sort of natural domain we are going to try to account for. Your computer models can never be truly vulnerable empirically because you can always side-step and say, "This is outside of the bounds of the particular thing I wish to account for!"

Simon: That is true of all theories: they are untestable if, when the theory is refuted, one is allowed to say, "That is not what I meant." If one wants to use the theories, it is more reasonable to say instead, "I predicted that was going to happen and it did not—I have to do something about the theory." I think that the refutability of theories rests a great deal on how we use them, and on our attitude when we have trouble with them.

Miller: I have been thinking about how many discoveries from learning experiments could tie in with neurophysiology. I can be very brief, unfortunately, because I have not found very much that I could recommend to the neurophysiologist as hard facts about learning to be taken into account.

I trust that everybody here knows that the greatest amount of forgetting seems to be produced by interference rather than by mere disuse, but there have been some rather elaborate experiments investigating the effect of disuse on the functioning of synapses in an attempt to isolate central phenomena relevant to learning.

Another fact is that learning seems to be unidirectional, with some minor exceptions which perhaps can be accounted for by overlapping processes. Forward conditioning seems to be substantially better than backward conditioning, and in nonsense-syllable learning forward association seems to be considerably stronger than backward association. Similarly, as Nagaty (21, 22) has shown, reinforcements seem to affect responses that occur before them, not those occurring after them. This directional nature of learning seems to be adaptive, for one would prefer to build a nervous system that knows where it is going rather than one which functions like the mythical little bird that flies backwards because it likes to see where it has been.

The third fact about learning is that it can occur extremely rapidly, particularly at the human level. As Dr. Grant pointed out, in many experiments we deliberately choose a poor learning situation in order to have more time to watch gradual changes. But under favorable conditions, a great many different things can be learned swiftly. If you have learned something from what I have just said and can repeat a considerable number of words and ideas, you must have formed a lot of associations very quickly. This means that at least the initial stage of the process has to be something that occurs rapidly. Assuming that the initial stage will cause a puff of DNA, which causes a particular type of RNA to be plated off, which in turn causes protein synthesis, which makes glial cells grow in a certain way, which guides the growth of the neuron, it can be seen that the process will take a relatively long time. Now, it might be possible for the initial stage to get started

quickly so that it would inevitably produce a long chain that would ultimately result in a memory. But the fact is that the memory can also be retrieved immediately after the learning experience, or at various intervals
thereafter. Therefore, every step in the process has to be one that allows retrieval, or there has to be a second mechanism for storage and retrieval to
occur during any hypothetical process that requires considerable time to
achieve the permanent engram. Fortunately the brain is large, so that there
is considerable capacity for intermediate storage; but even then I am not
sure that some of the neurophysiological mechanisms that have been proposed would account for the rapidity with which large amounts of information can be acquired under favorable circumstances.

I have mentioned three facts about learning that might possibly be some
guide to the neurophysiologist: it is not greatly weakened by mere disuse, it
seems to be unidirectional, and it can occur very rapidly. I hope that not
more than one of these "facts" turns out to be wrong.

Lindsley: In spite of what Dr. Miller said about human learning occurring so quickly, I think we have to recognize that much of animal learning
occurs rather slowly.

Miller: It can occur rapidly. Recently a new dog attacked our old cat; in
a few seconds the cat learned something about the dog which it remembered very well the next day.

Lindsley: It depends entirely on the complexity of the problem. You were
setting a very simple problem for your animal.

Miller: But we have to account for the fact that the cat's neurons can accomplish simple learning quickly.

Simon: When you say quickly, do you mean, say, three seconds?

Miller: Yes.

Simon: That is an enormous length of time, is it not?

Miller: What would that be in relation to the time required for DNA to
start producing RNA?

Calvin: They can unwind in milliseconds.

Miller: Can you get the whole sequence of enzymes down to the protein
synthesis in that time?

Calvin: Perhaps.

Miller: All right then, perhaps it will work. I do not think what I said
about learning was wrong, but what I said about molecular biology was
wrong, and that is not surprising. I am glad to be corrected and informed;
this gives me a different perspective.

Lindsley: Assuming for a moment that what I said was true, an animal
might require longer to learn at a comparably difficult level. The difference
would be smaller short-term memory storage capacity, that is, delayed response takes longer in the animal. I think we have to admit that in many
systems the time constant is faster in the human than in the animal.

I would like to see a comparison made in those terms. If we could find comparable terms to adjust the rate of learning *versus* the various capacities, we could list them for the human *versus* each of the animals concerned in this comparative series. The problem could be approached from this angle, which I have not heard anyone mention here.

Simon: You must be careful not to underestimate how small differences can change the processing time. As a test, try multiplying three or four digits in your head without using pen and paper, and see what happens to the time of performance as you begin to approach the limit of your immediate memory capacity. The difference between man and other species may well lie in this direction rather than in the basic processing.

Rothkopf: I would like to suggest that the second fact mentioned by Dr. Miller is only half right: when it comes to verbal systems, direction of association does not hold up very well. If you use mixed designs where, for example, half of the items on a list have to be tested in the forward direction and half in the backward direction, the effect disappears (12). It seems to be a learned factor that is peculiarly associated with the use of the anticipation method. There are several experiments which bear this out.

The reversal of association decrement is another example of a situation where some peculiarity in the experimental design produced an enduring "fact" that has been uncritically accepted for several years, at least since the Feldman & Underwood (12) and Jantz & Underwood (15) experiments.

Miller: Razran (25) believes that the difference between backward and forward conditioning depends upon the relative strength of the CS and the UCS. I do not think he is right, but nobody has thoroughly tested his idea. If we are to help the neurophysiologist, these parameters of relative strength should be experimentally tested to find out whether the directional nature of conditioning is a relatively invariant relationship or merely a function of the relative intensities of the CS and the UCS. The directional nature of association may be wrong, or partly wrong, as Dr. Rothkopf says. I do believe, however, that a reward immediately after a response is effective, while one immediately before a response is ineffective.

Pribram: I do not think it is that hopeless. If we use common techniques in common fashion, i.e., if we do not change situations so much that they become unrecognizable, we can obtain recognizable data. Then we still have the problem of talking in a common language. I do not like the pessimistic note: "Computers are much too complicated" or, "Computers are but a rough splinter of the whole"; "It is too elegant", and "It is not elegant enough"; or even, "This has no relationship to the brain", and "It has too much relationship to the brain." We have heard all of these arguments during this conference and they cannot all be right.

I think that, if we *actively* listen in a sophisticated fashion, work together on some of these problems (and by that I mean in one experiment), and use

conceptual tools properly, we can achieve a great deal of useful understanding. I do not feel that we must just stick to our own limited lasts for
the next century or two.

Miller: When I say that at present there are only relatively few hard facts
about learning that are highly relevant for the neurophysiologist, I do not
feel hopeless. Exciting things are happening; there is much promise. Trying
to think of which hard behavioral facts will be most relevant to the neurophysiology of learning will help the psychologist to perform more
significant experiments than he might if he confined his thoughts strictly to
his own field.

Pribram: I would like to say something about the difference in models,
though it might be somewhat irrelevant at the moment. Is it true that the
computer model differs from the statistical model in that there are very few
recursive functions in statistical models, while the computer model is built
on the concept of feedbacks? Is that an essential difference, or can the two
models be translated, one into the other, rather easily?

Simon: The answer to the latter is no.

Pribram: Is this due to the fact that there are so many recursions, subroutines, in the list structure?

Simon: The simulation model is much more detailed. Another important
difference is between representation of the situation by means of parameters *versus* representation of the situation by means of isomorphs to the
symbol structures.

*Lowenthal:** Dr. Simon, when you asked for the next letter in the ABM
CDM sequence, I though of E, and also of a couple of other sequences,
especially since you only gave two elements of the series. I began to think I
could create an infinite number of elements in the series, which gives me a
bit of a problem in equating the brain with the computer. In trying to bring
the two together, I wonder whether we can say that the computer could
begin to create new material? Do we have to say that the brain is not actually creating but using only material which has already been fed into it in
the past?

Simon: Mathematicians frequently flunk the Thrustone Series Completion Test because they know there is no unique answer to the problem as
posed. There are always many series that fit the given sequence. Most of
the rest of us take the test and do better because we write down the first
letter that seems to fit a pattern we see there. A limited answer to your
question is that there would be no particular difficulty in writing a program
that would not stop with the first pattern it found but would try to find
other patterns that would also fit.

Lowenthal: Is there a concept of creativity in a computer?

Simon: The concept of creativity is difficult to define whether in a computer or out of a computer—in the human brain. I would like to tell a story

---

* Auditor at the Conference.

as my best answer to the question of computer creativity. In 1912 two chess grandmasters, George Thomas and Edward Lasker, played a game. At a certain point in that game, Lasker announced that he was going to mate his opponent in eight moves, and proceeded to do precisely that. A few months ago we gave this same chess position to a computer program (32)—one I did not talk about tonight—and it also found the checkmate in eight moves.

Chess players think they are being creative when they discover such mating combinations; in talking about such feats, they use the same language about creativity that people use in describing achievements in other fields. The particular checkmate I have referred to has often been reprinted in chess books as a notable example of creativity. Of course, in one sense the computer was not creative, since this particular checkmate had been discovered 50 years earlier by Lasker. But since the computer was unaware of this and was not given any hints from the previous discovery, the fact that its discovery was not "original" from an historical standpoint is irrelevant to the issue of creativity—it was a case of independent invention, if you like. In any other sense, the computer was as creative in discovering the checkmate as Lasker had been. I leave this example to you, and let you decide whether you want to regard it as an instance of creativity or not.

REFERENCES

1. ATKINSON, R. C., and CROTHERS, E. J., A comparison of paired-associate learning models having different acquisition and retention axioms. *J. Math. Psychol.*, 1964, **1**: 285-315.
2. BRUCE, R. W., Conditions of transfer of training. *J. Exp. Psychol.*, 1933, **16**: 343-361.
3. BUGELSKI, B. R., Presentation time, total time, and mediation in paired-associate learning. *J. Exp. Psychol.*, 1962, **63**: 409-412.
4. CALFEE, R. C., and ATKINSON, R. C., Paired associate models and the effects of list length. *J. Math. Psychol.*, 1965, **2**: 254-265.
5. CHENZOFF, A. P., *The Interaction of Meaningfulness with S and R Familiarization in Paired-Associate Learning.* Ph.D. Thesis, Carnegie Institute of Technology, 1962.
6. FEIGENBAUM, E. A., The simulation of verbal learning behavior. In: *Proceedings of the Western Joint Computer Conference*, 1961: 121-129.
7. ———, Discussion in: Uttley, A. M., Does a cortical synapse transmit "Shannon" Information? In: *Learning, Remembering, and Forgetting, Vol. I: The Anatomy of Memory* (D. P. Kimble, Ed.). Science and Behavior Books, Palo Alto, 1965: 374-387.
8. FEIGENBAUM, E. A., and FELDMAN, J. (Eds.)., *Computers and Thought.* McGraw-Hill, New York, 1963.
9. FEIGENBAUM, E. A., and SIMON, H. A., Forgetting in an association memory. In: *Proceedings, National Conference of the Association for Computing Machinery*, 1961, **16**: 202-205.
10. ———, Generalization of an elementary perceiving and memorizing machine.

In: *Information Processing 1962* (C. M. Popplewell, Ed.). North-Holland, Amsterdam, 1962: 401-406.

11. FEIGENBAUM, E. A., and SIMON, H. A., A theory of the serial position effect. *Brit. J. Psychol.*, 1962, **53**: 307-320.

12. FELDMAN, S. M., and UNDERWOOD, B. J., Stimulus recall following paired-associate learning. *J. Exp. Psychol.*, 1957, **53**: 11-15.

13. HOVLAND, C. I., Human learning and retention. In: *Handbook of Experimental Psychology* (S. S. Stevens, Ed.). Wiley, New York, 1961: 613-689.

14. HUNT, R. G., Meaningfulness and articulation of stimulus and response in paired-associate learning and stimulus recall. *J. Exp. Psychol.*, 1959, **57**: 262-267.

15. JANTZ, E. M., and UNDERWOOD, B. J., R-S learning as a function of meaningfulness and degree of S-R learning. *J. Exp. Psychol.*, 1958, **56**: 174-179.

16. KELLY, H. S., and NEWELL, A. (Eds.), *Information Processing Language—V Manual*, 2nd ed. Prentice-Hall, Englewood Cliffs, 1964.

17. LINDSAY, R. K., Inferential memory as the basis of machines which understand natural language. In: *Computers and Thought* (E. A. Feigenbaum and J. Feldman, Eds.). McGraw-Hill, New York, 1963: 217-233.

18. McCRARY, J. W., JR., and HUNTER, W. S., Serial position curves in verbal learning. *Science*, 1953, **117**: 131-134.

19. MILLER, G. A., The magical number seven, plus or minus two: some limits on our capacity for processing information. *Psychol. Rev.*, 1956, **63**: 81-97.

20. MILNER, P. M., The cell assembly: Mark II. *Psychol. Rev.*, 1957, **64**: 242-252.

21. NAGATY, M. O., The effect of reinforcement on closely following S-R connections: I. The effect of a backward conditioning procedure on the extinction of conditioned avoidance. *J. Exp. Psychol.*, 1951, **42**: 239-246.

22. ———, The effect of reinforcement on closely following S-R connections: II. Effect of food reward immediately preceding performance of an instrumental conditioned response on extinction of that response. *J. Exp. Psychol.*, 1951, **42**: 333-340.

23. NEWELL, A., and SIMON, H. A., GPS, a program that simulates human thought. In: *Lernende Automaten* (H. Billing, Ed.). Oldenbourg, Munich, 1961: 109-124.

24. ———, Computers in psychology. In: *Handbook of Mathematical Psychology*, Vol. I (R. D. Luce, R. R. Bush, and E. S. Galanter, Eds.). Wiley, New York, 1963: 361-428.

25. RAZRAN, G., Backward conditioning. *Psychol. Bull.*, 1956, **53**: 55-69.

26. ROCHESTER, N., HOLLAND, J. H., HAIBT, L. H., and DUDA, W. L., Test on a cell assembly theory of the action of the brain, using a large digital computer. *IRE Trans. Inf. Theory*, 1956, **IT-2/3**: 80-93.

27. ROCK, I., and STEINFELD, G., Methodological questions in the study of one-trial learning. *Science*, 1963, **140**: 822-824.

28. ROSENBLATT, F., The perceptron: a probabilistic model for information storage and organization in the brain. *Psychol. Rev.*, 1958, **65**: 386-408.

29. SIMON, H. A., and FEIGENBAUM, E. A., An information-processing theory of some effects of similarity, familiarization, and meaningfulness in verbal learning. *J. Verb. Learn. Verb. Behav.*, 1964, **3**: 385-396.

30. SIMON, H. A., and KOTOVSKY, H., Human acquisition of concepts for sequential patterns. *Psychol. Rev.*, 1963, **70**: 534-546.

31. SIMON, H. A., and NEWELL, A., Information processing in computer and man. *Am. Scientist*, 1964, **52**: 281-300.

32. SIMON, H. A., and SIMON, P. A., Trial and error search in solving difficult problems: evidence from the game of chess. Behav. Sci., 1962, **7**: 425-429.

33. UNDERWOOD, B. J., Studies of distributed practice: VIII. Learning and retention of paired nonsense syllables as a function of intralist similarity. *J. Exp. Psychol.*, 1953, **45**: 133-142.

34. UNDERWOOD, B. J., and KEPPEL, G., One-trial learning? *J. Verb Learn. Verb. Behav.*, 1962, **1**: 1-13.

35. UNDERWOOD, B. J., and SCHULZ, R. W., *Meaningfulness and Verbal Learning.* Lippincott, Chicago, 1960.

36. WILLIAMS, D., *An Example-Driven Problem Solver.* C.I.P. Working Paper #68, Graduate School of Industrial Administration, Carnegie Institute of Technology, 1964.

37. WILLIAMS, T., *A General Game Playing Program.* Ph.D. Thesis, Carnegie Institute of Technology, 1965.

THE CONCEPTS OF DEVELOPMENT AND LEARNING
IN CHILD BEHAVIOR

LEWIS P. LIPSITT°
Brown University
Providence, Rhode Island

In the discussion of Dr. Simon's paper we heard the discouraging proposition that perhaps there were only three facts in psychology which could be commended to neurophysiologists for whatever neurophysiologists do with functional relationships. Following that remark, I feel that my paper might be somewhat overambitious, for I intend to talk about at least four functional relationships from my own laboratory.

The field we call Child Development has historically attracted researchers and thinkers from such a diversity of disciplines (22) that I think it would be well to start by identifying the goals and methodological orientation of the research I shall discuss, and compare these briefly with certain other techniques and theoretical viewpoints which researchers may and do bring to their studies of child behavior. From the earliest days, beginning with biographical reports of physical growth and behavior in individual children, up through the more elaborate and methodologically secure longitudinal and cross-sectional studies of large numbers of children, the field has been concerned primarily with the documentation of physical and psychological attributes as a function of increasing age (17, 48, 60).

This early emphasis on the age-properties of the child took its rationale from the biological tradition in which most child developmentalists were trained. Development is generally defined by reference to organismic changes which are essentially time-determined, so that, for the study of the physical growth characteristics which concerned many child developmentalists, the emphasis on the passage of time is of paramount importance. Goaded on by the success of physical-growth research in obtaining reliable measures—and because behavior, too, changes with age—child behavior researchers soon moved to refine their psychological measures as well. There was a consequent adoption of the physical-growth model for the study of "behavioral growth". Graphic and pictorial presentations of data abounded,

° Preparation of this manuscript was facilitated by USPHS Grant NB 04268, as were many of the studies cited herein. The writer is indebted to the staff of the Providence Lying In Hospital and to the Child Development Study of the Institute for Health Sciences at Brown University for their cooperation in these studies.

211

showing behavior changes as a function of age. Moreover, child psychologists were reinforced in their burgeoning concern with the temporal determinants of behavior by the indulgence of a practical society which very soon found age-norms, with their neat means and standard deviations, to be of ostensible psychometric value in assessing the progress of individual children. They devised and embraced the concept of developmental age (a reliable numerical representation of the behavioral status of a given child of a given age) in relation to the comparably tested performance of similarly aged peers.

This historical affinity of the field of child development for structural or morphological biology, and its alliance with the psychometric movement, produced two major effects on the study of children's development, neither of which I can regard as salutary. First, the field was slow in moving toward the behavioral study of children with experimental manipulative techniques which might have been quite readily adopted from general experimental psychology; second, the field carried with it for some years a rather thorough maturational bias which has inhibited the extensive study of environmental or experiential factors as they affect behavior, most specifically learned changes in behavior. I am also of the opinion that this maturational bias of the field led in some cases to the premature acceptance of certain data and propositions concerning the limitations of the human organism, particularly with respect to its capacity for being affected by potential learning circumstances in the early months of life. Here I refer to statements and data of Morgan & Morgan (44), Gesell (17), Krasnagorsky (28), and a number of other writers reviewed by Elkonin (11). Perhaps this suffices to indicate the empirical and methodological set with which my own research program in infant behavior was undertaken. In our orientation we are experimentalists rather than developmental testers; our primary interest is in understanding the lawful relationships underlying early experiential influences on the behavior of the human.

The studies I shall be reporting were conducted through the cooperation of a National Collaborative Project sponsored by the National Institute of Neurological Diseases and Blindness for the investigation of perinatal factors involved in the development of cerebral palsy, mental retardation, and other neurological and developmental aberrations. While this research is of an ancillary nature and is independently financed from the overall core project, the flow of infants to our sensory testing and conditioning laboratories is facilitated by the collaborative project. Through this convenient association, we have infants available to us at birth at the Providence Lying In Hospital, and again at 4, 8, and 12 months of age at the follow-up center of the Collaborative Project when they return for routine neurological, developmental and pediatric examinations.

Our newborn laboratory is shown in Figure 54, with a stabilimeter crib (33) in the foreground, a six-channel Grass polygraph with integrator unit,

Figure 54. View of the newborn sensory assessment and
conditioning laboratory, Providence Lying In Hospital.

and an upright panel containing an audio-oscillator and associated speaker,
a physiological stimulator and three Hunter interval timers for the timed
presentation of stimuli. On the edge of the stabilimeter rests an ordinary
bottle nipple attached to an appropriate transducer for the polygraphic recording of sucking responses. The stabilimeter provides continuous polygraphic records of the infant's movement, and allows recording of startle or
other activity in response to specific stimulation. Other equipment records
responses such as leg-withdrawal to stimulation of that leg, or breathing activity (recorded by means of an infant pneumograph linked with an appropriate transducer and the polygraph).

Figure 55 shows a newborn infant on the stabilimeter, which is essentially a suspended lever arrangement with one end containing a rod leading
into a light-proof box where the changing proximity of a light-sensitive resistor to a light source reflects the amount of the subject's movement. The
spring at the other end may be seen clearly, as can a small neon light at the
right, which is linked to our timer system and signals to the experimenter
events such as the start and stop of a trial. The accordion-pleated tube
around the infant's abdomen is the pneumographic pick-up, itself connected
to an appropriate transducer and leading to the polygraph. The pick-up de-

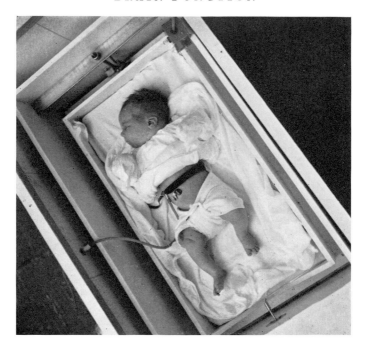

Figure 55. Newborn in the stabilimeter with pneumographic pick-up in place.

vice for leg-withdrawal is seen at the foot of the stabilimeter; to use it, we
put the baby's foot into a boot attached to the pick-up. The mechanism is of
the same light-sensitive resistor style as the stabilimeter.

Figure 56 shows the type of record that may be obtained. The example
shown is a record of a one-day-old infant's response to three successive ten-
second stimulations with a loud 1000 cps tone and about 30 seconds be-

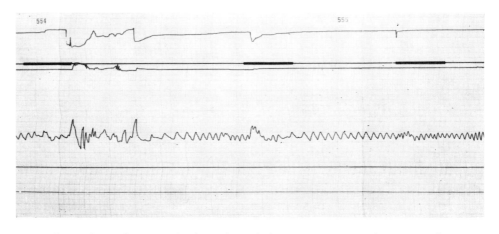

Figure 56. Polygraphic record of newborn habituating to an auditory stimulus. From
the top down, pen-lines represent leg-movement, stimulus (heavier portions: 1000 cps,
10 sec.), stabilimeter, and breathing. The two bottom lines are irrelevant.

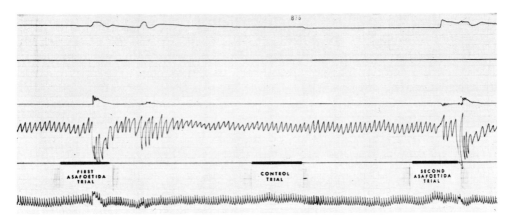

Figure 57. Polygraphic record showing infant's response to administration of asafetida on two occasions, with an intervening control trial. From the top down, pen-lines represent leg-movement, an irrelevant pen-marker, stabilimeter movement, breathing, stimulus presentation, and heart rate.

tween tones. The gradual diminution of response (adaptation or habituation) is seen in all three measures recorded: leg movement, stabilimeter activity and breathing.

Several studies on olfactory adaptation or habituation have been done in this laboratory in collaboration with my colleague, Dr. Trygg Engen (14, 15). Figure 57 shows the sort of response record that can be obtained in such studies utilizing olfactory stimuli. This record shows a set of three ten-second trials administered to the same infant: the second one involves the control presentation before the infant's nostrils of a dry cotton swab; a swab saturated with an anise oil or asafetida solution was used for the first and third presentations. Anise oil has a fairly strong odor; most infants will respond to it on the first presentation of the solution, yet it is not so strong that it fails to adapt or habituate. As can be seen, the response to the solution was striking, and the presence of response to that stimulus in comparison to its control is obvious. It is also characteristic of these youngsters to have a slow-latency response to olfactory stimuli. In one study of olfactory response and decrement, each of ten subjects was presented two odors, anise oil or asafetida (which, at least to me, smells like boiling onions). Half the subjects received ten trials with anise oil first and asafetida second, while for the other half the order was reversed. Stimulus presentation consisted of removing the cotton swab from a corked test tube and placing it between, and about 5 mm from, the infant's nostrils. Control trials involved the presentation of a dry cotton swab in exactly the same manner, and presentation of stimulus and control trials was alternated. The duration of trials was recorded on the polygraph as ten seconds, with one minute between trials. At the conclusion of the 20-trial series for each subject (each of these trials consisting of both a control and a stimulating presentation), two post-test trials were added with the same one-minute intertrial interval and using the first presented of the two stimuli, thus enabling a test of recovery from decrement to that stimulus. Utilizing the leg-withdrawal, general activity, and breathing measures, all of which tended to yield the same result, three judges evaluated the polygraph records independently and agreed on 86 per cent of the judgments as to whether a response to the olfactory stimulus had occurred; in the remaining 14 per cent, two out of three judges prevailed as to whether the response had occurred or not. The control trial was used as a baseline, and a response on a stimulus trial was judged positive only when it was greater than that on the paired control.

Figure 58 presents the percentage of responses* as a function of trials for the two odorants when each was presented first and second to subgroups of five subjects. A greater percentage of responses was obtained with asafetida than with anise, and for both there was a reliable decrement of response from the first to the last block of trials. There was also a recovery of response to the second odorant after diminution of response to the first. While the order of presentation had an apparent effect for both odorants, this effect was most striking—and reliable—only for anise. Finally, in the post-test trials with the first-given odorant, there was recovery of response to nearly the level of the first several trials with each odor. Similar tests with other odorants, such as an acetic acid solution and phenylethyl alcohol, further indicated sharp differences in level of response to various odorants, as well as rate of decrement. For instance, as might be expected, no response decrement occurred over ten trials with the acid solution.

While these studies demonstrated both a decrement in response as a function of repeated stimulation with some odors and recovery following stimulation with another odor, these effects† presented an interesting problem of interpretation. We were concerned with the problem of experimentally distinguishing between sensory adaptation (i.e., fatigue of receptor organs produced by repeated stimulation), and response habituation (i.e., extinction of response to an originally effective stimulus). Our study involved the presentation of a new and qualitatively different olfactory stimulus following presentation of the first stimulus; even the post-test trials could be regarded as "new" stimuli, since approximately 20 minutes had elapsed since the previous presentations with the same odor, and this interval was occupied with sniffing another odor. We could not be sure whether we were dealing with a response habituation or central phenomenon rather than with a sensory adaptation or peripheral phenomenon without doing a further study, which I would like to mention now.

This experiment (14) sought to discover whether recovery of response would occur to a second or novel odorant following response diminution, even when that "novel" odorant was in fact a constituent or component of

---

* That is, the number of occasions on which the response was larger to the presentation of the odorant than on the comparable control trial, as determined by the three-judge procedure outlined above.
† See also Disher (10); Bridger (7); Bartoshuk (5), Bronshtein et al. (8).

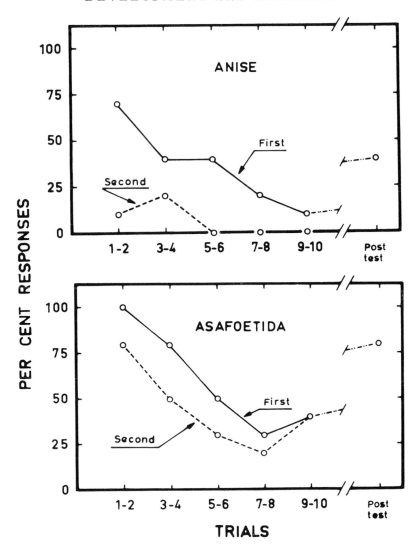

Figure 58. Percentage of responses to anise (top) and asafetida (bottom). Response to the two odorants is plotted separately depending upon whether that particular odor was administered first or second in the series of 20 trials. "Post-test" refers to presentation of the first-administered odorant following 10 trials of the second-administered odorant. (From Engen, Lipsitt & Kaye, 15.)

the stimulus first presented. Newborns, slightly older than two days in mean age, were the subjects. The apparatus and methods were similar to those used in the earlier study. Because breathing had seemed the most sensitive measure of response to olfactory stimulus change in that study, only this response was examined. The infants were first administered ten trials of an odorant consisting of a mixture. Test trials were then administered by presenting a component of that mixture with a non-odorous diluent.

For example, in Figure 59, the response and decrement of response may be seen for ten infants to a mixture of 50% diethyl phthalate, 33.3% amyl acetate, and 16.7% heptanal. These data are not plotted in terms of percentages but in terms of mean responsivity; the maximum value obtainable is 2. In other words, at the outset the child was responding maximally to the mixture solution; following these ten presentations, the 33.3% amyl acetate odorant in solution with diethyl phthalate was presented and did produce a recovery of response. Similarly, the presentation of the 16.7% heptanal solution yielded a recovery effect.

The point I want to make about these data is that when the amyl acetate and heptanal, which were presented in mixture or solution during the ten response decrement or habituation trials, were now presented alone with the non-odorous diethyl phthalate solution, recovery of response did occur. The data for recovery to heptanal are essentially the same.

In a replication of the same procedure, using a 50% anise and 50% asafetida mixture, post-test trials with asafetida alone yielded recovery while anise did not; that is, this effect will occur apparently for some odors and not

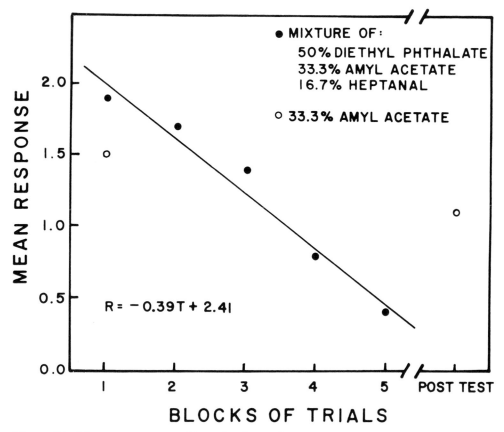

Figure 59. Mean responses to 10 trials of an odorant mixture at one-minute intervals, followed by a 2-trial presentation of a component (amyl acetate) of that mixture after the same interval. Response to the post-test component may be compared with response level obtained to that stimulus by a group of similarly aged infants not subjected to the mixture odorant (indicated by the open circle at 1).

for others. Initial responsiveness to anise oil, however, is low, so that a large recovery effect could not be expected with that odorant; response to a 50% anise oil solution is not as great as to the 100% solution mentioned previously. That is, if the stimulus does not initially elicit a large reaction, we do not have far to go to bring about recovery to it; it is hard to demonstrate recovery with an initially weak odorant. Therefore, one of the problems here is to utilize stimuli that are effective at the outset in eliciting response from newborns.

Under what conditions may response decrement in neonates be taken as evidence for a learning process? Another way to ask this question is: When is a response to a novel stimulus evidence for a subject's having *learned not to respond* to a familiar stimulus? Our position with respect to these data is that the recovery effect to components of a previously presented stimulus mixture argues strongly for the proposition that the decremental process is mediated centrally and cannot be easily ascribed to any peripheral changes induced by the stimuli. Moreover, to the extent that the decremental and recovery effects do reflect a memory process (and it would seem that reaction to a component of a previously presented mixture as if it were novel supports such a memory hypothesis), it would appear that we have a learning process of some sort, although not of the usual associative types represented by classical and operant conditioning procedures (32).

I would like now to review some data from sucking experiments conducted in our laboratory in collaboration with Dr. Herbert Kaye. One of these studies (36) documents another kind of perseverative effect which could also be taken to represent a memorial or learning process. A number of writers (e.g., Gunther, 21), have suggested that differently shaped nipples, both natural and unnatural, have differential capacity for eliciting sucking responses in newborns; our study was conducted for the purpose of documenting this difference in sucking obtained with an "optimizing" and a "non-optimizing" intra-oral stimulus. The stimuli used were, respectively, an ordinary bottle nipple and a piece of straight quarter-inch rubber laboratory tubing. No food was administered to the babies through either the nipple or the tubing. All were bottle-fed babies except one, whose data do not appear to be different from the others (it is not customary in Providence Lying In Hospital to have breast-fed babies).

Ten subjects in this study received stimulation with just the nipple (group N), ten with just the tube (group T), and ten with both (group TN) in order to determine whether sucking on one might be affected by experience in sucking on the other. All subjects received 50 trials of intra-oral stimulation, each lasting ten seconds, with an intertrial interval of approximately 30 seconds. The experimenter touched the infant's lips with the stimulus, inserted it when the mouth opened, and pushed a hand-button connected with a timer set at 10 seconds, thereby activating a light signal during which the observers counted the number of sucks. Observational counts of sucks per unit time have been found to be highly reliable, and the means of either two or three observers were used as this experiment's basic data.

Figure 60A shows the infant with the nipple inserted; Figure 60B shows the tube in place. Anticipating the results, the infant's facial expression suggests that he finds the tube somewhat less than agreeable.

Figure 61 shows the results of the study in terms of mean number of sucking responses made during the 50 trials by the three groups. The middle portion shows the responses given on five-trial alternations of the tube and nipple by group TN. The topmost line shows responses of group N to 50 trials of the nipple, and the bottom shows the mean response to the tube for group T. It can be seen that the order of magnitude is about 8 to the

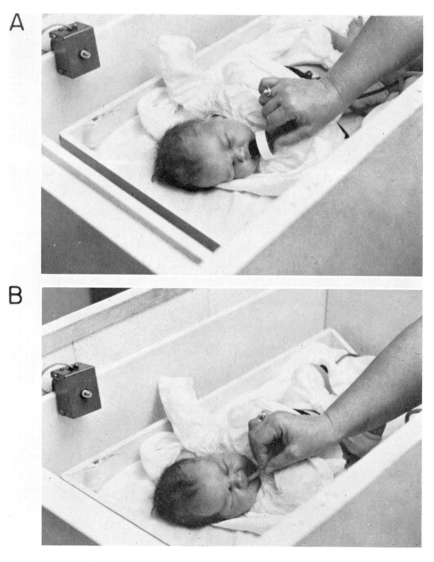

Figure 60. Newborn with nipple stimulus (A) and tube stimulus (B) inserted in mouth.

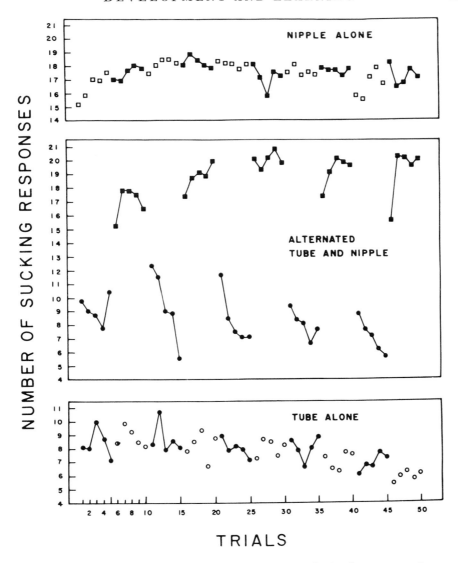

Figure 61. Number of sucking responses in 10-second stimulus presentations in the nipple-alone (N), tube-and-nipple (TN), and tube-alone (T) groups (top to bottom). The TN group received 5 trials of tube, followed by 5 trials of nipple, and so on, while the two control groups received 50 consecutive trials with either the nipple or the tube. (From Lipsitt & Kaye, 36.)

tube alone and about 15 or 16 to the nipple alone. The results are similar for subjects presented both stimuli in alternating fashion. For groups T and N, the pertinent comparison trials against which to assess the effect of alternating oral stimuli are given in the darkened lines.

Regardless of whether the tube and nipple are given alone or alternately, the nipple elicits more sucking than the tube. More pertinent to my present purpose, however, is the fact that within 5-trial blocks for group TN there appears to be a perseverational effect of response to the previous stimulus administered, such that response to each block of the nipple starts low and goes high, while response to the tube starts high and goes low, relative to the response on comparison trials in the T and N groups.

This effect is seen best in Figure 62, drawn by collapsing the last four blocks of scores (eliminating the first block, in which no such effect should be expected) for each subject and averaging over all subjects in a given group. The upward trend for nipple-sucking and the downward trend for tube-sucking within blocks are compared with the appropriate data from groups T and N. Statistical analyses confirmed that both trends for the alternating group are reliable, while on comparable trials the responding of the T and N groups does not show a reliable change. That is, response rate for those control subjects appeared to be constant across the pertinent trials.

These babies were fed approximately every four hours; they were brought to our laboratory for this study about an hour and a half after their last feeding, i.e., all subjects were brought into the laboratory at about the same time in their day's routine. I do not think hunger is a factor here; it so happens that sucking rate is lower when the child is given something to ingest than it is when he is given a pacifier; sucking rate is higher to a non-nutritive pacifier than to a nipple attached to a bottle from which the baby is fed. There are other mechanisms involved in the feeding process that inhibit the sucking rate.

These results indicate that the nature of an intra-oral stimulus determines the frequency with which a newborn sucks, and that sucking is affected by other oral stimuli with which the infant has experience. Further study will

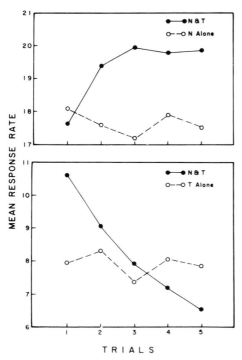

Figure 62. Mean response rate within blocks of stimulus presentation for the three groups described in Figure 61. The top graph represents nipple-sucking, the bottom graph tube-sucking. The solid lines show nipple-sucking and tube-sucking for the TN group. The dashed lines represent nipple-sucking (top) for the N group and tube-sucking (bottom) for the T group, on pertinent comparison trials. This graph was drawn by collapsing or superimposing the last four blocks of nipple-sucking and tube-sucking shown in Figure 61 as darkened lines; thus *trials* refers to trials within blocks of five. (From Lipsitt & Kaye, 36.)

be necessary to determine the parameters of stimulation conducing to an "optimizing" effect; both contour and texture may be pertinent. The perseverative behavioral phenomenon fascinates us, for it could be observed both qualitatively and quantitatively. In Group TN, the first trial of a tube-block often elicited vigorous "nipple-like" sucking at the outset of the 10-second trial, but was followed by a "surprise" phenomenon wherein the subject stopped sucking abruptly before proceeding to explore the tube at a slower rate. This "surprise" appearance, coupled with the quantitative demonstration of experiential influences on sucking rate, supports our predilection for our working assumption that "human newborns have retentive minds".

This study led naturally into the next, further convincing us that newborns do learn. The fact that the tube is a relatively poor elicitor of sucking provided us the opportunity to use the tube in the following conditioning study (37). Twenty infants ranging in age from 48 to 96 hours were given one of two treatments. An experimental group received six baseline trials of 15-second presentations of the tube, then ten conditioning trials, ten extinction trials, five reconditioning trials and five more extinction trials. During conditioning and reconditioning, a 5 per cent dextrose and water solution was given through the tube after the first ten seconds of sucking, 1 ml being given in each trial. A control group was run which received identical treatment, except that the dextrose and water solution was given by syringe between each of the trials comparable to conditioning and reconditioning in the experimental group. To control the amount of oral stimulation, an empty syringe was used at comparable times for the experimental subjects. Sucking throughout was recorded only for the first 10 seconds of each 15-second trial, with two observers recording response frequency independently.

Figure 63 shows the difference in response rate for the two groups throughout the experiment. The data for each subject were transformed at each plot-point to "proportion of baseline responding". That is, responding in baseline was considered 100 per cent for each subject, and subsequent blocks were assigned percentages relative to baseline, thus standardizing scores for each individual. Statistical analyses indicate that differences in response rate in conditioning were reliable, although the differences during reconditioning fell short of significance. Thus, it appears that a "non-optimizing" sucking stimulus can be transformed into a more effective elicitor of sucking by pairing it with a suitable reinforcing agent. This phenomenon had been previously established in newborn pups by Stanley et al. (59).

It may be added that in another study (35) classical conditioning of the sucking response was demonstrated using a loud tone as the CS and a nipple pacifier as the UCS. Sucking in response to the tone was greater, following a basal period, in infants who received paired presentations of the tone than in infants who received unpaired presentations of the same stimuli. These experiments were all done within a morning's period for each sub-

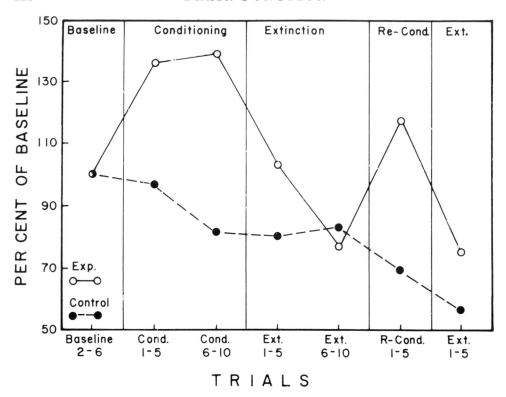

Figure 63. Percentage of responses to the tube in conditioning experiment, utilizing baseline performance as reference point. See text. (From Lipsitt, Kaye & Bosack, 37.)

ject; our next task will be to determine the stability of the conditioning, to see whether it persists for a matter of days.

Moving up the age scale to the four-month period, a post-doctoral trainee in my laboratory, Dr. Einar Siqueland, has recently developed a technique (54) for exploring operant conditioning, based on earlier work of Papousek (47) and using food reinforcement, which already promises to yield learned behavior in infants younger than four months as well. His apparatus consisted of an infant reclining seat on which was mounted a head cradle constructed of light-weight plastic and lined with foam plastic. A potentiometer circuit recorded on a polygraph changes in potential occurring with head rotations. In this study, a head turn was defined as a rotation of 45° or greater to the right or left of the central position. A white experimental chamber, open on one side and with the infant facing toward the back, provided the subjects with an environment devoid of distracting stimuli. The experimenter stood behind the subject and, during conditioning procedures, a nursing bottle was presented from behind, with each presentation being registered on the polygraph record by an event marker activated by a foot switch.

An 8-minute procedure consisted of a 1-minute baseline, 3 minutes of conditioning, 2 minutes of extinction, and a 2-minute reconditioning period. Reinforcement consisted of presenting the bottle in the subject's mouth for

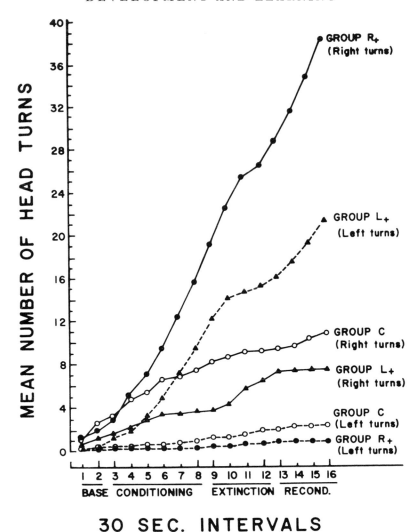

Figure 64. Mean cumulative number of head turns in the Siqueland experiment, over an 8-minute experimental period. Group R+ was reinforced for right turns only, Group L+ for left turns only. Group C received comparable reinforcements but not contingent upon head-turning in either direction. (From Siqueland, 54.)

three seconds. For Group R+, reinforcement was given following each right turn of 45°. Group C was a control for arousal effects on head rotations, with individual Group C children being matched with Group R+ subjects for number of milk presentations during conditioning and reconditioning; for Group C, however, reinforcement was not contingent on head rotations. A third group, Group L+, received the bottle contingent on left head rotations of 45°. The subjects' heads were repositioned at center following each head rotation.

Figure 64 shows the mean cumulative head-turns, both left and right, for the three groups, over 30-second intervals throughout the experimental

period. For the R+ group, the pertinent head turns, left and right, are
shown in the bottom and top curves. There were no reliable differences
among the three groups during the baseline period for either left or right
turns. Group R+ showed a significant increase in right turns from baseline
through the conditioning period, a decrease between the first and second
minutes of extinction, and subsequently an increase during reconditioning.
Similar comparisons for right head turns in Groups L+ and C showed no
such effects. Instead, Group L+ shifted significantly in number of left
turns on each of the above comparisons. Considering the brevity of the
experimental procedure (dictated, incidentally, by the scheduling circumstances in the follow-up center where these studies were conducted), and
considering that almost no control of the deprivation circumstances of the
infant was possible, these results bode well for further studies of the same
type of response at earlier ages and for differential conditioning studies at
four months of age.

I should like now to show very briefly some techniques for older infants,

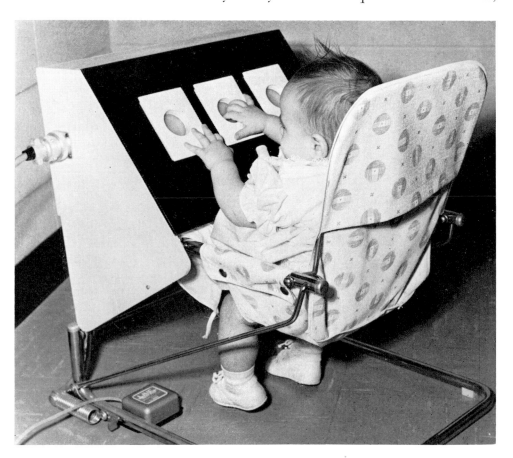

Figure 65. Three-panel apparatus for study of operant discrimination in young children.
Colors appear in stimulus apertures, and depression of "correct" panel may produce
buzzer sound or turn on room lights. (From Lipsitt, 32.)

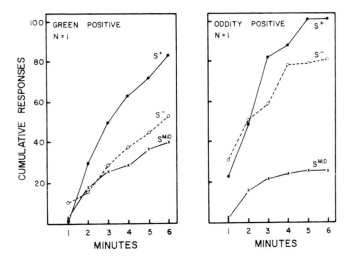

Figure 66. Data of two subjects in the 3-panel apparatus depicted in Figure 65, one receiving reinforcement for response to the green panel throughout the experimental period, the other for response to either red or green depending upon its being the "odd" stimulus present. (From Lipsitt, 32.)

currently under development in our laboratory. Figure 65 shows an operant discrimination procedure for 8- and 12-month-old children. The child is seated at an apparatus with three panels which may be depressed; counters on a remote control panel register relative numbers of responses to each. The stimulus apertures in the center of each permit the presentation of different colors through a Wratten filter system, and it is possible to show any of four different colors in each. The experimenter controls the stimulus presentation arrangement and reinforcement contingencies from the remote unit. Reinforcing circumstances in various studies have consisted of door chimes, buzzers, flashing lights in the stimulus apertures themselves, and operation of room lights.

The sort of data obtainable are represented in Figure 66, which shows the cumulative responses of two children over a six-minute period, one of them being reinforced for responding only to the green when both red and green were present, and the other subject being reinforced for responding to the odd stimulus, whether red or green. Considering that an infant at this age is generally a multiple-responder and typically uses both hands at once, differentiation of response such that the reinforced panel elicits response more frequently than the non-reinforced panels is not easy to obtain, but this technique shows promise for further studies now under way.

Another somewhat similar technique involves seating the child in front of two pendulums, as seen in Figure 67. The manipulanda consist of plastic capsules; inside each there is a bulb which may be turned on from a remote unit and used as a discriminative stimulus. When the child pulls on the cap-

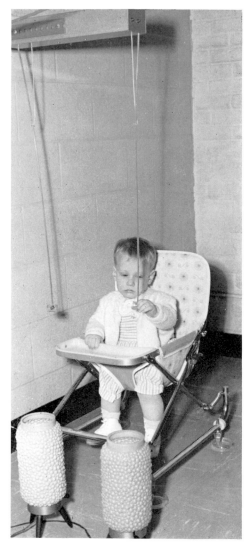

Figure 67. Two-manipulandum apparatus.
Flashlight bulb can be lit in either capsule.
When lighted capsule is pulled, reinforce-
ment lamps in front of child flash on. (From
Lipsitt, 32.)

sules, counters record the responses, and if the lighted capsule is pulled, the
floor lights are activated and serve as a reinforcing event during conditioning phases.

Figure 68 shows the cumulative record of an infant subjected to alternating baseline and conditioning phases, and reflects that the child's behavior
is under the control of the reinforcing circumstances, so that more responding occurs during the periods in which the lighted manipulandum is
effective in producing room illumination, and more responding occurs to
the lighted manipulandum than to the unlighted one.

We are currently exploring a technique (39) which promises to be a better learning arrangement than any we have yet explored for children this
age. It is adapted after some suggestions of Ogden Lindsley's (31), and involves the use of conjugate reinforcement, a technique involving the pre-

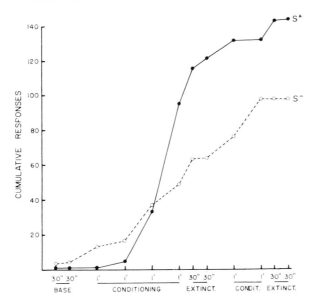

Figure 68. Data for one 12-month-old subject in the two-manipulandum apparatus depicted in Figure 67, showing increase in response during conditioning period and diminution during extinction, followed by a reconditioning and a re-extinction period. The entire procedure lasted nine minutes.

sentation of changing illumination, rather than discrete reinforcing events, contingent upon the rate of the infant's response. The baby is seated in front of a plastic panel mounted on a box. During conditioning phases, pressing on the panel turns on a light inside the box; by means of a capacitance device, the light intensity becomes greater with increasing rates of response. The reinforcing condition is such that the harder the infant pounds on the panel, the greater the brightness of the light inside the box and the greater the visibility. Increased illumination in the box reveals a colorful clown's face rotating inside. The considerable reinforcing power of such a circumstance is reflected in Figure 69, which shows a 12-month-old infant's responding about 240 times in the course of a 10-minute period, during seven minutes of which responses resulted in reinforcement, while no reinforcement of panel-pressing was involved in the remaining three minutes. As the figure indicates, it took 58 seconds to go through a baseline procedure involving the accumulation of five responses. That is, we put the child in the apparatus and let him sit there until he makes five non-reinforced responses, at which time we turn the reinforcement circumstance on. Our cumulative curves begin at 5 for all subjects. We record the amount of time it takes each subject to meet the five-response basal criterion.

Figure 70 presents group data averaged for fifteen 12-month-olds. Through trial and error, we are currently increasing the visual interest of events occurring inside the box, and it appears likely that we will soon be

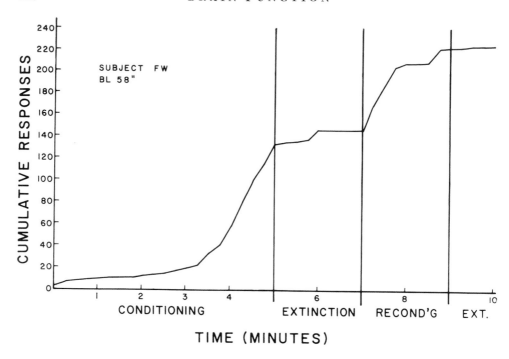

Figure 69. Cumulative response data from one 12-month-old subject in a conjugate reinforcement procedure involving progressively increased illumination for higher response rates during the conditioning period, and absence of light reinforcement during extinction. This subject produced almost 240 responses in a 10-minute period, following a 5-response baseline period of 58 seconds. (From Lipsitt, Pederson & DeLucia, 39.)

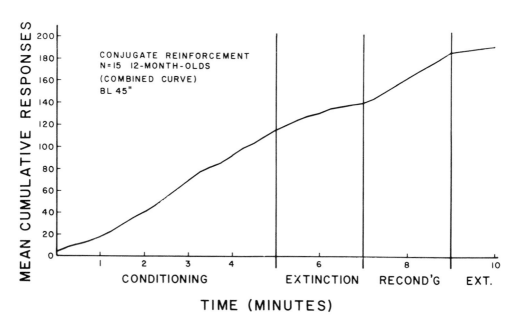

Figure 70. Mean cumulative response data for a group of fifteen 12-month-old subjects in the conjugate reinforcement situation. (From Lipsitt, Pederson & DeLucia, 39.)

able to study visual exploration and visual reinforcement in greater depth.

Pribram: In plotting the curves backwards, you might find better extinction and conditioning curves. That is, when you are combining the curves of individuals who have learned at different rates, an average of their daily scores often hides regularities that come to light when criterion is used as the anchor instead of the first test score.

Lipsitt: It is our intent to begin soon on a longitudinal study of a group of children within the first year of life (that is, at birth, 4, 8, and 12 months) with the best of the techniques we have developed thus far for exploring their learning processes, to determine whatever constancy or inconstancy there is in learning ability over this period of time.

I shall conclude by saying that I am enthusiastic about the feasibility of an experimental psychology of infancy which will take into consideration where appropriate, but not become obsessed by, the age determination of child behavior. I do not wish to imply that the developmental and experimental approaches to the study of the child are incompatible: they are not, and this has been made plain enough by numerous writers (20, 26, 65). Moreover, we have conducted developmental studies of tactile (38) and olfactory (34) thresholds in the same laboratories that produced the experimental manipulative studies on which I have concentrated today. It seems to me that we should soon be entering a research era in which experimental techniques for the study of sensory and learning processes will be employed increasingly in development-assessment research programs. I suspect, on the basis of information now accumulating concerning experiential influences on the behavior of very young children, that the maturational bias which has been historically characteristic of the field of child development will probably become less and less attractive. It may even become difficult to keep the pendulum from swinging too far toward the environmentalist's bias. Preventing this will be an important challenge for the more biochemically and neuropsychologically inclined child developmentalists.

Discussion

Konorski: Dr. Lipsitt, going back to the response latencies, your Figure 56 seems to indicate that the infant's response to sound was similar to his response to olfactory stimuli: it came at the termination of the sound, at least for the first of the three stimuli.

Lipsitt: However, it clearly came before the termination of the sound on the later trials. You are quite right; it sometimes has a long latency. With respect to olfactory stimuli, the latency is variable because of the breathing process: we find it to be longer when the infant is exhaling than when he is inhaling; if we happen to present the stimulus at an apneic period (not unusual in the newborn), the latency will of course be increased as well. Some of that breathing disruption, or what has been picked up by the breathing disruption measure, is no doubt partly due to movement; that is why we have pneumographs to record movement as well as pure breathing rate.

Lindsley: I might comment that the latency of the evoked potential to a flash of light, that is, to a sign of something happening at the cortex, is four or five times longer in the newborn infant than in an older child or adult. In the newborn infant the latency may be of the order of 180 or 200 msec., whereas later on it may be 50 msec. or less. But that, of course, does not account for the full 8 or 10 seconds of latency described by Dr. Lipsitt.

Lipsitt: I think the other mechanism I suggested would account for the 8-second latency; it takes time for the odor to get where it makes a difference.

Calvin: In your two-odorant experiments, did I understand correctly that the asafetida obliterates the anise response, but not the other way around?

Lipsitt: That is correct; anise responding falls to zero.

Birch: I am interested in the diminution in response over the six trials to any of the stimuli; I am more struck by coincidence than anything else because, in our own studies of human newborns, responses to auditory stimulation also decline quite rapidly, with the same slope. By the fifth or sixth trial we see the development of rather complete unresponsiveness to the stimulus itself.

Lipsitt: That is why I presented a model record (Figure 56) showing the diminution of response to an auditory stimulus, a 1000 cps tone. The diminution of response is clearly discernible, though not completely habituated, in the three trials.

Lindsley: Do you have any information as to how older children or adults react to these stimuli, in terms of dishabituation or adaptation? That is, how would they react to the same odors when you were using, say, galvanic skin response, or some other measure? Obviously, the stabilimeter could not be used.

Lipsitt: Verbal reports could be used. It is quite possible that if we questioned a child over ten trial presentations of smells, he would answer "yes" or "no".

Lindsley: I was thinking more of the galvanic skin response, of which the subject is not so much aware.

Lipsitt: I do not know what the comparable data would be.

O'Connor: All of these adaptations are unlike those of an adult; they decline in about eight trials, as I recall, in some of the studies with schizophrenics.

Pribram: With auditory stimuli our human and monkey subjects habituate in about three trials (4, 27).

Lindsley: I have done this many times with galvanic skin response or EEG, and obtained blocking of the EEG and continuous galvanic skin response for sometimes 10 or 20 stimulations.

Pribram: Our results are different; perhaps we do not use the same criterion to ascertain habituation. Our subjects are divided into labiles and stabiles and each group attains a baseline. We call the subjects habituated when they reach the baseline, though they still give responses.

Lindsley: I do not mean the spontaneous ones.

Birch: Habituation is the function of the time interval. For example, in the studies Demb and I (6) did on conditioning GSR to auditory stimulus, we were thwarted in obtaining the conditioned response by the efficiency with which the stimuli worked. We could present prepared stimuli with relatively short intervals between them; when we increased these intervals to about 3½ to 4 minutes between stimulus pairs, we were able to get a relatively stable response. With a shorter interval, the response to auditory stimuli was habituated within three or four trials, depending upon the duration of the interval.

Konorski: Dr. Lipsitt, did you observe some defensive response on the first trial? For instance, did the child cry or become very excited?

Lipsitt: The only odor we used that elicited what would be called an aversive response was our acetic acid solution; we found no habituation to it in ten trials. It is an extremely strong stimulus, and habituation or response decrement rate is a function of the intensity of the stimulus.

Birch: In your opinion, is the kind of learning you described similar to the type Thorpe (61) referred to years ago, when he spoke of habituation as pre-learning learning, as non-associative learning?

Lipsitt: Yes, I think it is becoming increasingly fashionable to refer to it as a learning phenomenon, though it is clearly different from the kinds which were classified, for instance, by Dr. Hilgard and Dr. Grant.

Jensen: Would this not be thought of as S-S type learning? A pattern is being recognized, and then habituation occurs to that pattern. Here there is simultaneous presentation of two stimuli which form a pattern; one stimulus in isolation does not form that pattern.

Lipsitt: Can we speak of it as an associative process, however? I think that is the problem. To speak about it in this way strains the vocabulary.

Birch: You are considering it an acquired response. Let us begin by going back into its history as a learned phenomenon. The basis for the study of this variety of learning derived from a concern with so-called "species-typical" characteristics in animals, and the modification of such characteristics on the basis of early experiences. Thorpe (61) placed larvae of the ichneumon fly upon an insect other than the one on which the fly characteristically fed and laid its eggs. When adult, the fact of having fed upon a foreign host during the larval period led many of these flies to sting and oviposit not the species-typical host, but their early infant feast as the new host through which their reproductive cycle took place.

Thorpe then argued that there was an acquired modification in responsiveness which had occurred as the consequence of stimulation, but was not associative in character. He considered it, then, as habituation in the course of the development of organisms and spoke of it as a non-associative variety of learning. I think this is the kind of phenomenon you have described.

Hilgard: A generation before Thorpe, George Humphrey (24) devoted half a book to it. I should think the problem is rather one of permanent memory. If the procedure is repeated the next day, will the subjects go right back to the beginning and start over again? In that case it would appear to be a kind of work decrement. The fact that it is central does not make it learning. There are all kinds of refractory-phase types of behavior. To consider it learning, I would be more concerned about the fact that, in being repeated another time, it showed some residue from having been done before.

Pribram: We have some data (4) on that. Dr. Lindsley suggested that perhaps habituation does not occur in three or four trials, and the subjects certainly do not become completely unresponsive so quickly. However, a repeat run one year after the original shows habituation to proceed even more rapidly. Whether this is the effect of familiarity with the total situation or a specific effect of experience with the stimulus, we do not know.

Thompson: We see the same thing for flexion reflex habituation of the cat spinal cord in our acute experiments; habituation occurs more rapidly in successive training sessions.

Rothkopf: It has been suggested that there are associative mechanisms which have some sort of an inhibitory character. Dr. Lipsitt, have you considered an experiment in which you attempt to suppress response by presenting an habituated odorant with other odorants that have not been habituated? Can this diminish a response?

Lipsitt: Are you suggesting doing some conditioning experiments with habituated responses?

Rothkopf: Essentially; the reverse of the procedure you showed.

Hernández-Peón: It has been our experience that there is some plastic inhibition left after each series of habituating stimuli, so that in succeeding experiments, either the next day or some days after, the next series of stimuli produce a quicker habituation than the first. Even though the response to the first stimulus of a new series is about the same size as the response to the first stimulus of the first series, the rate of decrement is faster for the succeeding series of stimuli. These results suggest that something remains even during dishabituation by rest. We have done the experiment suggested by Dr. Rothkopf, recording the olfactory evoked responses in the olfactory bulb of cats (23). The olfactory stimuli consisted of puffs of air, with different odors introduced through a polyethylene cannula permanently implanted into the cat's nose. We have confirmed habituation at the olfactory bulb and dishabituation produced by stimuli of different sensory modalities. For instance, if a nociceptive stimulus is presented to the cat after habituation to a given odor has been established, the next olfactory stimulus produces a response larger than the last one habituated. Dishabituation is also produced by conditioning, i.e., by associating the olfactory stimulus with a reward. Thus, if we monotonously repeat puffs of fish odor, the olfactory response in the olfactory bulb becomes reduced. Then, if we give the cat the fish to eat, the next olfactory stimulus produces again a large response. If we do not reinforce the stimulus, we can rehabituate the cat. I wonder whether Dr. Lipsitt has tested the effect produced by different varieties of stimulation upon the response he has been recording.

Lipsitt: The habituation process has been known, even in newborns, for some time. Disher (10) cites some 1896 Kussmaul data that suggest newborns habituate to olfactory stimuli. I do not present here newborn habituation to olfactory stimuli as a documentation of a new fact, although I believe our data showing decrement of response to mixtures, and subsequent recovery to a mixture component, are a new finding.

Donchin: I believe the olfactory system is usually considered a rather primitive system in the developmental scale. I wonder to what extent the fact that the findings you mention are most restricted to olfactory data is related to the developmental scale.

Lipsitt: I believe habituation occurs, though I have not personally documented it, in all sensory modalities.

Birch: In our laboratory, we have good habituation data on auditory responses which, as has been pointed out, have a curve very similar to the one presented by Dr. Lipsitt. Habituation is not restricted to this; in our experience, tactile stimuli have been the most refractory to habituation, even with relatively short intervals between the stimuli.

Miller: I think it would be interesting to try experiments of the kind done by Sokolov (56) in the Soviet Union on the effects of omission of an expected stimulus. The effect is somewhat analogous to that observed by Dr. Lipsitt for a mixture. Sokolov found that, if subjects were habituated to a sequence such as dah-dee-dah, and then the "dee" was omitted, they would show an arousal response to the omission of the sound. Would such an effect be a short-term memory lasting for only a few minutes after the last training presentation, or would it be a long-term memory that would show up on a test trial given the next day?

Brazier: Sokolov's model (55) is an information theory model.

Zigler: In the sucking experiments, there may be some innate mechanisms that make the nipple the appropriate stimulus. I would like to observe a control group fed continuously out of a tube, to see whether there is some reversal, before I could concur with any equanimity with Dr. Lipsitt's conclusion concerning the memory phenomenon.

Atkinson: In Figure 62, the T and N groups had absolutely flat curves, with no fluctuation over a long period of time. Is this characteristic of the response?

Lipsitt: Yes. Sucking behavior is remarkably constant to either tube or nipple over prolonged periods of time. We kept a nipple in an infant's mouth for at least 20 minutes without any diminution of sucking rate; it is a potent stimulus.

Pribram: Sucking can go on for many months without any milk or other liquid being sucked in, whether this be in the laboratory (kitten experiments, in progress) or at home (thumb sucking, also in progress).

Lindsley: We have seen evidence of a change in the spontaneous electrical activity of the nervous system at successive age levels from birth to twelve months (30), but we must also consider what has been observed in the electrical responses of a newborn infant to stimulation. It has been shown by Ellingson (12, 13) that an evoked response can be elicited in these infants in the visual or auditory area, but with a very long latency. Similarly, we can observe this effect in a kitten. At four or five days of age a flash of light produces only a long-latency negative response; by ten days there is a much shorter latency positive-negative response as well. Eventually, by 30 days, these two responses coalesce. We thought that the first-appearing long-latency, negative wave was a diffuse and general type of response we associated with a nonspecific sensory system, and the shorter-latency response was a more localized one associated with a specific system. We have been able to demonstrate that, by blocking what we think is the entrance of the impulses to the reticular formation (lesion of superior colliculus and pretectal region), the long-latency response can be eliminated; by making a lesion of the lateral geniculate body, the short-latency response can be eliminated (51).

The reason for mentioning this is that a newborn infant does not have persistent alpha waves. It may have something like alpha waves over the motor area when very drowsy but not when awake. Only at about the third month does the visual area develop alpha rhythms that are persistent; this has been confirmed by a good many workers.

It appears that the cortex is not really very "functional" for the first three months. I say "functional" because we can elicit an electrical response to stimulation, that is, an evoked potential. There are other indications of the fact that the cortex is not fully functional and that it changes markedly between birth and three or four or five months, functionally, structurally and behaviorally. Initially there is a Babinski response, grasp response, and a Moro response, all of which persist for the first few months; then the Moro disappears or reverses and becomes the startle response, the grasp reflex disappears, and the Babinski shifts from extension to plantar flexion. Similarly, Monnier & Willi (42, 43) have demonstrated that during this early period of life anencephalic monsters and normal infants are alike in all essential respects (reflex, postural and otherwise).

I therefore think one can argue that the cortex is not yet functional and is not playing the role it will play later. I raise this question because we are talking about learning and memory, and it would be interesting to know how persistent conditioning, probably subcortical, may be. Wenger (63), Marquis (40, 41) and others found conditioning in the very young infant, but it was quite unstable and not very persistent. I would be interested in knowing whether Dr. Lipsitt will find it to be persistent in his subsequent experiments.

Zigler: A correction is in order. Dr. Lipsitt's work is very exciting to workers in child psychology because of the ambiguity of the early conditioning experiments done in the first ten days of life. Certain positive results turned out to be artifactual. Dr. Lipsitt has come closest to finding learning in the classical sense in the first few days of life.

Lindsley: As far as I know, there is no reason for conditioning not to be persistent. It certainly occurs in organisms that have no cortex or very little in the way of cortex.

Lipsitt: In defense of my empirical forebears, Marquis (40), Wickens & Wickens (64) and Wenger (63), it might be said we have technological advantages today that were not available to them. Also, I think that the Marquis data concerning a classical conditioning sucking response (40) are quite defensible within the first ten days of life as demonstrating a conditioning phenomenon; I do not think one could argue very forcefully that in that study sensitization occurred, for there were controls for it. On the other hand, the Wickens & Wickens study (64) certainly did demonstrate theirs was not a clear-cut classical aversive conditioning.

Lindsley: A response can be evoked with a flash of light in the human newborn as well as in the kitten. It simply will not occur with ten flashes of light per second; the flashes must be spaced about a second or more apart in order to evoke a repetitive response to the same light which, when presented alone, produces a response.

I mentioned previously that the latency is very long; the conduction is obviously very slow. There are many factors which I think ought to be brought into correlation, in one way or another, and I am sure they will be, as the work of Dr. Lipsitt, which represents a resurgence of interest in experimental child psychology and which we are all so glad to see, continues. But, unfortunately, when looking for things to correlate (as I have searched for behavioral data to correlate with my electrophysiological results, i.e., the work from H. F. Harlow's laboratory on the infant monkey), one finds that there is some beautiful work, but that it was not collected with the intention of correlating it with something else in which one happens to be interested. Therefore one has to struggle to find corresponding data to compare or try to integrate with one's own.

Feshbach: I had the advantage of having read Dr. Lipsitt's manuscript in advance, and most of my comments are about his concluding remarks, in which he returns to some statements he made in the introduction to his paper regarding certain deficiencies in traditional child development approaches and contrasting these with the advantages of an experimental approach. I simply want to put in a kind word or two for some aspects of the traditional approach which might be usefully integrated into current research procedures.

I think Dr. Lipsitt has presented a fair appraisal of what was essentially a rather stagnant state of affairs in child development until the last decade or so. I think I might add one minor reason to the more fundamental ones he gave in his paper for experimentalists not having entered the field earlier. Not infrequently a carefully designed, basically hard, experimental study would sometimes take on a very soft appearance which is somewhat inhibitory to the investigator. At least I remember experiencing inhibition a number of years ago when I requested research support from my department for the following list of items: 4 Indian headdresses, 2 Davy Crockett rifles, 1 baby doll, 1 teddy bear, and 150 candy bars.

With regard to the more serious limitations of procedures to which Dr. Lipsitt has referred, it is important that these limitations be clarified before one discards or disregards the developmental orientation. It is not enough, in my view, to acknowledge, as he did in his paper, that the developmental and experimental approaches are not experimentally incompatible. I would maintain that the development orientation is essential to a successful experimental child psychology. Briefly, "development orientation" entails the two related contexts of time perspective and organism perspective. With respect to the former, Dr. Lipsitt appropriately criticized the maturational bias of the traditional child developmentalists. Their error was not in providing age norms (which I think was an extremely useful kind of information) but in using, as explanatory concepts, age or time sometimes disguised in the more elegant garb of maturation.

The structural changes that occurred during maturation and how they interacted with experiential factors were rarely specified or analyzed. Thus, one might offer as a supposed explanation for temper tantrums or stuttering, "These are three-year-olds". This is the kind of "explanation" that might be offered by Gesell (18), for example. This account is hardly satisfactory, but a time perspective does have utility. Without it, one ignores questions such as the kind of early cognitive experiences that are necessary for the development of complex cognitive skills, the conditions governing the importance of early attachments upon subsequent object preferences, the period of development in which the child is docile or vulnerable to a particular kind of response acquisition, or the more mundane problem of the factors governing the disappearance of letter reversal. The utility of a time perspective is readily acknowledged and I need not belabor the point.

I think a rather different situation obtains for that aspect of the development orientation which I have labeled organism perspective. The ethologists' complaint about the disregard by experimenters of species differences in capacities and characteristic response modes can be applied with almost equal cogency to various experimental studies with children. Dr. Lipsitt quotes a complaint by Harris (22) to the effect that the "child" is ignored in many experimental studies. What is being ignored is not, as suggested, the emotional dimension of the child's behavior. Rather, the issue is whether relevant response modes are being studied. For example, a Skinner box arrangement is very useful in studying various kinds of discriminations and determining different sensory capacities in the young child. However, it may or may not tell us very much about generalization and the ease or difficulty with which the child makes similar discriminations when bar press is not used as an operant, and very little about how the child learns to discriminate between what belongs to him and what is alien to his body. In brief, I am suggesting that there are ranges of problems that sometimes are ignored, problems which are extremely important insofar as child development is concerned, and which ought to be experimentally analyzed but tend to be disregarded if we become overly concerned with specific kinds of procedures.

Zigler: I would like to underline the other point. As developmentalists, we are concerned with the process which is mediating the response. Dr. Lipsitt is not guilty of this, but many who use these techniques call us metaphysicians when we raise such questions. Developmentalists have always been aware of the fact that the exact same content, end product, or correct response is mediated by quite different processes.

Feshbach: Actually, a very rigorous experimental attitude, combined with some perspective of the changes that occur in the course of the organism's development, will often lead to serious questions about the kinds of experiments that can be used in making developmental comparisons.

Suppose we wish to compare children of different age levels in the same learning situation. We present the same learning task, observe variations in rates of learning, and then conclude that the children vary with respect to their skills in solving this task or in some more general learning ability. It is evident, from a host of studies of, and experience with, these children that they vary in many other respects that are relevant to the learning problem: they vary in the meaning of the situation for them; they vary in motivation; they vary in the magnitude of reinforcement that is offered, the same reinforcement having different effects at different age levels; they vary in the attention they pay to the stimulus. Concern for these factors, and changes in these factors as they covary with other developmental changes, becomes central to the comparative study of differences in discrimination or differences in learning at various age levels. The problem of equating these variables is extremely forbidding; it is not altogether obvious how some of the difficulties can be solved. It is much like comparing learning in different animal species while trying to insure that strength of motivation and other conditions are comparable, and then determining if there are differences in acquisition skills.

There is one final point about the kinds of questions that a developmental approach might stimulate. An interesting question which the typical "experimental" advocate—I do not include Dr. Lipsitt in this category—is likely to ignore, arises in the course of his testing of various types of reinforcers. He will find that a jack-in-the-box is reinforcing or that a bright light is not. He rarely asks what is it about these events that makes them reinforcing and why they change in their reinforcing properties at different age levels. The analysis of the antecedents of reinforcers seems more interesting to me than the fact that they can be used in various kinds of schedules.

Zigler: A research project now going on at Yale is designed to attack this very problem of developmental changes in motivation.

Feshbach: Finally, I think some reference to the central nervous system is in order. The importance of neurophysiological correlates of development is obvious. I might suggest one difference between the interest here and the previous discussions of correlates of learning. We were concerned before with the neurophysiological correlates of the learning event. Our present interest is in the correlates of those structures and processes which make learning possible so that we should now be oriented to the correlates of intelligence and related capacities. Our interest then is not so much in what happens when learning takes place, but rather in what happens before learning takes place.

Lindsley: I think we have moved from the direction of just what is being learned, what specific things, what controls, and so forth, to a new type of data Dr. Feshbach has brought into the picture, namely to factors related to the problem and the setting. Some time ago Dr. Urie Bronfenbrenner from Cornell University spoke at UCLA about his experience in a kind of "living-in" schools in the USSR. He spent six months in some of these, where children had been taken out of their homes because the fathers and mothers worked, or for other reasons, and were brought up from infancy without really seeing very much of their parents. The developing infants were given a lot of sensory stimulation, i.e., they had an opportunity to experience all kinds of colors and textures; it was a rich sensory environment, perhaps reflecting the fact that Sechenov (53) a hundred years before had spoken about sensory hunger, or the tremendous need for sensory input, and that an organism apparently strives for, and actually needs, sensory stimulation for the nervous and receptor systems to develop. At any rate, Dr. Donchin has been a member of a Kibbutz in Israel which, in many respects, resembles some of the facilities of the schools of the USSR. I will let him tell about his experiences.

Donchin: As I listened to Dr. Bronfenbrenner's speech on the educational system in the Soviet Union, I was struck by the close similarity of that system to the child-rearing and educational practices of the Kibbutz movement in Israel. Of course, the scale of the Soviet experiment is vastly different; it currently involves millions of children (1, 2). Unless the plans are modified, 30 per cent of the total school and pre-school population in the USSR will be educated in the new system. The plan calls for a complete coverage of all Soviet children by the 1980's. The total Kibbutz population in Israel is about 100,000; this probably includes about 40,000 children. On the other hand, while the Soviet experiment was initiated in 1960 or 1961, the Kibbutz educational system has been in existence for the last 50 years. In many cases it is now handling its second or third generation, including children whose parents and grandparents were born and raised in a Kibbutz and who stayed in the Kibbutz during their adult life (57, 62).

The Kibbutz provides an important environment in which the effects of child-rearing practices can be studied. Various theories of child development should be able to predict what the results of child rearing in the Kibbutz manner should be, thus providing an excellent testing ground for the theories. The Kibbutz provides an important research environment (52, 58) because it is a system which is decidedly different in its child-rearing practices from most accepted systems within Western society. The Kibbutz is also unique in that it is a culture with which the researcher can communicate with greater ease than he could communicate with a tribal culture in New Guinea, for example. Since the Kibbutz shares a wide variety of cultural concepts with Western society, language and conceptual barriers are more manageable. In fact, some of the very innovations of Kibbutz education are in a sense an attempt to carry out to their logical extreme some of the contemporary notions in child psychology.

Apart from its intrinsic interest, the Kibbutz educational system should be accorded serious study as an attempt for partial evaluation of the Soviet system. Granting the vast numerical and basic differences between the Israeli and Soviet environments, the similarities between the two systems warrant that any serious student of the Soviet system should be aware of the long-term effects of these educational practices.

A definition of the Kibbutz was recently given as follows:

"Kibbutzim are communal settlements constructed on the basis of Socialist principles of collective ownership of the means of production and collective ways of producing, marketing and consuming, excluding paid labor. Using less abstract concepts, and seen from the point of view of the conscious expectations of the people who get together to form a collective of their own free will, one might formulate the basis of kibbutz life as follows: The kibbutz expects every individual to contribute all he is capable of, and the kibbutz is under the obligation to cover all his needs. Among these needs, including food, housing, clothing, care for the sick and aged, cultural requirements, entertainment, etc. the education of the children always takes first place . . ." (46, p. 201).

I would like to point out the importance of the fact that the Kibbutz is a wholly voluntary society. Nobody is compelled to be a Kibbutz member and every member is in the Kibbutz because he wishes to be there. About 95 per cent of the children raised in a Kibbutz become members when they reach adulthood.

Thus the Kibbutz is a rural community, where all the inhabitants own and operate jointly a large economic establishment, both agricultural and industrial; out of the proceeds they provide jointly for their total needs in housing, food, clothing, entertainment and child rearing. The structure of the educational system was largely developed in the earlier communities as the founders were faced with the problems of raising their children under this particular social and economic plan. However, the particular solutions they chose were determined to a large extent by their ideological outlook (19, 29, 57).

One of the major factors determining the structure of the Kibbutz system is the fact that in a communal society the family cannot serve as a consuming economic unit. Rearing of the children by the parents, in their own quarters, would call for a major change in the structure of the community in terms of housing arrangements, distribution of food, clothing, etc. In addition, rearing the children within the family inevitably takes the mother out of the general labor pool where she can (theoretically) choose any job that suits her, and places her back in the family kitchen. For a society that is committed to the full equality of women in terms of complete freedom in job selection, such a development would be unthinkable. Thus child rearing is considered the professional duty of specially trained members of the community rather than the "biological" function of the mother.

This notion of professionalism in child rearing is often mentioned in the Soviet literature and is associated with another important idea, namely that the building of a "new" society calls for a "new" man (2, 3, 25) whose outlook and education are more attuned to the needs of the new community. In both the Kibbutz and the Soviet movements this can only be undertaken successfully by the community and its specially trained members, who are responsible to the community, and in a system that is more appropriate to the communal structure of the society (1, 19). It is also suggested that child rearing is too serious a matter to be handled by amateurs. The parent-child relationships are seen as a source of major conflict, due mainly to the ignorance of the parents (some Kibbutz theoreticians cite as evidence the list of Freudian complexes). The above, at least in the case of the Kibbutz, is honored more in theory than in practice. It is extremely difficult to obtain and maintain the high level of professionalism in the very large staffs required. In fact, maintaining a stable professional staff has always been one of the major problems of the Kibbutz.

The sequence of events in the life of the Kibbutz child has been described quite often—Spiro (57) gives a detailed account of a rather extreme case. From birth to maturity the children live in a boarding school situation. During the first year the mother nurses or feeds the child within a nursery. Most of the other services to the child are provided within the nursery by the staff of upbringers. One upbringer is assigned to four babies. At the age of 12 to 18 months the children are moved into the kindergarten. There a group of up to 16 children is established in "their own" house, with two major upbringers and occasional help from a maintenance staff. The kindergarten combines both the living quarters and the playrooms of the children. The groups are coeducational, with usually up to six children in the house, with two or three children in a sleeping room. That depends very much on the conditions of the particular Kibbutz, how many children it happens to have at any given stage of development, and how much money it can afford to use for building.

When the groups reach school age (six years), they move to a third house, where a group of 8 to 12 children constitutes the major social environment and one of the most important objects of identification for the children. This is again quite similar to the Soviet system, where the major socializing agent is the peer group, or the "children's society" (3, 25). The general atmosphere is that of a self-governing group, where discipline and ethics are maintained by the children. This is, of course, accomplished under the guidance of the upbringers, who exercise great control over the process, but the control is much subtler than that exercised, say, over "student government" in an American college. The peer group does not change in composition until the children finish high school at the age of 18.

One of the most important differences between the Kibbutz and the Russian systems concerns family ties. In the Soviet system the connection with the family is partially severed (2). The family might visit the child once a week, once a month, or even more infrequently. The child's life centers in the boarding school and the upbringer is expected to be the central adult figure in his life. In the Kibbutz the system is quite different: the child's major emotional environment is the family environment. He maintains a close and intimate relationship with his parents and siblings and identifies quite closely with the family. Each child spends at least three to four hours a day with his parents in their quarters. At the end of the working day the parents pick up their children at the various homes, and the following hours are totally dedicated to the children until dinner time, which parents and children take in different dining rooms. After dinner, the parents put their children to sleep in the children's quarters. Parents and offspring have numerous other sources of contact; the child may visit his parents in their working places, the weekends are given to the children, and holidays and trips to town may provide other sources of parent-child interaction. All this results, of course, in very close interactions, and the family unit maintains its integrity as a social unit in spite of the fact that it is no longer an economic one. Dr. Bronfenbrenner noted an emotional blandness in the Soviet children. To the extent that his observations are valid, it would be interesting to determine whether this blandness is not reported for Kibbutz-reared children as a function of their closer family ties.

Brazier: Since the period when I visited one of the children's places in the Soviet Union, I had an opportunity to discuss it with Professor Luria. He told me the system had changed. They were giving up the scheme by which the parents had so little access to their children. They already were feeling this was not to be held to so rigidly, and the whole scheme was in the process of change. Also, is it not true that the Kibbutzim vary from one to another, as to how much the parents are with their children? In some of them the children go home for the weekend.

Lindsley: Dr. Bronfenbrenner spent six months in the USSR fairly recently, primarily visiting the schools. At that time it was apparently not true, at least in the various boarding schools he visited, and I believe these were several. The parents followed the plan Dr. Donchin described.

Donchin: I have found it very difficult to obtain published material on the reorganization of Soviet education. Dr. Bronfenbrenner gave his talk at UCLA in 1964, and I believe that he had returned from Russia not too long before that. There is a discussion of this reorganization dating from 1961 (1), which definitely describes the particular pattern I mentioned, and there is another report from 1964 (3) confirming the details I described in terms of a five-year plan. The details can be gleaned from various translations published by the Joint Publications Research Service (1, 2, 3). I have, of course, no idea to what extent the more recent leadership changes have affected the planning in this area. As to the variability in the Kibbutz format, it is indeed quite extensive, the age of the Kibbutz, its particular political affiliation, and many other factors determining the exact pattern; but the basic lines I have described are invariant—namely the extra-familial rearing pattern and the close emotional ties with the family.

We thus have an educational system which is quite different from current Western practices. One of the more interesting facets, at least from the point of view of the child development theorist, is that most of the research done to date on the Kibbutz child (16, 50, 58) failed to find any systematic differences between him and the city child reared in Israel (in spite of the fact that an Israeli would probably recognize a Kibbutz child, or at least has a definite stereotype). Kugelmass (29) has studied the development of moral judgment in Kibbutz children and did not find it to be any different from that observed in city children. Nagler (46) has recently reported on the behavior disturbances observed in Kibbutz children; he finds that there are no basic differences in the patterns, in terms of both symptomatology and etiology, between the Kibbutz children and the generally reported results in the literature. The single difference is that the upbringer and her relationship with the parents becomes a source for behavior pathology.

Koestler: Are there not some peculiar phenomena such as a trend toward exogamy, a kind of incest-taboo felt by the members of the community towards each other?

Donchin: That is true. Kibbutz children tend to marry outside their own Kibbutz. But before any significance is attached to that, one has to determine to what extent marriage within the circle of very intimate infancy and childhood friends is prevalent in the general population.

Brazier: In 1963 I had the experience of visiting a Kibbutz. At the University of Jerusalem they told me that a study had been made of enuresis, and that its duration extended to a much later age in Kibbutz children than in Israeli children living at home.

Donchin: That is also mentioned by Nagler (46). Enuresis does seem to be the one disturbance that is reported more often in the Kibbutz than in the general population. On the other hand, feeding difficulties, aggression problems and other effects are quite markedly reduced.

Jensen: Would Mowrer's (45) conditioning analysis of enuresis provide an explanation? Might it not simply be that the training procedure for the teaching of responding to bladder distention is less effective in the communal situation?

Feshbach: The apparently greater degree of enuresis may be an artifact in that you can get much more accurate information from people in the Kibbutz. Enuresis is more frequent in non-clinical populations than is generally recognized (9). It has been reported, incidentally, that homosexuality is very rare among Kibbutz children (58).

Donchin: As far as I know, it is very rare, but again this might be more indicative of the situation in the Israeli population than of the Kibbutz as a special part of that population. I could enumerate other instances in which differences sought between Kibbutz and non-Kibbutz children did not materialize; whether this is due to the insensitivities of the measuring instruments applied or to inadequacies in the theories of child development that predicted the differences is a very important problem. It seems a pity, therefore, that this rich mine of information on the differential effects of child rearing practices has not been tapped more often.

REFERENCES

1. AFANASENKO, Y., *Reorganization of Education—USSR.* U.S. Joint Publ. Res. Serv.—No. 11874, Washington, D.C., 1962.

2. ANWEILER, O., *Social Problems of Soviet Education.* U.S. Joint Publ. Res. Serv. No. 11049, Washington, D.C., 1961.

3. ARISKIN, I. T., Teaching practice of students in boarding schools. In: *Soviet Educational Methods and Aims.* U.S. Joint Publ. Res. Serv. No. 23508, Washington, D.C., 1964: 29-39.

4. BAGSHAW, M. H., KIMBLE, D. P., and PRIBRAM, K. H., The GSR of monkeys during orienting and habituation and after ablation of the amygdala, hippocampus and inferotemporal cortex. *Neuropsychologia,* 1965, **3**: 111-119.

5. BARTOSHUK, A. K., Human neonatal cardiac acceleration to sound: habituation and dishabituation. *Percept. Mot. Skills,* 1962, **15**: 15-27.

6. BIRCH, H. G., and DEMB, H., The formation and extinction of conditioned reflexes in "brain-damaged" and mongoloid children. *J. Nerv. Ment. Dis.,* 1959, **129**: 162-170.

7. BRIDGER, W. H., Sensory habituation and discrimination in the human neonate. *Am. J. Psychiat.,* 1961, **117**: 991-996.

8. BRONSHTEIN, A. I., ANTONOVA, T. G., KAMENETSKAYA, A. G., LUPPOVA, N. N.,

and Sytova, V. A., On the development of the functions of analyzers in infants and some animals at the early stage of ontogenesis. In: *Problems of Evolution of Physiological Functions* (S. Shoshan, Transl.). Acad. Sci. USSR, Moscow, 1958: 106-116.

9. Coleman, J. C., *Abnormal Psychology and Modern Life*, 2nd ed. Scott, Foresman, Chicago, 1956.

10. Disher, D. R., The reactions of newborn infants to chemical stimuli administered nasally. *Ohio State Univ. Stud. Inf. Behav.*, 1934, No. 12: 1-52.

11. Elkonin, D. B., The physiology of higher nervous activity and child psychology. In: *Psychology in the Soviet Union* (B. Simon, Ed.). Routledge & Kegan Paul, London, 1957: 47-68.

12. Ellingson, R. J., Electroencephalograms of normal, full-term newborns immediately after birth with observations on arousal and visual evoked responses. *EEG Clin. Neurophysiol.*, 1958, **10**: 31-50.

13. ———, Cerebral electrical responses to auditory and visual stimuli in the infant (human and subhuman studies). In: *Neurological and Electroencephalographic Correlative Studies in Infancy* (P. Kellaway and I. Petersen, Eds.). Grune & Stratton, New York, 1964: 78-116.

14. Engen, T., and Lipsitt, L. P., Decrement and recovery of responses to olfactory stimuli in the human neonate. *J. Comp. Physiol. Psychol.*, 1965, **59**: 312-316.

15. Engen, T., Lipsitt, L. P., and Kaye, H., Olfactory responses and adaptation in the human neonate. *J. Comp. Physiol. Psychol.*, 1963, **56**: 73-77.

16. Faigin, H., Social behavior of young children in the Kibbutz. *J. Abnorm. Soc. Psychol.*, 1958, **56**: 117-129.

17. Gesell, A., The ontogenesis of infant behavior. In: *Manual of Child Psychology*, 2nd ed. (L. Carmichael, Ed.). Wiley, New York, 1954: 335-373.

18. Gesell, A., Halverson, H. M., Thompson, H., Ilf, F. L., Castner, B. M., Ames, L. B., and Amatruda, C. S., *The First Five Years of Life. A Guide to the Study of the Preschool Child.* Harper, New York, 1940.

19. Golan, S., Behavior research in collective settlements in Israel. 2. Collective education in the kibbutz. *Am. J. Orthopsychiat.*, 1958, **28**: 549-556.

20. Gollin, E. S., A developmental approach to learning and cognition. *Adv. Child Dev. Behav.*, 1965, **2**: 159-186.

21. Gunther, M., Infant behaviour at the breast. In: *Determinants of Infant Behaviour*, Vol. I (B. M. Foss, Ed.). Methuen, London, 1961: 37-44.

22. Harris, D. B., Child psychology and the concept of development. In: *Research Readings in Child Psychology* (D. S. Palermo and L. P. Lipsitt, Eds.). Holt, Rinehart & Winston, New York, 1963: 21-31.

23. Hernández-Peón, R., Neurophysiological correlates of habituation and other manifestations of plastic inhibition. *EEG Clin. Neurophysiol.*, 1960, Supp. **13**: 101-114.

24. Humphrey, G., *The Nature of Learning in Its Relation to the Living System.* Harcourt Brace, New York, 1933.

25. Kassof, A., *The Soviet Youth Program: Regimentation and Rebellion.* Harvard Univ. Press, Cambridge, 1965.

26. Kessen, W., Research design in the study of developmental problems. In:

Handbook of Research Methods in Child Development (P. H. Mussen, Ed.). Wiley, New York, 1960: 36-70.

27. KOEPKE, J. E., and PRIBRAM, K. H., Habituation of GSR as a function of stimulus duration and "spontaneous activity". *J. Comp. Physiol. Psychol.*, 1966, **61**: 442-448.

28. KRASNOGORSKI, N., Über die Grundmechanismen der Arbeit der Grosshirnrinde bei Kindern. *Jb. Kinderheilk.*, 1913, **78**: 373-398.

29. KUGELMASS, S., *Development of Values in Kibbutz and City Youth*. Research Report M-6423(A), 1962-1963, Psychology Dept., Hebrew Univ., Jerusalem.

30. LINDSLEY, D. B., The ontogeny of pleasure: neural and behavioral development. In: *The Role of Pleasure in Behavior* (R. G. Heath, Ed.). Hoeber, New York, 1964: 3-22.

31. LINDSLEY, O. R., Experimental analysis of social reinforcement: terms and methods. *Am. J. Orthopsychiat.*, 1963, **33**: 624-633.

32. LIPSITT, L. P., Learning in the first year of life. In: *Advances in Child Development and Behavior*, Vol. I (L. P. Lipsitt and C. C. Spiker, Eds.). Academic Press, New York, 1963: 147-195.

33. LIPSITT, L. P., and DeLUCIA, C. A., An apparatus for the measurement of specific response and general activity of the human neonate. *Am. J. Psychol.*, 1960, **73**: 630-632.

34. LIPSITT, L. P., ENGEN, T., and KAYE, H., Developmental changes in the olfactory threshold of the neonate. *Child. Dev.*, 1963, **34**: 371-376.

35. LIPSITT, L. P., and KAYE, H., Conditioned sucking in the human newborn. *Psychon. Sci.*, 1964, **1**: 29-30.

36. ———, Change in neonatal response to optimizing and non-optimizing sucking stimulation. *Psychon. Sci.*, 1965, **2**: 221-222.

37. LIPSITT, L. P., KAYE, H., and BOSACK, T., Enhancement of neonatal sucking through reinforcement. *J. Exp. Child Psychol.*, 1966, 4: 163-168.

38. LIPSITT, L. P., and LEVY, N., Electrotactual threshold in the neonate. *Child Dev.*, 1959, **30**: 547-554.

39. LIPSITT, L. P., PEDERSON, L. J., and DeLUCIA, C. A., Conjugate reinforcement of operant responding infants. *Psychon. Sci.*, 1966, **4**: 67-68.

40. MARQUIS, D. P., Can conditioned responses be established in the newborn infant? *J. Genet. Psychol.*, 1931, **39**: 479-492.

41. ———, Learning in the neonate: the modification of behavior under three feeding schedules. *J. Exp. Psychol.*, 1941, **29**: 263-282.

42. MONNIER, M., and WILLI, H., Die integrative Tätigkeit des Nervensystems beim normalen Säugling und beim bulbo-spinalen Anencephalen (Rautenhirnwesen). *Ann. Paediat.*, 1947, **169**: 289-308.

43. ———, Die integrative Tätigkeit des Nervensystems beim meso-rhombospinalen Anencephalus. II. Anatomischer Teil. *Mschr. Psychiat. Neurol.*, 1953, **126**: 259-273.

44. MORGAN, J. J. B., and MORGAN, S. S., Infant learning as a developmental index. *J. Genet. Psychol.*, 1944, **65**: 281-289.

45. MOWRER, O. H., and MOWRER, W. M., Enuresis—a method for its study and treatment. *Am. J. Orthopsychiat.*, 1938, **8**: 436-459.

46. NAGLER, S., Clinical observations on Kibbutz children. *Israel Ann. Psychiat.*, 1963, **1**: 201-216.

47. PAPOUSEK, H., Conditioned head rotation reflexes in infants in the first months of life. *Acta Paed.*, 1961, **50**: 565-576.

48. PRATT, K. C., The neonate. In: *Manual of Child Psychology*, 2nd ed. (L. Carmichael, Ed.). Wiley, New York, 1954: 215-291.

49. RABIN, A. I., Some psychosexual differences between Kibbutz and non-Kibbutz Israeli boys. *J. Proj. Tech.*, 1958, **22**: 328-332.

50. RAPAPORT, D., Behavior research in collective settlements in Israel. 7. The study of kibbutz education and its bearing on the theory of development. *Am. J. Orthopsychiat.*, 1958, **28**: 587-597.

51. ROSE, G. H., and LINDSLEY, D. B., Visually evoked electrocortical responses in kittens: development of specific and nonspecific systems. *Science*, 1965, **148**: 1244-1246.

52. SCHWARTZ, R. D., Behavior research in collective settlements in Israel. 5. Some problems of research in Israeli settlements. *Am. J. Orthopsychiat.*, 1958, **28**: 572-576.

53. SECHENOV, I. M., Reflexes of the brain. In: *Sechenov: Selected Works* (A. A. Subkov, Transl. and Ed.). State Publishing House, Moscow, 1935: 263-336.

54. SIQUELAND, E., Operant conditioning of head turning in four-month infants. *Psychon. Sci.*, 1964, **1**: 223-224.

55. SOKOLOV, E. N., Neuronal models and the orienting reflex. In: *The Central Nervous System and Behavior*, Trans. 3rd Conf. (M. A. B. Brazier, Ed.). Josiah Macy, Jr. Foundation, New York, 1960: 187-276.

56. SOKOLOV, Y. N., *Perception and the Conditioned Reflex* (S. W. Waydenfeld, Transl.). Pergamon, New York, 1963.

57. SPIRO, M. E., *Kibbutz: Venture in Utopia*. Harvard Univ. Press, Cambridge, 1956.

58. ———, *Children of the Kibbutz*. Harvard Univ. Press, Cambridge, 1958.

59. STANLEY, W. C., CORNWELL, A. C., POGGIANI, C., and TRATTNER, A., Conditioning in the neonatal puppy. *J. Comp. Physiol. Psychol.*, 1963, **56**: 211-214.

60. THOMPSON, H., Physical growth. In: *Manual of Child Psychology*, 2nd ed. (L. Carmichael, Ed.). Wiley, New York, 1954: 292-334.

61. THORPE, W. H., *Learning and Instinct in Animals*, 2nd ed. Harvard Univ. Press, Cambridge, 1963.

62. WEINGARTEN, M., *Life in a Kibbutz*. Reconstructionist Press, New York, 1955.

63. WENGER, M. A., Studies in infant behavior. III. An investigation of conditioned responses in human infants. *Univ. Iowa Stud. Child Welf.*, 1936, **12**(1): 7-90.

64. WICKENS, D. D., and WICKENS, C., A study of conditioning in the neonate. *J. Exp. Psychol.*, 1940, **26**: 94-102.

65. ZIGLER, E., Metatheoretical issues in developmental psychology. In: *Theories in Contemporary Psychology* (M. H. Marx, Ed.). Macmillan, New York, 1963: 341-369.

PROGRAMMED LEARNING AND TEACHING MACHINES[*]

ARTHUR A. LUMSDAINE[†]
University of California
Los Angeles

Several reasons make me feel somewhat diffident about my topic. For one, what I have to talk about may seem rather practical and therefore mundane. We have been in the stratospheric ranges of the cerebrum and basic science; now I am supposed to descend to what might be viewed as the "quick and dirty" applied level.

A survey of the total field of research and development applicable to teaching machines, programmed learning or related aspects of instructional technology would not be possible here. Even a sketch of the main features of this field would be unduly repetitious of various previous papers (14, 15, 19, 20, 36), to which the reader can refer for general orientation to the field. Aside from giving only a minimum of background, I shall limit my remarks to points that have special relevance to the present symposium and which have not been previously presented as such. Those interested in the experimental literature on instructional programming variables should consult Schramm's 1964 annotated bibliography (37), the 1965 literature review by Lumsdaine & May (23), and papers in the 1965 NEA volume edited by Glaser (9). More detailed background information is contained in the 1960 Lumsdaine & Glaser source book (22).

What I would like to say falls mainly under four topics: science and technology, models and instrumentation, application of theory, and problems in experimentation.

SCIENCE AND TECHNOLOGY

When I was an undergraduate, I was taught that psychology is the science of understanding, predicting, and controlling human behavior. Like all such characterizations, this neat scheme is an oversimplification. For example, if we are to verify predictions, we also have to cope with problems in *measurement* of the behaviors predicted. Moreover, at least in an applied

[*] The preparation of this paper was aided by research projects supported by the Ford Foundation and by the Educational Media and Cooperative Research programs of the U.S. Office of Education. Reproduction by the U.S. Government in whole or in part is authorized for any purpose.
[†] Now at the University of Washington, Seattle.

field such as programmed instruction, the logical primacy of understanding as a presumable prerequisite does not quite fit; rather, we have to try to do something about controlling behavior without being able to understand fully the reasons for effects we produce or observe.

This situation is at variance with the implications of what I believe was a well-intentioned falsehood perpetrated a few years back, that there exists in inventory (developed in Cambridge and elsewhere) a fully developed science of learning which we have only to apply in order to acquire an adequate technology of education. I think it is quite manifest from the discussions thus far that we still have a great deal to learn about understanding and predicting the phenomena of learning, not to mention the cerebral processes which are presumed to underlie them. But, as practicing educators, we can hardly stand still and wait for the achievement of complete understanding before we improve our methods of instruction. Without becoming dramatic about H. G. Wells' "race between education and history", we clearly have to do our best to control the learning processes and to improve instruction before a science of learning or instruction is fully developed. With or without adequate guidance from a science of learning, a technology of instruction must attempt to control, regulate and manage the learning process (10, 20, 21).

Three Foci of Inquiry for Research.

For the present purpose, we can regard the brain as a "black box" inside the head of the learner (Figure 71B). In other words, we are concerned here only with input-output relationships, not with what happens inside. Data concerning such relationships may lead other investigators to hammer the box on the top and drill holes through it and peer inside (Figure 71A); that is completely bypassed here.

Perhaps the most common focus of interest in research on programmed learning is the manipulation of variables in an instructional program (Figure 71B). Another kind of research, more applied or technological in orientation, is concerned only with determining the effects attributable to a particular programmed-learning sequence by means of scientifically valid techniques of experimental measurement. This form of product-testing research is useful in providing educational specifications for programs applicable to a potentially wide educational market, but it further bypasses the functioning of intra-program instructional variables that contribute to the program's effectiveness. It thus regards the program (whether or not actually packaged in a "hardware" form of teaching machine) as *another* black or gray box (Figure 71C). We are then asking not even *how* this gray box works, but only *how well* the whole system works in terms of overall input-output relationships. However, in thus dealing with the teaching machine, or with any form of programmed learning, the symbolic representation by a black

A. Scientific study of brain function in learning

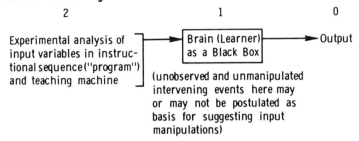

B. Behavioral science of learning or instruction

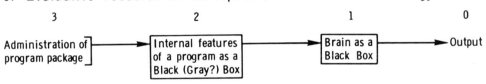

C. Evaluative research as an aspect of instructional technology

Figure 71. Schema illustrating different loci of inquiry. A: Basic research on brain function in learning; B: basic behavioral research on instructional variables; and C: applied or evaluative research on effectiveness of a particular instructional program or system. (Numbers indicate main locus of inquiry in terms of steps removed from system output.)

box, or a series of black boxes, does imply inner workings which, while unanalyzed, do have predictable outputs in relation to specifiable inputs.

For reasons stated elsewhere (20, 21), much of my own recent research interest has been in the technologically oriented area of applied research. This aims to determine and describe the effects which particular programs can be shown capable of producing (1, 2, 17, 21). I would like to emphasize the importance of adhering to the methods of science in applied technological research. Even when we are not looking inside the gray box (which is in the form of a program we purchase from The Grolier Society, A & P, or the IBM Corporation) we need, in order to determine its effects, to use essentially the same standards of experimental rigor we apply to inquiries into the internal workings of the box.

The other, or scientifically oriented kind of research—dealing with programming variables that influence learning—is clearly more relevant to the purposes of this symposium. Such research aims to discover or demonstrate the validity of rules or principles of instructional programming which would contribute to a science of instruction. Following Skinner's initial paper in 1954 (40), a large number of such experiments, many of them quite inconclusive, have been conducted.*

MODELS AND INSTRUMENTATION

As suggested above, we may consider scientifically oriented research as concerned with the internal features of a programmed black (or gray) box (Figure 71C, left). As this research progresses, however, it becomes increasingly clear that it should be accompanied, or even preceded, by developments in the technological field, for our interest lies, not in looking inside a box constructed by Mother Nature and seeing what is already there (as brain researchers do), nor merely in building *models* of programmed learning, but in examining the characteristics of programmed materials and devices which we must, perforce, construct ourselves. We are interested in building machines. We are particularly interested in developing programmed materials to put in those machines, though perhaps designing these in accordance with certain theoretical notions. This goes beyond tinkering with what was previously put into a box by someone else; it actually means, in a sense, building the box from scratch and then seeing how it works, in order to improve it.

Of course, our attempt to investigate, manipulate, control, and optimize the effectiveness of the whole system presumes manipulating experimentally the conditions inside the gray (teaching machine) box. This is done partly with the hope of deriving generalizations suggested by less applied branches of learning science, by intuition, and by accident. Regardless of their source, it involves testing propositions which will make the box work better.

These generalizations relate to factors that are often expressed in terms of stimulus-response psychology—e.g., factors concerning the prompting or cuing of the learner, the nature of his response in relation to antecedent and consequent stimuli, or the nature of inputs in a feedback loop from the student back to the box (program).

Feedback Loops in Programmed Instruction.

I think it is important to note that the feedback inputs involved in programmed learning are of several different kinds (Figure 72). The first, perhaps more obvious kind (Figure 72A), assesses in some way what the student does, which makes some difference in the next display given him by the box; this may involve altering the program in a branching sequence by employing various sorts of relatively simple or more complex mechanisms (mentioned later on).

Two other uses of feedback involve information fed back to the programmer or the purchaser of programs, rather than to the student. They

---

* For reviews see Schramm (37), Lumsdaine & May (23), and papers by J. G. Holland, J. L. Evans and others in the volume edited by Glaser (9).

A. Preprogrammed contingent alteration of sequence within a given program

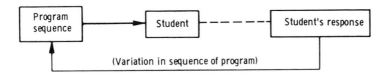

B. Use of response data to revise a program

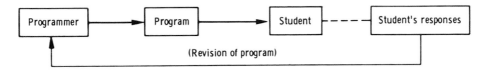

C. Use of evaluative data to affect selection or use of programs

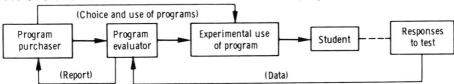

D. Use of experimental data on alternative programs to revise principles or rules of programming

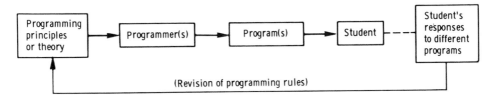

Figure 72. Uses of feedback data from student's responses in the operation, development, selection, and theory of instructional programs.

therefore apply to the development (Figure 72B) and selection (Figure 72C) of the programs rather than to their inner workings. These two uses of feedback, which occur during the empirical development and evaluation of programs, are crucial to the technologically oriented kinds of research. The usefulness of these kinds of feedback from the student's performance stems from the relatively high degree of reproducibility characteristic of instructional situations mediated by a machine or program (as contrasted with the lesser degree of reproducibility we customarily associate with human instruction such as a lecture, tutoring session, etc. This reproducibility has practical as well as scientific consequences: a program not only stays constant as an experimental vehicle as long as it is maintained as such, but it can also be improved on the basis of information feedback from the learner's output. Such information includes data on the student's step-by-step responses to the program and, later, retention or savings data, indicating how well the whole system achieved the outputs desired. In principle, the system can be modified until it achieves optimal efficiency.

The fourth kind of feedback (Figure 72D) is essentially what is involved in scientifically oriented research. As previously indicated, this type of research seeks to use response data as a basis for modifying principles or theories of programming rather than aiming toward the improvement or assessment of a particular program. Feedback of type C considers the program as an intact program "box"; the others are concerned in various ways with its inner workings.

Student Response and Instructional Objectives.

In the use of response data for the purposes of program development and assessment, program performance and needs for program modification can be pinpointed to a very considerable degree. This can be done not only by examining moment-to-moment responses to the program, but also in terms of a later, fairly exhaustive analytic testing sequence. By this means, the particular components of the learning sequence that went wrong can be identified, even for subsequent retention. This sort of test profile does not always identify the reasons or the points in time at which the program went wrong, but at least indicates the specific points one failed to teach.

Simon: Your statement assumes that you really know what can be regarded as satisfactory performance from the black box called "S". I wonder about the basis for your optimism. Are you assuming you can judge that without knowing what is inside that black box?

Lumsdaine: I think that, beyond superficial truisms, the answer to what should be regarded as satisfactory performance is not an easy one, yet it is not clear to me that the answer necessarily lies in looking inside either of the boxes. In deciding what we want S to learn, a great deal depends on value judgments about what we want the student to learn in the first place; this might be more apparent in attempting to work with a school system or department of education. Deciding on educational goals to aim for runs into some real difficulties representing differences of opinion as to what competences the student should acquire. This, I think, must be regarded as lying in the realm of value judgments. Should he learn principles of estimation and fiducial probability, or learn to derive proofs in geometry? Should he learn to speak with a flawless Parisian accent, or learn a smattering of several languages, in order to adjust to a variety of relationships? Should he learn linguistics, which will mediate the learning of subsequent languages, or just learn one language well?

Simon: Are these not the questions: If I teach this, will its applicability transfer to other tasks? If I teach that, will it not transfer?

Lumsdaine: Yes—up to a point we do indeed have to deal with the gray box problems involved in programming for transfer. But some of the further questions that arise do not seem to be of this character—we still have to decide on the more ultimate outcomes to which we want the training to transfer. Perhaps it is a matter of degree. Some of those questions, including the linguistic example, are definitely amenable to this kind of approach. Certainly, the question of whether learning structural linguistics is a better way to use the student's time than learning three languages directly is, in principle, open to experimental approach. But, as we go further into kinds of attitudes the student should acquire about, for example, democracy or child-rearing, then we go beyond realms that seem readily amenable to experimentation; ultimately, we push the question further and further in terms of what kind of world we would like to have several millennia hence. I am merely saying that there are some real uncertainties—involving what might be called "knowledge for what?"—concerning the kinds of competences we ultimately want the student to have. Determining which ultimate goals should have primacy does not seem to yield very neatly to experimental attack. However, I do not mean that such questions are not amenable to *any* kind of research.

Stopping short of these more ultimate objectives, there are certainly, as you suggest, a variety of questions about what specifics should be taught (and in what order they should be taught, at what level, and so on) that are amenable to experimental attack not only in principle but also in practice. One such question concerns problems in transfer of learning. Further, a very important though non-intrinsic aspect of the development of teaching machines and programmed instruction is the emphasis that these developments have placed on identifying much more clearly than is customary—in much more specific behavioral terms—what outcomes of instruction are to be sought and/or measured (8, 25). I say "non-intrinsic" because the notion of defining objectives of instruction in detailed terms by indicating the competences which one expects the student to acquire (instead of supplying a one-line or three-line description of the course "content" in a catalogue) dates a long way back. Ralph Tyler (45) at the University of Chicago, and others such as Bloom (3), have tried to promote this way of looking at curricular objectives in terms of specific behavioral outcomes. This tendency has, however, acquired additional momentum in relation to developments in programmed instruction. One reason is that the programming of learning generates an instructional sequence which is reproducible not only regarding instructional materials and events, but in the achievement of desired outcomes. This requires a very clear idea of exactly what it is we are trying to teach—a much clearer idea than is needed to lecture and assign grades on the basis of a distribution at the end of the semester. Being very precise about what we exactly want to accomplish is, in fact, an essential aspect of the entire notion of programmed instruction.

Software and Hardware: Programs and Computers.

As such, however, this emphasis on precise specification of objectives has little to do with teaching-machine instrumentation. Indeed, some of my colleagues feel that teaching machines are unimportant, that the hardware is only a trivial aspect, that "everything is in the program", and that a presentation by programmed booklets is sufficient to implement the full potential of the programmed-learning concept. I agree with Skinner (42) in thinking otherwise: I believe that hardware, as well as software, can play a very important role in providing the kind of reproducibility that not only assures a predictable outcome but makes the learning process more readily amenable to scientific inquiry.

Pribram: Are you suggesting that we teach children the way we teach computers, perchance? Do we simply want a child to learn, or do we want him to become educated? What we want a computer to do for us is something very different from what we want children to become.

Lumsdaine: It certainly was not my intention to suggest that teaching students to follow rote instructions is the only objective of education. I would say, however, that in talking about computers and teaching machines it is no accident (although unfortunately misleading) that the term "program" is used for both. Actually, the "program" in a teaching machine is not really the same thing as the program for the computer, even in a branching program. In programmed-instruction "programs", the student, contingent on his response to a stimulus frame (e.g., a question), would be sent to a certain place or address; had he made a different response, he might be sent elsewhere. Both the material to which he responded and the new material to which he is sent are, like data, stored material to be brought into the operation at an appropriate time, even though they are called frames of a "program". But in computer terms the "program" is, rather, the contingent directions that govern *where* the student goes, not what he finds when he gets there. In a sense, therefore, most program content, as commonly used in the term "programmed instruction", is perhaps more analogous to the *data* in a computer than to its program. I prefer not to push that analogy too far just now, however.

Some Characteristics of Teaching Machine Systems

I would now like to discuss some features of teaching–machine systems that may be of special interest in the present context. These relate particularly to variants of the kind of feedback loop depicted in Figure 72A, involving the consequences of the student's response to the progression or sequencing of an ongoing program (as distinct from feedback to the programmer, purchaser, or instructional theorist). Associated with the implementation of such feedback are differences in the features of response evaluation or response discrimination (by the machine and/or the student). These serve to initiate the feedback signals which regulate the progression of instructional sequence for any particular student. While other features of some machines may be noted in passing, my main interest in the present discussion is in these two related features, feedback models and response discrimination.

Characteristically, teaching machines present items of stimulus material consisting of information plus questions or, in some instances, just questions. Many teaching machines also incorporate some kind of response-registration or scoring device. The items of presentation are generally called "frames" because they appear in a frame-like aperture or window in the machine. Such items or frames characteristically tend to be rather short, and the student is generally required to give at least one appropriate response to each frame.

One reason for my present concentration on machines rather than on instructional programs is that the question of programming of material has tended to dominate most recent discussions in the field. By no means do I wish to minimize the importance of the kind of subject-matter analysis and empirically guided development of verbal (and in some cases pictorial) teaching materials with which these programming efforts are concerned; on the contrary, I believe such work is of great importance for improving the effectiveness of instruction, as well as for trying to understand the dynamics of complex learning sequences. However, I do feel some need to redress the balance of attention that has lately slighted the hardware in favor of the "software."

An important side effect of the emphasis on programming has been the tendency, perhaps inadvertent, to focus attention on the stimulus and to neglect the learner's response and its consequences. Though active responding (and frequent subsequent "reinforcement") has been touted as an important aspect of programmed instruction, the actual role, or roles, of the response has been somewhat disregarded.*

Figure 73 shows a variety of teaching machines that illustrate several main patterns of item-sequence regulation, mediated by different ways of discriminating the adequacy of the student's responses. Such devices and the kinds of instructional stimulus sequences (programs) they present have been described elsewhere (14, 15, 19); here we merely want to take a brief look at the machines in order to classify them according to the feedback and sequence-modification patterns they permit (see Figure 74), and to the response-discrimination capabilities that mediate this feedback.

Machine #4 in Figure 73, a recently mass-produced version of the gener-

---

* See Lumsdaine & May (23), especially pp. 501-502, for further comment on various roles of student response.

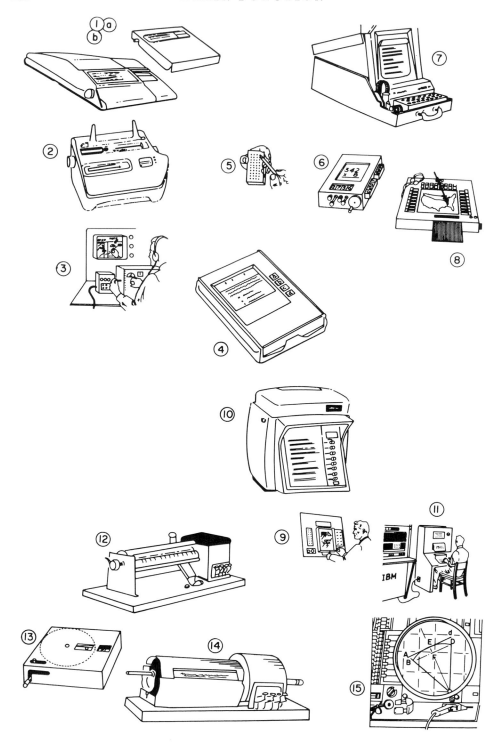

Figure 73. Some teaching machines and related devices (teaching-system components) differing in capability for automatic response-discrimination, and also illustrating differences in sequence-variation capabilities. See text.

A. Feedback to S without altering program sequence

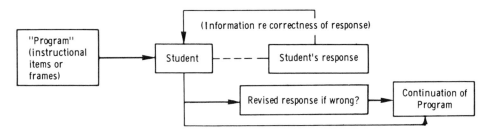

B. Student-mediated program alteration based on feedback to S

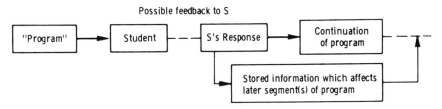

C. Automatically-mediated immediate control of program sequence or progression

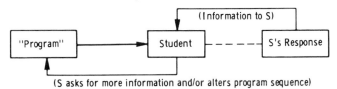

D. Automatically-mediated deferred effect on program sequence

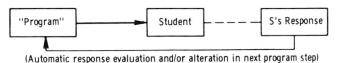

Figure 74. Differences in the way in which a student's responses may be used to alter the instructional sequence he will receive.

al type first built by Pressey (30, 31) in the 1920's, runs on flashlight batteries and is capable of nearly everything that machine #10 (which has been on the market for some time) can do, at only about one per cent of the cost of machine #10. The machine presents the student with successive frames carried on a roll of paper, each containing a small amount of material to read, followed by a question to which he may choose any of four responses. It can be "programmed" (by means of punches in the paper that close electrical circuits) so that it will "balk" if he does not pick the right answer; i.e., it stops and makes him try again before proceeding to the next

frame. The lesson's progression thus becomes directly contingent, in a simple way, on the student's response, as schematized in Figure 74C.

We call this device a "teaching machine" (in the sense that this term is
currently used) because it presents material individually requiring some sort
of response from the student as a condition for the lesson to proceed; "tutoring machine" is perhaps a better term. At any rate, the instructional sequence does not just run on like a lecture or like most motion pictures (see
below), without regard to what the student does, although what the student
must do in order to make the instructional sequence continue varies from
one type of machine to another. In machine #4, the lesson sequence will
not display the next frame until the student gives an answer which the machine discriminates as correct (see Figure 74C).

Machines #12 and #14 (Figure 73), which we will discuss again presently,
were Pressey's early models, on which #4 is essentially based. Machine #5,
a simple punch board, was another device developed by Pressey (32) to give
automatic feedback to the student in the form of right-wrong indicators,
but leaving it up to him to correct his mistakes by answering a question
again, before proceeding to the next one, if he had erred. The questions
were presented on a separate sheet of paper, so that there was device control
over the feedback information to the subject but no stimulus control over
the instructional material.

In these simple multiple-choice devices, in which the student selects his
response from a small number of choices, learning depends on transfer from
selective to subsequent constructed-response performance. The adequacy of
such transfer remains a moot point. Skinner (41) took the position that the
student should construct or compose his answer rather than merely select it
from a limited set of alternative choices. The difficulty of providing automatic response-discrimination for responses more complex than four-choice
ones increases rapidly as the complexity of the response increases. Quite a
bit of sophistication can be developed in this respect (if one is willing to pay
for it), as will be seen in a moment. As an alternative, Skinner (41) decided
to abandon automatic discrimination in machines designed for mature students, who were instead left to judge the adequacy of their responses after
comparing them with a correct-answer display shown after the student had
responded. This far-reaching decision meant, in other words, that feedback
from his response was to the student rather than directly to the machine or
program.

Skinner's compromise led to the development and marketing of a large
number of write-in machines, such as #1a and #1b in Figure 73. In such
machines no provision is made for modification of the "linear" program
sequence, though slightly more elaborate devices allow some modification
when the student adjudges his responses inadequate. (These devices, shown
as #2 and #13 in Figure 73, will be further discussed later.) The simplest
of these so-called teaching machines (some forms of which can be bought
in a supermarket) consist simply of cardboard masking contraptions. Thou-

sands of such devices have been sold, many more than of the more sophisticated types. Basically, whether activated manually (as are most) or electrically, they are merely ways to try to insure that the student responds, in writing, before the correct answer to a question is revealed. But in such devices the student can make the program proceed regardless of his response, for there is no response discrimination other than what the student himself provides; the progression of the program depends only on his giving the machine a "go" signal after he has responded and/or has checked his answer; continuation of the program does *not* depend on his showing that he can respond correctly.

The recognition of this fact led Homme & Glaser (12) to propose the substitution of "programmed textbooks" for teaching-machine presented sequences. This suggestion, eagerly taken up by the book-publishing industry, was accompanied not only by a desirable emphasis on the arts of program construction, but also by a tendency, less desirable in my opinion, to neglect the program-regulation properties of teaching machines. This tendency was aggravated by the publication of oversimplified interpretations of experimental comparisons which failed to show statistically reliable differences between "programs" presented in book form and by simplistic machines such as #1a and #1b in Figure 73.*

In the "linear" kind of programs introduced by Skinner in 1958 (41) for such machines, the student is given a good deal of prompting, at least initially, and his rate of errors is therefore low; feedback to the learner tends to be corroborative rather than corrective. When the student is well-prompted, it would seem that feedback of the correct response loses much of its relevance. In fact, children working with highly prompted programs often ignore the correct answer, evidently because they know their answer is right without looking. In any case, the nature and importance of the feedback function will obviously depend on the kind of instructional-stimulus "programming", especially on the degree of prompting.

The use of a machine rather than a programmed book may be required because of the kind of stimulus input desired, as well as to provide automatic response discrimination and consequent program regulation. Before returning to the latter, we may consider as an example audiovisual device #3 in Figure 73. The functional properties of a programmed-instructional sequence depend on what is done with a medium or device, as well as on the device itself. Motion pictures are not normally thought of as programmed learning, at least within the programmed learning fraternity, but they can be used as programmed-learning devices with the right kind of projector used properly. This is exemplified by device #3, where the projector can be stopped to show a segment of a demonstration, which the student is to imitate as a step in an operational sequence, before proceeding with further demonstration and practice. Such a step-by-step procedural demonstration can also be used to "program" the performance of an individual in a job sit-

---

* See reviews by Schramm (37) and Lumsdaine & May (23).

uation, which he need not learn at all so long as the demonstration continues to be available. On the other hand, guiding him step by step through a
lengthy, complex sequence can also be used for his eventually learning it,
i.e., for teaching him serial learning tasks.

Used either as a job performance aid or as a learning aid, such a device
can be very important economically. For example, the former application
(substituting continuously available job instructions for prior instruction)
has been utilized in a number of industrial installations, including Hughes
Aircraft. Use of the device as a learning aid raises some interesting theoretical problems and opportunities for the application of S-R theory-guided
cue-vanishing gradients, if one thinks of the transition from earlier, less
guided performance to later, more completely guided performance.*

The use of such a device for teaching serial-procedural tasks is actually
quite similar to the use of "linear" instructional programs for teaching conceptual subject matter in devices such as #1a, #1b, #2, and #13 (Figure
73). Despite the differences in what is to be learned, both employ responses
constructed by the learner guided by prompting from the instructional
sequence. Incidentally, the limited experimental research on the efficacy of
cue-vanishing has been about equally divided between the two kinds of
linear instructional sequences (23, 37). In both cases, also, the student rather
than the device serves as the comparator of response adequacy, by matching
his answer to a correct-response display revealed by the device. The feedback paradigm here is thus similar to that in Figure 74A, except that in
devices such as #3 (Figure 73) only a partial check (still picture of terminal
point in demonstrated action) is given as information on correctness of
response, and that this same picture, being continuously visible while S
is responding, can also function as a partial prompting cue.

Returning now to kinds of devices which provide automatic response
discrimination, device #6 in Figure 73 is a simplified representation of one
of Skinner's first machines (40), used for teaching arithmetic. A similar one
was also constructed by David Zeaman, also in the 1950's. Device #6 requires constructed responses (e.g., the student multiplies two numbers and
sets in the answer) rather than selection of an answer from an arbitrarily
constrained set of alternatives. But here the response construction is performed as a digital operation, by setting plungers or pressing keys, etc.,
rather than by making a free (or analog) response such as writing. This
makes it fairly easy for the machine to discriminate automatically the correctness of a constructed answer, even without any very sophisticated hardware, in contrast with such devices as #1, #2, #3, and #13 (Figure 73),

---

* This particular pattern of instruction grew out of some work done in the Air Force. Interestingly enough, the speaker and the two main discussants derived their interest and background
in the programmed-learning, teaching-machine field from work sponsored by the Air Research
and Development Command and augmented by some support from the Air Force Office of
Scientific Research.

in which the student has to serve as his own comparator by judging whether his response approximates adequately the model shown him as correct.

The distinction between simple multiple-choice selection and such digital "constructed" responses really involves, of course, a continuum representing the number of digital choices that are discriminable. Thus, extending the number of discriminable choices to a few dozen gives a full alpha-numeric repertoire which can be discriminated, as in the typewriter keyboards used in device #11 (which uses an electronic computer to match the student's response against possible answers stored in the computer's memory), or device #7 (which uses photoelectric discrimination of code spots on a film strip that also projects the instructional material). Though our subject here is not economics of engineering, it is of interest that the recognition of a typed response does not require a computer but can be done quite well with a slide projector, a few photoelectric cells, and a fairly simple keyboard arrangement; some earlier experimental devices merely used sliders instead of a keyboard, as in device #6 and in the lower part of device #8.

There are some interesting questions here concerning functional requirements for accuracy or certainty of correct-response discrimination. Perhaps, instead of the full keyboard, just a telephone dial (in which A, B, and C are confounded) might work as well for many purposes. In this case, the discriminator mechanism obviously might make a mistake and score the student right when he was actually wrong. Thus, it is possible he might have spelled in "act" when the correct answer was "cat", and this would not automatically be discriminated as an error. However, the nature of English is such that in general the probability would be very low for most responses actually given by students being scored incorrectly, even with a device affording something far short of complete discriminability. If the choice of the response is sine, cosine, or tangent, for example, just the "s", "c", or "t" serve to discriminate. For many of the sub-domains of any subject matter, mere recognition of the first letter or two as correct will be a fairly sure indicator of whether the student is, in fact, going to respond correctly. Obviously, use of a probabilistic discriminator based on this fact greatly simplifies the hardware required.

To my knowledge, there are as yet no devices available for adequate discrimination of oral responses. That is, automatic speech-pattern recognition seems to be at or beyond the fringes of the present state of the art. Some non-digital responses can feasibly be discriminated, however, such as pointing or tracing a path or a display. This is illustrated in device #8, an experimental apparatus designed by Dr. Rothkopf (33). In addition to other capabilities, such a device can discriminate the correctness of a student's tracing of a route on a map or signal flow through on an electronic diagram, or even the adequacy of his writing a letter or short word. More recent computerized devices, involving complicated back-up hardware, currently seem to do little more than that; they use a "light pencil" or "light gun" (see #15 in Figure 73) as a photoelectric reactor to spots on a cathode ray tube, but some are able to discriminate only points and will not score the tracing of a path or line. However, I see no fundamental limitation for automatic discrimination of almost any two-dimensional written or graphic response.

There are obviously more serious problems in evaluating three-dimensional responses such as might be involved in doing the rumba, performing an appendectomy, or in other skilled motor acts. If we do not want to rely for response discrimination on the learner's matching his own performance against a model, we will probably seek the skills of a human discriminator. Such an instructor need not function as information presenter, but only as a response evaluator for those responses which a machine system cannot discriminate, or at least cannot discriminate economically. This, of course, is merely one aspect of the need to consider the entire instructional problem as one of the allocation of man-machine resources.

Let us turn now from primary emphasis on response discrimination as such to the related question of its possible consequences for instructional sequence modification. In the consideration of devices thus far, whether response discrimination is automatic or not, the effect of incorrect responses on program progression has been limited at most to "balking"—i.e., stopping until the student corrects his response. Much of the current interest in computerized devices lies in their capability for mediating "branching sequences" as well as for providing response discrimination for words and sentences.

There are some further advantages in using a moderately sophisticated computer system such as the IBM installations at Yorktown Heights (46) and the similar one installed at UCLA's Western Data Processing Center. A single computer can be used on a time-sharing basis to regulate the sequence for a number of students, each using a typewriter console like that represented in #11 of Figure 73 (see also Bushnell, 5). In the "Coursewriter" system developed by IBM, the same console can also be used for the instructor to write the instructional material directly into the teaching-machine system, using such a simple system of instructions to the computer that it really is not programming language at all; the instructor can write in the statements and questions he wants to have in the instructional program, using a dozen or so code symbols to give directions for contingent sequencing of this material based on the responses the student may give.

Branching sequences can also be arranged with much simpler hardware than a computer. The kind of arrangement devised by Crowder (6) has been by far the most widely known to the public—to an extent that the notion of "branching" is often erroneously assumed to be synonymous with Crowder's particular style of instructional programs, used for the "Autotutor" (see #10 in Figure 73) or for his "scrambled textbooks". Crowder's earlier machines, based on a prototype developed in the Air Force (#9), were random-access, address-seeking devices; the later Autotutor is an incremental device in which the response choices selected by the student generally result in either direct progression to the next frame if the response is correct or, if it is wrong, digression to a short remedial sequence of a few frames, followed by return to the original frame for a further try. Much the same function can be served even more easily and inexpensively by simply inserting the remedial frames in the main sequence and bypassing them when the student responds correctly to the initial frame. This option is available even in the very inexpensive device shown as #4, which is so arranged that, if the student answers correctly, it may skip the next three items and put him ahead; thus it "branches" in at least a limited fashion. In each of these cases, the paradigm is of automatically-mediated sequence alteration (Figure 74C).

Although quite complex branching arrangements are possible, in principle, with a somewhat more elaborate device such as the Autotutor, branches much more complex than those permitted by the simple bypassing arrangement do not seem to have been very widely used to date, even in computerized systems. Relatively infrequent branching at major points can, of course, be achieved with any machine by changing the program packet (roll, disc, cartridge, etc.). Thus, in a film-projection device like #3 in Figure 73, the student may come to a contingency point where, depending upon what he has found out by what he has done, he can branch by pulling out the film magazine and putting in another one to start off on an alternative sequence. The branching in this case, however, (and also in Crowder's scrambled books) is not automatic, but must be mediated by the learner (Figure 74B). The same is true of a very limited form of "branching" provided in device #2, with which the learner, if unable to respond correctly, may ask for additional prompting.

Each of the above kinds of branching involves only *immediate* effects of a response on the selection of the next frame in the sequence. Delayed effects (e.g., in subsequent repetition or review of material) require of course some form of register or memory system that can be invoked at later points in an instructional sequence (Figure 74D). Mechanical arrangements for this purpose were, in fact, incorporated in early devices such as Pressey's 1927 machine (#14, Figure 73) and Skinner's 1958 machine (#13), both of which recycle to provide repetition, but with provision for later omission of items that had been responded to correctly on one or more prior trials. Pressey's 1926 machine (#12) did not vary sequence of item appearance, but did allow for deferred influence of earlier responding by providing a reward after a pre-set number of correct answers. One of the main advantages of computerized devices in their potential for similar deferred effects (or cumulative effects of a series of responses by the student) on later portions of an instructional sequence. Curiously enough, however, this potential does not seem to have been fully exploited thus far. For example, the currently (1964) available version of the IBM Coursewriter system lacks this capability—thus its branching capability conforms essentially to the paradigm characteristic of much simpler devices (Figure 74C).

Application of Theory

I would like now to comment briefly on a question of applicable theory in the construction of instructional program frames. Consider the kinds of instructional frames most commonly used in what usually are called Skinnerian-type programs (e.g., for write-in machines like #1a and #1b in Figure 73). A dominant characteristic here is the tendency to help the student, particularly to prompt him a great deal at first. This decreases the emphasis, at least at the practical level, on the functional importance of feedback, "reinforcement", or confirmation-correction of the student's responses, and directs attention to prompts designed to elicit a correct response.

In terms of the classification presented earlier by Dr. Hilgard, the paradigms of most interest here are those for classical conditioning, and those for instrumental reward or trial-and-error learning. The classical conditioning paradigm, in the form I prefer, is a stimulus-substitution model (not an S-S but an S-R model), in which the association of a previously ineffective cue, in temporal contiguity with a given response, tends to make it a subsequently effective cue for that response. This model disregards the effect of consequences of the response on its being learned, and thus is in contrast with any model requiring reinforcement as a primary condition for learning to occur. As Dr. Hilgard indicated, the substitution principle or model seems directly applicable to the classical conditioning situation, and that of reinforcement seems to apply directly to trial-and-error learning or instrumental-reward situations. (See Table 11.*)

I am concerned here only with the usefulness of each principle or model for program construction, not with any question of the ultimate validity of the theory of learning implied by either. I have felt the latter to be a somewhat uninteresting question ever since Hilgard & Marquis (11) showed that each of these principles can be derived logically from the other, by merely making some plausible ancillary assumptions about contextual and/or maintaining stimuli. Either removing the organism from a situation or giving it a reward can change the total stimulus situation. Thus the effect of a reward can be explained on a straight substitution basis, in terms simply of leaving the response that occurred last in a particular situation conditioned to the cues of the situation. Similarly, the substitution principle can be logically derived from the effect principle.

The real question then (at least for the practical man interested in managing learning) is not what the "truth" of the theory is, but what its utility is. Dr. Hilgard has pointed out that if a theory is of any value it can be used to control behavior. One can go further and simply profess disinterest in the ultimate truth of the theory, merely questioning its utility for the business at hand—in this case the business of programming an instructional stimulus sequence for a teaching machine. In the present context, the applicability of the contiguity and reinforcement paradigms depends on which is the more

---

* Page 146, in Dr. Hilgard's presentation.

useful guide to the programming of instruction. I think there is no uniform answer to this question. I previously made (18, 20) a simple generalization: if we already have a dependable cue for evoking the response we want (as is very often, but not invariably, the case with human subjects), then we prompt the response so that it will occur in the context we desire; if we do not have a dependable cue for eliciting the response, it then is an operant (by the exigencies of the situation rather than the inherent nature of the response), and we must, in effect, wait for it to occur and then reinforce it. This pragmatic point of view says that the choice of applicable paradigm depends simply upon how readily available a basis we have for evoking the response we would like to have occur.

As far as current practice goes, one can draw pertinent inferences from the behavior of programmers. I have previously pointed out (18, 20) that, although the reinforcement paradigm is often cited as the theoretical foundation of the so-called programmed-instruction "movement", what most programmers actually do when they write a tutorial sequence (or train people to write such programs) does not invoke a reinforcement-feedback paradigm but rather follows a stimulus substitution model. The idea is to find suitable prompts that will *elicit* the desired response, rather than to wait for it to occur and then reward it so as to shape it up and strengthen it.

On the other hand, the operant-reinforcement model seems to be more applicable for some very important classes of responses that are very difficult to elicit, to call out on cue—e.g, the responses of "paying attention" or persevering at a task. Efforts to *demand* attention as a response to a lecture or a textbook commonly fail. If dependable eliciting cues for such responses cannot be found, we have to fall back on shaping them up by differential reinforcement.

Some Problems in Experimentation.

A great deal of the research that has been done in the programmed instruction field has been quite unilluminating, partly due to preoccupation with the wrong problems—e.g., whether programmed instruction is better than conventional instruction, and similar unanswerable questions. Aside from such trivial comparisons, it seems to be quite difficult to conceive and execute fruitful "hard" experimental research on the programming of complex subject matters. Some of the difficulties involve measurement and realistic experimental control, but the most serious problems are those of conceptualization and identification of really stable and pertinent independent variables. Perhaps most of the experimentation to date (including, I must say, most of my own work) has not yet achieved the level of sophistication and reproducibility one would aspire to in relating the input to the "black box" to its output (see Figure 71B).*

---

* Note that, despite the central role of the student's response in the learning process, we cannot directly manipulate the response as such; we can only vary the conditions under which the instruction is presented, including, of course, the kind of opportunities for response given to the student.

In considering the relationships between instruction and S-R learning theory, it seems convenient to think of two or three major classes of independent variables that can be investigated.* One class may be termed primary S-R variables, and includes those characteristics in instruction which can be conceived to operate within a single frame in the instructional program—e.g., variations in the strength or amount of prompting and some aspects of the feedback or reinforcement pattern. These can be distinguished from a second class of variables which involves the organization and sequencing of a series of frames or of an entire course of instruction. Third is a miscellaneous group comprising some special variables that are not appropriately described in the usual kind of S-R terminology—for example, factors such as "identification" with a protagonist in motion pictures.

Simon: How about variables which refer to the intrinsic structure of the task?

Lumsdaine: I suppose that the structure of the task is most conspicuous in terms of the interaction of task features with such programming variables as the seemingly most appropriate kind of sequencing. There are several studies of this kind. For example, in the work of Sheffield and Maccoby (24, 38), differential predictions about the optimum sequence of presentation and practice were made differentially, depending upon the organizational features of the task. These were procedural tasks, and there are too few similar studies for other kinds of tasks. Dr. Gagné may want to comment further on the matter of task analysis and task structure.

Nevertheless, I would like to point out that the relationship of programming principles to task features is one aspect of the broader problem of the modifying variables that determine possibilities for generalizability or reproducibility of experimentally demonstrated relationships. A similar set of contingent variables includes those that describe the initial characteristics of the learner. We need to know whether any proposed principle or posited relationship is relatively invariant with respect to such variables, or whether it is contingent upon them to an important degree (20, pp. 394ff).

Studies have been done on both relative invariance and contingency with respect to certain learner characteristics (cf. 16, Ch. 31). There have even been a few verifications of contingent predictions that, for learners of class X, method A works better than B, whereas for those of class Y the reverse is true (e.g., 13, Ch. 8). There seems to be less evidence on generalizability, or on a predictable kind of contingency, with respect to sampling of subject matters or sampling of contextual conditions.

Too few studies thus far have reported analyses with respect to the modifying influence even of learner characteristics, even where the information was potentially available. Much more data are needed on reproducibly demonstrable relationships concerning how the effects of particular instruc-

---

* May and I adopted this classification in our recent review of instructional literature for the *Annual Review of Psychology* (23).

tional variables are modified by other variables—characteristics of the learner, characteristics of the task, or characteristics of other aspects of the situation.

The need is even greater for better assurance of the reproducibility of the independent "variables" (e.g., response mode, size of step, prompting) manipulated in experiments. At a minimum this requires more complete description than is commonly given of the way in which such nominally-identified variables are actually implemented. We really need to go further and show that data offered in support of programming rules stated in terms of such variables are actually reproducible in the sense that rules for implementing them are effectively communicable to other programmers. In a sense, the "subjects" in experiments bearing on a science of instruction need to be the programmers (or teachers) rather than the learners, because ultimately we need principles which can be communicated in such a way that they instruct the instructor or instructional programmer on how to teach efficiently (Figure 72D).

Discussion

Lipsitt: To get down to my area of special interest, which has to do with children's learning, I wonder if you would comment briefly on the efficacy of O. K. Moore's (27) programmed learning techniques for facilitating reading behavior.

Lumsdaine: I do not know enough about them to say much. It looks very interesting, and Moore presents his case very persuasively, but thus far I have not seen any real data which convinced me that his system does a better job than some alternative procedures that might be considerably less costly. Also, it is quite difficult to distinguish the system's critical features. In some of the work the instruction is not at all fully programmed; there is ambiguity as to what the teacher contributes and what the student learns from the machine (26).

Miller: I would like to second Dr. Lumsdaine's impression. A few years ago I had occasion to review carefully O. K. Moore's work and could not find any real data to substantiate his conclusions, or an experimental design from which one could obtain such data. His work was ingenious and interesting, and his conclusions may well have been correct, but there was no way of evaluating them. Essentially, all he presented were a few striking anecdotes about children who learned to read at an exceptionally young age. There was no indication of how highly selected these cases were, but one can always find a few child prodigies no matter what technique is used to teach them to read.

Lumsdaine: It is quite clear that with Moore children do learn to read and write, even retarded ones. How much of this is due to a given feature of the system is another question. There seems to be something remarkable there, but it is not quite clear what it is. I do not think we need necessarily challenge the statements about the six-year-olds editing a newspaper, or about some retarded children having learned to read. But it is disconcerting not to have seen any comparative data for reasonable alternative approaches, and not to have a description that would permit reproducing his conditions.

Miller: In the publications as of a couple of years ago (when I reviewed Moore's work), data suitable for evaluation could not be found.

Atkinson: In my opinion, there is too much concern about the cost of computer-based instruction and related techniques. Often we are told that we can accomplish the same goals more cheaply and with less elaborate equipment. For the present, I do not think the point at issue is how to carry out instruction in the classroom; the real concern is to get computer-based laboratories where pedagogical research can be carried out. For the moment the cost of the equipment is not crucial; what *is* crucial is that we have a highly flexible computer-based system which would permit us to manipulate pedagogical variables in a precise way, and at the same time allow for complete recordings of data.

Lumsdaine: It depends on who we are. If we are school board members or taxpayers, we naturally have to be concerned with costs in practical application. But perhaps the sky ought to be the limit for experimental laboratory situations, and I am happy to see IBM investing in systems which are not economically feasible at present. Obviously, though, someone must also worry about whether systems developed as research and development ventures will, in the next five or ten years, lead to applications that are economically feasible.

Atkinson: There are two dimensions to be considered in evaluating computer-based instruction: one is the research dimension which is paramount at this point in time, where cost should not be the primary factor; the other dimension is computer-based instructional systems supplying entire school districts—this is far in the future. When we have enough research experience to know how to carry on computer-based instruction, then it will be time enough to let the engineers build an optimal system.

Gagné: Dr. Lumsdaine mentioned that the learning experimenter is concerned with the brain's inputs and outputs. The question uppermost in the minds of the participants in the conference is, how can one find neurophysiological correlates of learning? This, of course, leads to the second question which to many is perhaps the most important one: what is learning?

My answer to the second question is that learning is not a single process, but a number of processes (7). Suggestions of this sort have been made previously, and Dr. Simon stated earlier that a number of different kinds of processes (e.g., listing, sorting, etc.) had to be put into the computer for it to learn anything significant. Similarly, Dr. Atkinson suggested that there were three different processes that took place in learning. Therefore, if we are going to look for neurophysiological correlates, we must look for correlates of each of these processes.

Process No. 1 is association, which we have heard discussed several times during this conference. Almost everyone agrees that an associative process, by means of which one behavioral event is connected with another, must be a fundamental characteristic of all varieties of learning. In the study of the process of association, however, there is a really difficult problem: how can one isolate this phenomenon? In the human being this appears to be an exceedingly difficult thing to do. Presumably, human acquisition of an association would be represented by a situation such as the following: I give this direction to a subject: "Remember what number I say after 'boy'. Boy five". Then I say, "What did I say after 'boy'?" This is about as close as we can come, I think, to the process of association in its pure form in man. Experimental psychologists actually do study this process, or something close to it, nowadays, although they did not for many years, as Dr. Grant pointed out when he said that long ago psychologists seemed to have decided that this kind of process was an unsatisfactory thing to study. So they began to try to make things more difficult for themselves, and tried the classical conditioned response in various forms and in various animals. There are circumstances in which classical conditioning seems to be a relatively simple thing, analogous to associative learning in the human being. I remember that Watson & Rayner (47) struck a bar behind the head of an infant in the presence of a rabbit, and from that point on the infant feared the rabbit. I do not know what gave rise to the notion that a large number of trials is necessary to establish a CR.

Another situation employed in the attempt to study the association is instrumental conditioning, in which experimenters encounter somewhat similar difficulties. Consider Thorndike's (43) cats, for example, which I suppose are the prototype of this kind of learning. One cat learned a problem of getting out of a box by pulling a string; another cat, when put in a box in which it had to turn a handle, learned that way instead. If both of these are association, what happened? I do not think this variation in response represents association at all; it seems to me it must be some kind of search and selection procedure, by means of which the animal finally found the kind of response it needed to get out of the box. So I would say that the instrumental response, particularly, seems to imply that there is a need for a process that might be called "search and selection", or "discovery", as some people have called it.

Simon: In typical sequential maze experiments, we can isolate quantitatively the search or discovery part from the fixation part, and we can build a model that predicts quite accurately how much there will be of each as a function of the nature of the task (39).

Pribram: The data-based brain model I presented also distinguished between "search" and "fixation".

Gagné: That is where I found those terms. There are certainly other processes in learning. If we take the kind represented by paired-associate learning, it seems to me that practically every investigator now agrees that this is at least a three-stage process. Association is of course present, but one of the important steps involved in the process is coding. We may be trying to associate a word such as "sun," or, to put it the other way around, a word such as "soleil" with the word "sun". This is done by coding; that is, the individual does something to it. Of course, people do different things; one might say to oneself something like "ol' Sol", or might imagine a picture of a sunrise, but coding occurs, as many studies have shown. I think many people believe nowadays that no set of associates of this sort enters into the memory without being subject to interference. So, interference is another process which I would mention.

A little higher up in the complexity of things to be learned, there is a process concerned with learning a concept, or learning to classify a set of stimuli having widely different physical appearances. A common concept that has been mentioned in some studies, is "odd"; others would be "middle", or "left", or "right". These can be studied in animals as well as in human beings. They are different from the other kinds of things learned because, in fact, they have built into them a kind of immediate generalizability, so that, even if the individual sees new stimuli for the first time, he can nevertheless respond correctly by putting them into the class represented by the concept.

Another process I would like to mention combines concepts into principles. Proceeding in this way, we are coming a little bit closer to the sort of things we see in the frame of a teaching machine, such as English sentences. Of course these are only words, but presumably they represent combinations of concepts, which might be called principles. If we say to a learner, in a teaching machine or otherwise, "Birds fly", we are, in fact, giving him a combination of two concepts, "birds" and "fly". If he is to understand this in any but a sheer verbal sense, this means he must, in fact, know the concepts of "bird" and "fly".

Finally, the much-studied process called problem-solving is a kind of higher-order organization of what I have called principles. This, too, is a learning process. As we go into these kinds of learning they become more complex because the greater part of their content is contributed by the individual in idiosyncratic fashion. Thus, even when we are talking about coding, what the individual does in coding is something idiosyncratic which he contributes himself; we can furnish him with a code and find that it is fairly effective, but there are studies (cf. 4) which show that learning is most effective when the individual provides his own code. As these processes become more complex, the contribution from within the individual is greater than that which is provided by external stimulation.

Rothkopf: I think that Dr. Lumsdaine's presentation and Dr. Gagné's comments have a common feature. I would like to draw attention to it because I think it characterizes a special tactic in approaching the general problem of how to instruct people; it happens to be one which I have tried but which has disappointed me.

It seems to me that Drs. Lumsdaine and Gagné look into the literature of learning with a purpose of deriving from it, somehow, a calculus of practice. Some of Dr. Atkinson's ideas in this respect were also along the same line. They want to understand the learning process and then, by understanding its various events, figure out some combinatorial solution that will result in the most efficient learning. What I propose is that this approach, while it may eventually provide us with an elegant solution to some of the problems, is not very practicable at this time.

One of the peculiar difficulties with the problem is that, while the experimenter or the instructor has excellent control over the stimulus energies he transmits to his subjects or to his students, he can make very bad guesses as to the effect of stimulus in the situation. This is an old and vexing problem in psychology, the problem of *stimulus object* versus the *effect* of stimulus. I do not want to be considered unduly pessimistic in this matter; I think this simply means that it would be wiser, with respect to the instructional question, if we focused on a different class of problems, namely the kind of behaviors that the subject undergoes in order to change the stimulus object into an effective stimulus.

I believe I can illustrate this approach with examples from the field in which I am particularly interested, the area of written instruction. The great bulk of what is ordinarily subsumed under programmed instruction is simply a special case in written instruction. I like to think of what I am doing as trying to bridge the gap between verbal learning theory and written instruction.

In learning from written material, it is immediately apparent that the student is really in command of what the stimulus inputs are in the situation. Illiterate subjects do not learn from written material anything that is relevant to training objectives; they may learn other things, such as the size of the book or the color of the print, but they will not learn much of value to training objectives. You have, I am sure, personally observed yourselves carefully reading the first paragraph of a passage, then reading a couple of sentences of the second paragraph, and then finally just wandering across the page, frequently stopping to look out the window. You may have experienced the phenomenon of reaching the bottom of a page and recognizing you have not read anything at all on that page.

What I submit is that these are sets of phenomena that a person interested in practical instructive problems might profitably consider. He might try to find out what are the events that control whether people translate the printed words on the page into effective stimuli consistent with the formation of the appropriate skills, habits, associations, etc.

I have carried out some experiments on the control of these behaviors. As a matter of fact, I have been so impressed with the importance of the activities that the student has to maintain in order to learn something that, if you will pardon me, I have even coined a special word for them (35). Recognizing that neologisms already clutter the psychological landscape, I finally broke down and coined the word "mathemagenic" behavior, from the root "that which is to be learned", and "genic", "to be born". I had used before "inspection" behavior, but it was much too narrow a term. Anyhow, "mathemagenic" affords lively possibilities. We could talk about "mathemagenic seizures".

Such a class of behaviors can be thought to have a number of hypothetical functions. These functions, in the case of learning from written material, include simple translations—that is to say, this is the process of converting the printed material into some kind of internal representation. I have also identified a process which one might call "segmentation", which may seem like an excessive elaboration but is necessary if one is to account for the kind of phenomena that have been the basis for Thorndike's law of belonging (44). Suppose an individual speaks a series of sentences such as, "Art Lumsdaine is a psychologist", "Ernie Rothkopf is an astrologer", and people are asked afterwards, "What is Ernie Rothkopf?" Few will call him a psychologist, even though in this string of words that is the most proximal term. The speaker has done something: he has segmented the string of sentences in some way. This concept of segmentation is also needed to account for the following kind of data, reported in the classical literature of learning (28, 29). If pairs of nonsense syllables are read in troches; the stressed term can be recovered from within a troche from the unstressed term, and *vice versa*, but if we go outside the foot, there are real decrements in response even though dealing with adjacent syllables. That, again, looks as if some sort of segmentation function were operating here. The segmentation notion is within the empirical domain, but I must confess I have not had much luck with direct empirical exploration of the phenomena. We can observe people reading sentences aloud and record the distribution in time of those physical measures of speech that we think are interesting. A group of subjects can then be asked to read the material silently and then be tested by the free recall method, say, to see whether breaks in recall are correlated with the way the material was read aloud.

We tried this about two years ago, and obtained some rather interesting results. Unfortunately, it was confounded by the fact that people seem to read and remember in seven-word units. Perhaps there is some truth in this, but it ruined the experiment.

Another kind of hypothesized mathemagenic function involves the invention of various kinds of mediators, mnemonics or echoic reviews. The character of these functions, though interesting, is very speculative. It is difficult to handle them empirically. I have, however, made some progress in isolating events which are controls of mathemagenic behavior. The data seem to fit in with many other things known in verbal learning. One of our findings is that test-like events tend to exercise powerful control over mathemagenic behavior. If people are asked to read a long passage, such as a chapter in a book, and then some questions are interposed throughout the passage, a number of things can be observed. First, we find that reading time increases immediately after the test questions are administered. Then, in subsequent pages, reading time decreases again. If the subject is given another test question, the reading time goes up again. The subsequent drop resembles a decay function. It is also the case that delayed retention test performance is improved if questions are asked after the materials relevant to the questions have been read.

I would like to point out the critical features of the experimental logic that make inferences about mathemagenic responses possible. The anticipation method is a test-like event. It is well known that it also has practice-like properties. From the results of Estes, Hopkins & Crothers (6a), as well as other experimenters, we also know that test-like events are in themselves instructive even without feedback of any kind. It is therefore not possible to conclude that, simply because one has used tests and found some facilitation in performance on a retention test, this evidence of mathemagenic responses has been obtained. My technique is somewhat different. The questions used throughout the passage have been designed so that there is no transfer to the retention test which is the basis for comparison among treatments. That is to say, the little tests administered during reading of a passage have no direct substantive relationship to the retention test given after reading the passage. When the experimental materials meet these criteria, it can be shown (34, 35) that certain questions which are answered during reading can produce a substantial increase in retention test performance. It looks as though the subjects pay more careful attention. We have some evidence that these mathemagenic behaviors are under direct stimulus control, that is, it is possible to point to characteristics in the passage to which particular special attention will be paid. The questions have to be given after the relevant paragraph has been read, and it does not matter whether correct answers are provided or not. Many of the reading questions simply consist of sentences taken from the reading material from which a term has been deleted. We also have data which show, interestingly enough, that the kind of term deleted is critically important. If we delete some reasonably trivial terms, mathemagenic behavior is not changed much; I cannot yet define a trivial term very precisely, but there is good agreement among judges that some terms are trivial. We are working on the definition problem now.

I am attempting to say here that the question of what keeps the subject involved in a situation and what keeps him from falling asleep while he is reading is of great practical importance. Trying to understand this class of phenomena seems to me an encouraging prospect for research in instruction, primarily because it is a general question, that is, not specific to subject matter. The calculus of practice, on the other hand, is very intimately associated with subject matter. It is well known that at least some people learn from poorly written instructive material; others just get out of the badly written material, refuse to deal with its content and therefore do not learn anything from it. This seems to offer a wonderful prospect for behavioral variance to be subdivided and developed. I find this very encouraging.

REFERENCES

1. AMERICAN EDUCATIONAL RESEARCH ASSOCIATION, AMERICAN PSYCHOLOGICAL ASSOCIATION, DEPARTMENT OF AUDIOVISUAL INSTRUCTION, NATIONAL EDUCATION ASSOCIATION: JOINT COMMITTEE ON PROGRAMED INSTRUCTION AND TEACHING MACHINES. Criteria for assessing programed instructional material. *Audiovis. Instr.*, 1963, **8**: 84-89.

2. ———, *Recommendations for Reporting the Effectiveness of Programed Instruction Materials.* National Education Association, Washington, D.C., 1966.

3. BLOOM, B. S. (Ed.)., *Taxonomy of Educational Objectives; the Classification of Educational Goals. Handbook 1. Cognitive Domain.* McKay, New York, 1956.

4. BRUNER, J. S., The act of discovery. *Harvard Educ. Rev.*, 1961, **31**: 21-32.

5. BUSHNELL, D. D., The role of the computer in future instructional systems. *Audio-Visual Commun. Rev.*, 1963, **11**, Supp. 7 (TDP Monogr. No. 2).

6. CROWDER, N. A., Intrinsic and extrinsic programming. In: *Programmed Learning and Computer-Based Instruction* (J. E. Coulson, Ed.). Wiley, New York, 1962: 58-66.

6a. ESTES, W. K., HOPKINS, B. L., and CROTHERS, E. J., All-or-none and conservation effects in the learning and retention of paired associates. *J. Exp. Psychol.*, 1960, **60**: 329-339.

7. GAGNÉ, R. M., *The Conditions of Learning.* Holt, Rinehart & Winston, New York, 1965.

8. ———, The analysis of instructional objectives for the design of instruction. In: *Teaching Machines and Programed Learning, II. Data and Directions* (R. Glaser, Ed.). National Education Association, Washington, D.C., 1965: 21-65.

9. GLASER, R. (Ed.), *Teaching Machines and Programed Learning, II. Data and Directions.* National Education Association, Washington, D.C., 1965.

10. HILGARD, E. R., A perspective on the relationship between learning theory and educational practices. *Yearb. Nat. Soc. Stud. Educ.*, 1964, **63**(1): 402-415.

11. HILGARD, E. R., and MARQUIS, D. G., *Conditioning and Learning.* Appleton-Century-Crofts, New York, 1940.

12. HOMME, L. E., and GLASER, R., Relationships between the programmed textbook and teaching machines. In: *Automatic Teaching: The State of the Art* (E. Galanter, Ed.). Wiley, New York, 1959: 103-108.

13. HOVLAND, C. I., LUMSDAINE, A. A., and SHEFFIELD, F. D., *Studies in Social Psychology in World War II, Vol. III: Experiments on Mass Communication.* Princeton Univ. Press, Princeton, 1949.

14. LUMSDAINE, A. A., Teaching machines and self-instructional materials. *Audio-Visual Commun. Rev.*, 1959, **7**: 163-181.

15. ———, The development of teaching machines and programmed self-instruction. In: *New Teaching Aids for the American Classroom.* Stanford Univ. Institute for Communication Research, Stanford, 1960: 136-173.

16. LUMSDAINE, A. A. (Ed.), *Student Response in Programmed Instruction*. National Academy of Sciences, National Research Council (NAS-NRC) Publication 943, Washington, D.C., 1961.

17. ———, Criteria for evaluating self-instructional programs. *School Life*, 1962, **45**(2): 15-17; 39.

18. ———, Some theoretical and practical problems in programmed instruction. In: *Programmed Learning and Computer-Based Instruction* (J. E. Coulson, Ed.). Wiley, New York, 1962: 134-151.

19. ———, Teaching machines and programed instruction. In: *The Science of Human Communication; New Directions and New Findings in Communication Research* (W. Schramm, Ed.). Basic Books, New York, 1963: 139-151.

20. ———, Educational technology, programed learning, and instructional science. *Yearb. Nat. Soc. Stud. Educ.*, 1964, **63**(1): 371-401.

21. ———, Assessing the effectiveness of instructional programs. In: *Teaching Machines and Programmed Learning, II. Data and Directions* (R. Glaser, Ed.). National Education Association, Washington, D.C., 1965: 267-320.

22. LUMSDAINE, A. A., and GLASER, R. (Eds.), *Teaching Machines and Programmed Learning; a Source Book*. Dept. of Audio-Visual Instruction, National Education Association, Washington, D.C., 1960.

23. LUMSDAINE, A. A., and MAY, M. A., Mass communication and educational media. *Ann. Rev. Psychol.*, 1965, **16**: 475-534.

24. MACCOBY, N., and SHEFFIELD, F. D., Theory and experimental research on the teaching of complex sequential procedures by alternate demonstration and practice. In: *Symposium on Air Force Human Engineering, Personnel, and Training Research* (G. Finch and F. Cameron, Eds.). National Academy of Sciences, National Research Council, Washington, D.C., 1958: 99-107.

25. MAGER, R. F., *Preparing Objectives for Programed Instruction*. Fearon, San Francisco, 1962.

26. MOORE, O. K., Autotelic responsive environments and exceptional children. In: *The Special Child in Century 21*. Special Child Publications, Seattle, 1964.

27. MOORE, O. K., and ANDERSON, A. R. *Early Reading and Writing. I. Skills; II. Teaching Methods; III. Development*. Film, Basic Education Inc., Hamden, Conn.

28. MÜLLER, G. E., and PILZECKER, A., Experimentelle Beiträge zur Lehre vom Gedächtniss. *Zschr. Psychol. Physiol. Sinnesorg.*, 1900, Supp. **1**.

29. MÜLLER, G. E., and SCHUMANN, F., Experimentelle Beiträge zur Untersuchung des Gedächtnisses. *Zschr. Psychol. Physiol. Sinnesorg.*, 1894, **6**: 81-190.

30. PRESSEY, S. L., A simple apparatus which gives tests and scores—and teaches. *School & Soc.*, 1926, **23**: 373-376.

31. ———, A machine for automatic teaching of drill material. *School & Soc.*, 1927, **25**: 549-552.

32. ———, Development and appraisal of devices providing immediate automatic scoring of objective tests and concomitant self-instruction. *J. Psychol.*, 1950, **29**: 417-447.

33. ROTHKOPF, E. Z., Some research problems in the design of materials and devices for automated teaching. In: *Teaching Machines and Programmed*

Learning; a Source Book (A. A. Lumsdaine and R. Glaser, Eds.). National Education Association, Washington, D.C., 1960: 318-328.

34. ROTHKOPF, E. Z., Some conjectures about inspection behavior in learning from written sentences and the response mode problem in programed self-instruction. *J. Progr. Instr.*, 1963, **2**(4): 31-45.

35. ———, Some theoretical and experimental approaches to problems in written instruction. In: *Learning and the Educational Process* (J. D. Krumboltz, Ed.). Rand McNally, Chicago, 1965: 193-221.

36. SCHRAMM, W., *Programed Instruction Today and Tomorrow.* Fund for the Advancement of Education, New York, 1962.

37. ———, *The Research on Programed Instruction: an Annotated Bibliography.* U.S. Department of Health, Education and Welfare, Office of Education, Washington, D.C., 1964.

38. SHEFFIELD, F. D., and MACCOBY, N., Summary and interpretation of research on organizational principles in constructing filmed demonstrations. In: *Student Response in Programmed Instruction* (A. A. Lumsdaine, Ed.). National Academy of Sciences–National Research Council Publication 943, Washington, D.C., 1961: 117-131.

39. SIMON, H. A., Amounts of fixation and discovery in maze learning behavior. *Psychometrika*, 1957, **22**: 261-268.

40. SKINNER, B. F., The science of learning and the art of teaching. *Harvard Educ. Rev.*, 1954, **24**: 86-97.

41. ———, Teaching machines. *Science*, 1958, **128**: 969-977.

42. ———, Why we need teaching machines. In: *B. F. Skinner, Cumulative Record* (enl. ed.). Appleton-Century-Crofts, New York, 1961: 182.01-182.22.

43. THORNDIKE, E. L., Animal intelligence; an experimental study of the associative processes in animals. *Psychol. Rev.*, 1898, **2**(4), Monogr. Supp. No. 8.

44. ———, *The Fundamentals of Learning.* Teachers College, Columbia Univ., New York, 1932.

45. TYLER, R. W., *Basic Principles of Curriculum and Instruction.* Univ. of Chicago Press, Chicago, 1950.

46. UTTAL, W. R., On conversational interaction. In: *Programmed Learning and Computer-Based Instruction* (J. E. Coulson, Ed.). Wiley, New York, 1962: 171-190.

47. WATSON, J. B., and RAYNER, R., Conditioned emotional reactions. *J. Exp. Psychol.*, 1920, **3**: 1-14.

MENTAL RETARDATION AND LEARNING

NEIL O'CONNOR
Institute of Psychiatry
The Maudsley Hospital
London, England

When I first pondered on the position of mental retardation and learning in a conference concerned with brain mechanisms, I could see that there was one clear association: defectives cannot learn, and it is well known they have very undeveloped or maldeveloped central nervous systems. Quite obviously, there are a number of objections to this point of view, the main one being the fact that both the damage and the learning retardation are extreme; since the damage is widely generalized in the cortex, it is impossible to classify easily, as has been done in studies such as those of Teuber (44) and Luria (29), by damage localization.

There are also some rather important lessons in the psychology of mental deficiency which I think we have to consider in trying to determine ways of studying learning in the defective in relation to brain mechanisms. One of these, of course, is Binet's concept of intelligence. I would like to discuss briefly some of the issues that arose at the turn of the century and earlier in the psychology of mental deficiency, a field not as well known as the history of general psychology. Binet's view was that the educability of defectives had not been demonstrated, and he criticized (4) those of his predecessors who, like Seguin and Itard, worked on the problem of training defectives. In his study (4) of Paris school children, Binet showed that most educational efforts had been wasted on the children, whose progress had been very poor. He himself believed in the necessity of educating children of this kind, but the instrument he developed to check scientifically the effectiveness of education has tended, I am afraid, to put the dead hand of a cast-iron IQ entry against studies in this field. Thus the instrument provided by Binet to psychology and the field of mental deficiency, although in some respects valuable, put blinders on the study of the subject, as far as mental deficiency was concerned. I sometimes think that Binet might be described in a sense as the Galileo of psychology, but it is not yet clear whether he devised a telescope or a leaning tower.

Binet, and perhaps Burt, established at the turn of the century certain fairly rigid philosophical notions that influenced psychology in general.

279

Much later, through experimental and developmental studies, general psychology escaped this hierarchical concept of general intelligence. I believe the first break in the IQ shell around the study of mental deficiency resulted from attempts to demonstrate the unusual potentialities of defectives in the 1930's and postwar 1940's, and also from humanistic studies demonstrating the value of regimes for the improvement of the potentialities of persons classed as having IQ's below 50 or 70. The difficulty of demonstrating dynamism and need for studies of interactions of processes in relation to the psychology of defect has been very serious, so much so that not until after the war did it become feasible for anyone to consider working in this field, and many still have reservations. I want to suggest, however, that it is a field for research, and shall describe some experiments, but first I would like to mention two or three examples of the sorts of subjects that have "physiological" counterparts, using the term in a figurative sense.

I have in mind primarily the question of sinistrality in relation to some aspects of learning, studied as long as 70 or 80 years ago. Zangwill (49) has recently attempted to show the correlation between certain aspects of sinistrality and backwardness; another study by Strauss & Lehtinen (42) involved perceptual problems. General perceptual anomalies were also investigated in the study of mental defect, and these have been taken up again by, for example, H. H. Spitz (40), working from a Gestalt model. I think that some of the Gestalt models introduced into the study of mental deficiency in the last 20 or 30 years have been very productive, although they can of course be criticized because much of the developmental work has not attempted in any way to relate to the conceptual central nervous system. Lastly, and most importantly, the very obvious failure of language in mental deficiency and its relation to learning has long been noted. The relatively recent work of Vygotsky (46) and Luria (29) are very good examples of how this kind of knowledge can be exploited.

There are, of course, many studies of the biochemical anomalies in children with IQ 50 and below, as well as of the developmental phases. I would like to suggest, however, that it is possible to adopt an approach which considers both processes and tries, at least in a conceptual way, to tie up function with what one imagines might be going on at the physiological level—which is no more than what Pavlov attempted. I often reflect that, although he was anxious to dissociate himself from psychology, a number of his models were of the sort that psychologists would be proud to accept today.

We have tried to follow a model in this respect, somewhat like that of Broadbent (7), and which also seems to approach a model that Dr. Simon might like to have, with one notable exception I shall explain. Such a model is of course very mechanical as we have used it; it consists simply of thinking of the individual in terms of input, attention, and immediate memory lumped together, plus long-term memory and some kind of selection or revival process, with the various other scholastic operations I suppose are required to explain learning, such as transfer of training and coding of some kind, or what has been called interpretation and classification. These, together with cross-modal transfer and cross-modal coding (of which we have done a certain amount) come in, of course, at various stages as yet unspecified in this model of learning function.

Examining these particular operations individually, and then studying the way in which they might work in relation to each other, we can consider various possibilities in relation to the effect. For example, we might subdivide the effect by comparing mongols with imbeciles and non-mongols, and trying to examine the overall pattern of CNS damage in mongols (which we know excludes, in most cases, any unusual amount of epilepsy, for example) to see if their functions are similar to those of other defectives of the same IQ level. As an illustration, Dr. Hermelin and I (21) have found great differences between the stereognostic recognition for mongols and non-mongols: if a set of Russian letters cut out of cardboard is presented to a subject, who is asked to identify them a minute later from a group of other similar Greek and Russian letters, we find that the normal imbecile is as good as we are in this sort of problem, but the mongol is not. In this regard, the mongol operates at a level equivalent to his mental age, whereas the non-mongol imbecile operates at a level equivalent to our mental age. This one possible discrimination is given simply as an illustration of how the different impairment patterns could be differentiated. I would like to summarize this previous work before proceeding to describe what we have been attempting to do in the last year or so.

Let me first mention that the one especial difference, as I see it, between our program and the kind of program Dr. Simon is interested in relates to the coding of speech. Computers do not have to code speech, but human beings do and, according to Inhelder & Piaget (25), these suffer a certain developmental arrest if they have to relearn verbally the manipulation or perceptual interpretation of the world, i.e., if they have to integrate it a second time in terms of speech.

Beginning with conceptual studies, we led through a series of experiments concerned with perception, including the perception of proportion and direction, to a number of studies of coding into language, that is, cross-modal coding. We thought language was involved in such coding in the translation of a spatial into a symbolic form, and went on to examine operations such as memory and transfer of training and attention. From our studies we formed the impression that defective children are not handicapped (as many assert) in memory, but rather in a function such as attention or coding into speech. Problems seem to occur in functions concerned with input and with coding, but not in those involving transfer or long-term memory, both of which turn out to be rather good under certain circumstances.

Such observations tend to cut across the concept of IQ. Several of the operations mentioned are included in the average test, but differential handicaps cannot be determined from it. While our studies have not been conducted in as thorough and effective a fashion as we would have liked, for the amount of work we have actually done is very small, I think that, on the whole, they conform with findings of other workers in the field, such as Zigler (51), House & Zeaman (24) and others. Our work deals with a set of operations concerned with attention as well as with a peculiar set involving speech. I would now like to concentrate on these two sets of operations to illustrate how we analyze their interrelationships, and to offer some suggestions to our physiological colleagues about the way in which we can try to refine our psychological concepts in keeping with physiological findings.

If (as our previous experimentation suggests) we reject the notion that defectives suffer from poor memory, the concept held by the average teacher (e.g., "You tell him one thing one day and he has forgotten it the next") seems to be incorrect. Why, then, are defectives unable to learn? We thought one possible reason could be poor immediate memory. In our previous memory experiments, we had used a set of intensities of presentation and numbers of repetitions but, more especially, we had also used a set of recall periods of one minute, two days, and one month after presentation. We found that, in general (accounting for reminiscence), the material learned after one minute was retained after one month, so that the scores for both normal controls (of the same mental age) and defectives tended to remain the same throughout the longer period. The defectives and normals differed at one minute, however, at which period the normals retained better than the defectives, so that their learning processes were presumably better in that sense.

We decided to explore the preceding period. Our experiment consisted simply of auditory presentation of a successive series of numbers within the immediate memory span of the defectives concerned; defectives and controls were matched for memory span, and we always used a task below maximum. The retardates we used are what we call in England "undifferentiated imbeciles", which in general means imbeciles without specific diagnosis; we also used some mongols. Their ages ranged between 11 and 20, and their IQ's between 35 and 55, so that they were matched with normal children above five years old. The average memory span of the children we chose was four numbers, so we tested them on three numbers presented orally.

They were asked to recall eight sets of three numbers over periods lasting 2, 6, or 12 seconds. During these recall periods there was verbal interference, involving the reading of a list of words prepared by my colleague, Richard Mein (32) from the vocabulary used by defectives in London hospitals for the mentally deficient. For one group we used words occurring in over 60 per cent of the vocabulary of imbeciles, for another group we used rare words (i.e., those appearing in only 4 per cent of their vocabulary), and a third group had no interference. In this particular experiment the number

TABLE 15

RECALL SCORES OF GROUPS BY DELAY TIMES

	Immediate	2 Seconds	6 Seconds
Imbeciles	26.6	21.8	21.7
Normals	29.6	29.2	29.5

of recall errors increased dramatically for defectives between the two- and the six-second periods, while for the normals there was a very gradual increase, which was not significant, throughout that time. By doing a second experiment which did not involve interference, we confirmed that somewhere in this period there was a considerable loss of material on the part of the defectives.

We explored the two-to-six-second period further in another experiment. This was a rather crude auditory presentation, with numbers being read to the subjects on tape, but with no control of read-out on their part. We were attempting to go beyond the two-second gap and find out what happened earlier, because it might be that the two- to six-second period was too close to the two seconds for our crude methods to discriminate between them. We were now concerned with trace decay, a phenomenon in which Ellis (16) has been particularly interested, as I expect you know, and we wondered whether or not this was the explanation for the decline in performance. We were trying to refine the delay interval.

The errors in recall digits at the immediate and two-second periods result in recall scores by delay times which show that the drop is, in fact, between an immediate recall situation and the two-second recall period. Table 15 shows the significant scores in terms of group-score means; normal score was about 30 all the way through. It looks, therefore, as if the significant period for decline in performance for defectives lies between immediate recall and two-second delay. That was the conclusion we would like to have drawn at this point, but perhaps I should add a cautionary note: it concerns the work of my colleagues, Hermelin & Venables (22), involving the question of arousal in defectives. Following an investigation he had done with Dr. Lindsley,[*] Berkson, when working in London with Hermelin and me (2) did a study on the effect of a brief light flash on the alpha rhythm in defectives and in controls; the effect—delay or interruption—was longer for normals than for imbeciles. The investigation attempted to explain this transient effect in terms of shorter reverberation, or something similar. In another study, Hermelin (20) showed that the gap in reaction time between normals and defectives widened as a forewarning period increased. Could we infer, therefore, that the arousing effect of a warning, which blocked the alpha rhythm, had subsided relatively quickly, as the faster return of the alpha rhythm indicated? Hermelin & Venables (22) tested this hypothesis

---

[*] Unpublished.

by varying the length of the forewarning period in two conditions: in one
they produced a light flash, followed by a period of darkness varying from
0.5 to 16 seconds, followed by a tone which served as the stimulus for the
reaction; in the second part of the experiment, the same time intervals between the onset of the light and the onset of the tone were used, but the
warning light remained on throughout the forewarning period. Obviously,
the alpha rhythm was blocked for a longer time under these conditions than
when the light warning was a brief flash. Reaction times between the two
conditions did not vary, however, and the signals falling into a period of
blocked alpha rhythm did not evoke a faster response than those falling into
a period when the alpha rhythm had returned after the warning. It therefore seems that arousal as measured by alpha block duration, and arousal
measured by reaction time, are not closely related in imbeciles. This work
of Hermelin & Venables (22) is a little worrisome if one wants to build a
model for decay of trace.

The second major group of experiments I would like to discuss concerns
the question of input or the immediate memory limitations in defectives.
We speculated that, since some defectives cannot manage to reply to a recall question in under one second, whereas mental age-matched normals can
do it, the subnormals may have lost the item concerned from the immediate
memory store before it could be coded into a spoken response. Our interest
was in determining the critical time for loss of trace in imbeciles, and other
relevant mechanisms which might be operating.

Our second major aim was the determination of the relationship between
input and storage mechanisms in the imbecile. This question brings us back
to the problem of attention, which was mentioned before. Do defectives
have a problem in storage, or is it a question of whether or not they first
have to ascertain what they must exclude as noise and what they must select as the stimulus?

In our next experiment, 12 normal and 12 imbecile subjects of like mental
age were matched on their memory span for digits. Only those with visual
spans of four digits were used. They were presented with three-digit numbers in which the digits appeared either simultaneously or successively.
Each simultaneous presentation lasted three times as long as each digit of
the corresponding successive presentation. Durations ranged from 0.38 to
10.0 seconds for simultaneous numbers. Corresponding successive digit duration naturally ranged from one third of 0.38 (0.13) to one third of 10.0
(3.3) seconds. The subjects were given a series of training trials, and they
knew they had to start recalling as soon as "3" disappeared. So, if it was 1,
2, 3, when 3 disappeared they had to say "1".

It was predicted that in simultaneous presentations fast display rates
should limit test capacity and thus reduce overall scores. With long displays, of course, reading and re-reading would be possible, and scores
would improve, presumably because decay was prevented. In fact, the

groups differed only at one very fast speed (0.5 second), at which the imbeciles were inferior. This result seemed to suggest a difference in input capacity between the groups rather than one in short-term storage. Conversely, with successive presentations it was predicted that longer presentation times would create conditions in which the first digit would have time to decay between its presentation and the time that it was finally recalled. No possibility of rehearsal occurs under these conditions because other numbers are always either being presented or recalled. If imbeciles have, for example, poorer reverberating circuits than normals, then longer successive display times should affect them more than normals. In fact, there was no group-by-rate interaction, suggesting that there was no differential effect of decay in the imbecile group. There was an overall significant difference between the groups irrespective of rate, but this result cannot be held to bear on the issue under discussion.

It would seem therefore that this experiment showed input differences between normals and defectives, whereas the previous experiment, while suggesting a critical period of about two seconds between display and recall, showed that this period was critical primarily for defectives. As presentation was only successive in the first experiment, and the problem of input was not controlled for by the simultaneous presentation technique, we prefer our conclusions from the second experiment.

Sometimes the three numbers were given correctly, but in the wrong order. Many people doing this kind of work in England, notably Conrad (12) and Brown (9), have tried to develop different methods of evaluating the results. I think the only one which avoids solecisms of various kinds is consideration of the correct digit in the correct order. Some people have tried to consider order, and others have tried to consider simply the correctness of digits.

The subjects did not receive anything tangible as reinforcement for a correct response; I do not think they knew if they were correct or not. We simply said "good" every time. Imbeciles are exceedingly motivated for any kind of task, it seems to me.

Zigler: There is a question in this country as to just what they are motivated to do. I also find them highly motivated to interact with adult experimenters. The question I would put to you is whether they are also as motivated as the normal group to be right for the sake of being right.

O'Connor: That is a good point. Another of my colleagues, Peter Bryant (10), did a series of studies in which the object of the exercise was to judge the effect of verbal instruction on transfer. He found, in the learning task which preceded the transfer, that the average defective spent a lot of time being wrong. There is no question that they tolerate many more wrong responses, and the lack of reward that goes with them, than a normal person would. Bryant formed the opinion that defectives learn by storing, looking at, and eliminating negative cues rather than by searching out positive cues.

TABLE 16

MEAN ERROR SCORES OF GROUPS, METHODS OF PRESENTATION, SPEEDS AND DIGITS

(Maximum Score 8.0)

	Times	0.38-0.13			0.50-0.17			1.0-0.33			2.0-0.66			3.0-1.0			6.0-2.0			10.0-3.33		
	Digits	1	2	3	1	2	3	1	2	3	1	2	3	1	2	3	1	2	3	1	2	3
Imbeciles	Simultaneous	1.0	2.9	3.7	1.3	2.9	4.4	1.4	2.1	3.6	0.8	2.4	3.3	1.6	1.5	2.8	0.6	1.5	2.4	0.8	1.9	2.3
Imbeciles	Successive	2.3	5.1	3.8	2.5	4.3	4.3	2.1	3.9	2.8	2.3	4.2	2.7	2.5	3.6	2.7	3.1	3.8	2.8	3.4	4.1	3.4
Normals	Simultaneous	0.7	1.1	3.4	0.1	0.6	2.1	0.2	1.1	2.6	0.7	1.1	1.8	0.6	1.1	1.6	0.9	1.0	2.3	0.5	1.5	2.2
Normals	Successive	1.1	3.4	2.8	1.3	3.1	3.9	1.3	3.1	3.3	0.6	1.3	1.4	1.1	1.5	1.5	1.9	2.1	1.9	2.8	2.9	2.4

In Table 16 we see the simultaneous scores for the longer presentation times. For example, let us take the third digit of the 10-second simultaneous presentation. The score for the normals is 2.2 compared to 2.3 for the subnormals, and for 3-second simultaneous delay the scores are 1.1 and 1.5 for the second digit. There is one thing I must make clear here. This particular experiment does not necessarily have a delay period at the end of the presentation and before the recall; it really is concerned with the presentation time: the model is fairly complex because, if we are making a successive presentation which takes ten seconds in all, then each one of the digits will be visible for 3.3 seconds. If there is a constant rate of read-out, say, 1 second, the time between read-out of the first digit will be twice 3.3, namely 6.6 seconds, and the time for the recall of the first digit will be twice 1 second, or 2 seconds. The amount of delay time presents complexities that time does not allow me to discuss here.

I hope that the results I have described illustrate the possibilities of looking at cognitive functions in defectives in such a way that an attempt can be made to define them a little more precisely, as to what is in fact involved, whether it be immediate memory or something else.

I would like next to present data concerning psychotic children. As psychotic children are defined in England, the majority are imbeciles with hyperkinesis, and some of them lack speech. We worked with these children primarily because we were interested in their speech. A number of our studies indicated that they were capable of discriminating between certain sensory inputs, such as sound and light of different intensities. We could condition them to sound, although they showed a marked preference for light signals. While they were capable of picking up ordinary objects and finding their way about a room, they failed to develop patterns of response which would maximize rewards in a choice situation.

To examine further the nature of their percepts, we began to offer them more complex choice situations. At first we had used a light as opposed to a sound, then a sound as opposed to touch. Next we used three choice task situations with the usual Gellermann (17) arrangement. For the first we presented two plain upturned boxes, under one of which was a sweet; using the usual alternations we always presented one on a higher plane than the other. In the second task we presented the same kind of choice between two upturned boxes on the same level; one box was plain and the other marked on the side with an arrow. The third task was the same as the second, but each box was painted with an arrow, one pointing up and the other down. The subject was required to choose the box which concealed the sweet.

Two groups of psychotic imbeciles were chosen from among speakers and non-speakers. The two groups were matched for Seguin performance and chronological age. All subjects carried out all three tasks. There were ten subjects in each group, and each was given 60 trials on the three tasks or until each one scored 9 correct trials out of 10. The results show that the three tasks were successively more difficult for the non-speaking group, but not for the speakers. Whereas seven of the speaking psychotics found the third (two arrows) task solvable, none of the non-speaking psychotics could solve it. Everyone in both groups solved the first task. A group of undifferentiated imbeciles showed results similar to the speaking psychotics. The intermediate (one arrow) problem was solved by nine speakers and six non-speakers.

What is the basis for this sort of differentiation of speaking and non-speaking groups in relation to the solution of such a task? We tried to study some of these factors by doing another set of experiments. We considered that the inability to distinguish between the two arrows might be, for example, due to the direction of the arrows, the amount of reflectance, the actual size of the symbol on the box, or it might be a question of shape discrimination. Our aim was to determine something about the gradients of discriminability in these children for different dimensions of visual perception. If, in fact, the discrimination of shape, or something approximating shape, such as directionality, is primarily affected in parietal lobe injuries, and if, in fact, we are dealing with speechless and non-speaking psychotic or defective children, then what is the relationship between cortical injury and performance?

In an attempt to answer these questions, we gave each group a set of similar choice tasks, using four dimensions prescribed as black line drawings on 3×5 inch cards. The cards, two at a time, were presented over open boxes, one of which contained a sweet. The subject was required to choose one pattern. Each child was allowed to have 20 trials at the tasks or to work to a criterion of 9 out of 10 correct. Two groups of 12 psychotic children were used, one speaking and one non-speaking. They were matched for chronological age and for Seguin Performance age. The dimensions were albedo (a black square and a white square), shape (two triangles, one with concave sides and one with straight sides), direction (a vertical and a horizontal line), and size (a large and a small circle). The results showed a very clear difference between the capacities of the speakers and the non-speakers to discriminate: the non-speakers were much inferior. The second point we think interesting, Analysis of Variance, showed that the dimensions differed in difficulty: albedo and size were easiest, shape was significantly harder (0.05), and direction was hardest of all. (Size and direction differed at the 0.001 level.)

We considered that we had, in part, explained our difficulty with the arrows by this further experiment. Directional cues at least were extremely difficult for this group of children. Rudell has reported[*] that, for young children, up and down are easier to discriminate than right and left. We have found, none the less, that this discrimination is too difficult for non-speakers such as our subjects; all non-speakers had scores close to chance.

---

[*] Personal communication.

We are inclined to infer that both these experiments suggest brain damage as a component in this particular group of psychotic imbeciles, and we have plans to extend this work.

Discussion

Koestler: The finger-maze experiments with humans (48) might be relevant to your last inference, Dr. O'Connor. They show that those subjects who remembered by verbalizing did so much better than the visualizers, who, again, did much better than the simple motor-learners.

O'Connor: It is a function of memory.

Koestler: The emphasis is on verbalizing.

O'Connor: It could be. I do not know.

Koestler: Is there any work on the effect of mental deficiency on optical illusions?

O'Connor: There is some by Hermelin (19), primarily on illusion and learning. I am not quite sure whether this was a perceptual or a learning problem.

Feshbach: In your statement about strong neurological correlates of mental deficiency, did you mean the entire range?

O'Connor: Obviously, one must restrict it, but information is inadequate. The only definite study I know is by Crome (13) and is concerned with imbeciles and idiots, around IQ 30. He found 93 per cent of his autopsy cases to have extensive CNS damage; whether or not this would apply to others still alive, we do not know. There is always the other side of the picture: normal people can have damage to the CNS in various ways, too. So, it is undecided whether there is a very gradual gradient or a slump at the bottom of the IQ scale.

Birch: There is certainly clear information in our study[*] of the total population of mental defectives in Aberdeen, Scotland, to indicate that in groups of individuals with IQ's below 60 there is a very marked rise in the number of identifiable neurologic signs on the basis of clinical examination. As the IQ drops below 60, this finding begins to characterize the overwhelming majority of the population. The problem is in the group between IQ 60 and 75, in which information on the nervous system is more equivocal.

O'Connor: That is just the point; Strauss & Lehtinen (42) deal with brain injury but, of course, they might very well have studied it more effectively at the lower IQ levels, for that is where the brain is extensively damaged.

Guilford: I would like to come to the defense of Binet. You cannot blame him for saddling us with one large intellectual ability. Binet himself was an experimental psychologist who was impressed with the great complexity of intelligence. In his operations and practice he did not act entirely in accordance with his doctrine. If there is any blame, it should be placed on two sources; one is Spearman, who was obsessed with the idea that there is only

---

[*] Unpublished.

one ability, and the other is the American mental testers who, having no theory at all, found one score very simple in practice and therefore appealing.

O'Connor: I agree with you. I did not wish to single out Binet entirely but, of course, he gave the impetus by writing to people like Burt (cf. 6) and, I suppose Spearman (39), giving them the idea, which they developed.

Pribram: I would like to come to the defense of Dr. O'Connor. I think this is an ingenious and beautifully done study. Though tedious to do, it does not take much more effort than that expended on monkey-running in neurobehavioral experiments. We have been waiting for this sort of effective experimental approach to be applied to retardates for a long time. I wish him well.

Zigler: I, too, would like to add my words of praise for Dr. O'Connor, who has long been a stalwart in this area. One can take no offense at the kind of studies that Dr. O'Connor has presented to us; they are hard-headed, well-designed, empirical efforts. They provide some notion of what might be going on in retardation. However, there is presently on the scene in mental retardation a plethora of theories that worry me. They appear to represent firm commitments to a view of mental retardation which I think is highly questionable.

I am speaking of the defect notion in mental retardation, which asserts that whenever we encounter a mentally retarded child, we are dealing with a defective organism. This problem is made very difficult by the fact that there is no question in anyone's mind that a certain percentage of the retarded population is defective in the orthodox physiological sense. If we look into their skulls or examine their biochemical systems, it is very easy to find the defect. There has been a tendency to view all retardates in this way. Thus we find retardation conceptualized as a homogeneous and unitary phenomenon. This view has been facilitated by textbooks in which we find a single curve representing the distribution of intelligence, a cut-off at 70 or 75, and the assertion that everyone beneath this point is retarded. There is a tremendously complex problem in respect to the etiology of that most sizable group of mental retardates, namely that group which we have come to call the "familial retarded." These retardates typically have IQ's between 50 and 70 and constitute 75 per cent of all retardates. In my opinion the distribution of intelligence should be represented by two curves. This view has also been advanced by Lewis (28) and Penrose (35).

I would suggest that intelligence be conceptualized in the following way. A normal distribution of IQ's from 50 to 150 and, superimposed on such a curve, a second curve that would start at zero, peak at about 35, and have a long tail going to 150. This second curve would include all those cases which are defective in the orthodox sense. It would include all the mongoloids, all the brain-damaged, and phenylpyruvic oligophrenia. The long tail is necessary, since the brain-damaged can be found at every point along the

IQ continuum. Although a number of physiological and psychological processes remains to be unraveled, in respect to etiology this second group presents little mystery to either the psychologist or the physiologist; this became clear at the recent meetings in Denmark (34). It is the more sizable first group which presents the theoretical difficulty, and causes the most controversy.

Two basic positions have been advanced in respect to the familial retarded. My own position, which of course is not unique to me, is that there is nothing wrong with these retardates except that they are dull. The view here is that intellectual dullness does not require that a physiological defect or disease entity be postulated. This position would take as its physiological base the view that the normal distribution represents a polygenic phenomenon, and that the retardate found on one end of the curve is just as normal (in the sense that he is a normal representation of the genetic pool) as the person found on the other end. Using a stage approach to human development, we would view the familial retardate as moving from stage to stage more slowly than the normal child, and not attaining the higher stages of development. Again, emphasizing cognitive structures, the ten-year-old familial retardate with an IQ of 50 would be viewed the same as a five-year-old child having an IQ of 100. It must be emphasized that this sameness refers to the formal characteristics or, if you will, the nature of the program of the underlying cognitive structure. Does this mean the two children would behave the same? Obviously not. One child is ten; one child is five. This, plus a variety of other factors, guarantees differences in behavior. However, the central issue remains: the nature of the formal features of the cognitive processes with which these two types of children attack problems presented by their environment. The view that the familial retardate is essentially "normal" asserts an identity in these formal features across the two children.

An opposing view is that familial retardates, like organic retardates, suffer from some specifiable defect. The most convincing evidence in favor of such a position would come from pathological studies, biochemical analysis, and other physiological indices. While one may find an occasional validating report of this sort, no very impressive evidence has been mounted to indicate that the familial retarded suffer from any particular physiological defect. Indeed, most evidence has been to the contrary. This has not stopped workers from postulating such a defect. Their argument goes something like this: "There is a defect here, but we have not pinned it down yet. Given our poor physiological techniques, we just have not isolated it." This is the position that has been taken by Masland (31), Spitz (40), and others.

It is very difficult to argue against such a position. These theoreticians operate very much as the physicists of a not too distant era who asserted that there must be an electron without being actually able to see one. Not unlike the physicists, these thinkers in the area of mental retardation validate the existence of a defect by asserting that the defect should manifest itself in particular phenomena, i.e. in particular behaviors of the retarded.

Then they devise experiments to see if the hypothesized defect spells itself out in some predicted behavior. This approach is not only legitimate but has become increasingly popular. Most of the theories in the area of retardation are basically defect theories and, of course, differ among themselves. One difference concerns the theoreticians's effort in relating the postulated defect to some specific physiological structure. The theoretical language of some defect positions is explicitly physiological, that of others explicitly non-physiological, while that of still others has remained extremely vague. In respect to this last possibility, the theoretician's language smacks of physiology, but the theoretician insists that he is dealing with hypothetical constructs conceptualized at a molar level of analysis.

Let us briefly enumerate some of the defect positions. Lewin (27) and Kounin (26) thought that retardates suffer from a relative impermeability of the boundaries between regions in the cognitive structure; it was this theory that gave rise to the generally accepted view that retardates are more rigid than normal children of the same mental age. Kurt Goldstein (18) insisted that retardates suffer from primary and secondary rigidity caused by subcortical and cortical malformations, respectively. David Zeaman (50), has restricted his work to a molar level of analysis, maintaining that retarded children suffer from some impairment of their attention-directing mechanism. Siegel & Foshee (38) see the retarded as victims of a malfunctioning disinhibitory mechanism. Spitz (40) views the problem of the retarded as that of inadequate neural satiation related to brain modifiability or cortical conductivity. We have the position of Ellis (16) (somewhat supported by Dr. O'Connor's presentation) that the problem is in the relative brevity in persistence of the stimulus trace. We also have the position of Luria (30), for which O'Connor & Hermelin (33) have given supportive evidence, that the retardate suffers from an improper development of the verbal system resulting in a dissociation between the verbal and motor systems.

Can one of these positions be correct? Yes. Can they all be correct simultaneously? No, simply because certain of these positions generate antithetical predictions in behavior. For instance, the Lewin-Kounin rigidity position generates the prediction that retardates would have more difficulty than normals of the same mental age on a reversal-learning task. From Luria's position, O'Connor and Hermelin derived the prediction that normals would have more difficulty on a reversal-learning task than retardates of the same mental age; their reasoning was that, since the retarded child underuses the verbal system during the original learning, he has less to unlearn during the reversal. We need not go into the data on any of these points. Naturally, these theoreticians have little difficulty finding evidence in favor of their positions; across positions, however, the evidence has remained inconsistent and ambiguous. In my estimation none of the positions has provided truly convincing evidence. It should be noted that, although many of these defect positions refer directly or implicitly to underlying physiological mechanisms, little or no work is being done at a physiological level, nor is much work being done by trained physiologists. It thus appears that the various defect camps would be inviting areas of investigation for the physiological psychologist.

But care must be exercised by both disciplines. We psychologists would like the physiological investigators to tell us something that will direct us in our own thinking. I am sure that the physiologists would like the reverse to be true: they would like the psychologists to give them some kind of datum that would make them wonder what kind of physiological system would be necessary to encompass such an oddity in behavior. The psychologist should be extremely careful before he passes data along as indicative of a physiological defect.

This caution is necessary, since it is so easy to demonstrate that many of the behavioral differences thought to indicate some physiological defect have little bearing on it. Let us examine briefly the typical experimental paradigm in this area. First we obtain retarded children (without too much attention to etiology) from the nearest state school. We then obtain the same number of children from our university nursery or a nearby elementary school. We make certain that they are equated on sex and mental age. Then we determine if there is a difference in performance in the experimental task; usually there is, with the normals performing better. We then attribute this difference to some defect related to the low IQ of the retarded subject. There is an assumption here, which I feel is completely unwarranted, that there is no other difference between the two groups that could have produced this difference in performance. We must certainly attend to the variables of institutionalization, early histories of pre-institutional social deprivation, social class, as well as certain other factors that have been shown to play a role in producing the kinds of behavioral differences that are now being employed as evidence to support the defect position.

I would rather not use my own data here, preferring to quote someone else's, since I have been working this particular side of the street for a good number of years and may well have fallen victim to the Rosenthal effect discussed earlier. I do want to report some data that have recently come to my attention, knowing full well that this entire issue will ultimately be resolved on the basis of mounting experimental evidence rather than polemics. In order to demonstrate the subtleties involved in interpreting differences in performance, let us look at some findings of an outstanding worker in this field, and one for whom I have a great deal of respect, David Zeaman (50). He reported some years ago that retarded children institutionalized at the Mansfield State School did more poorly on learning problems than normals of the same mental age. As I noted earlier, he attributed this inferiority in performance to some deficit in the retardate's attention-directing mechanism. I have often wondered about this, since in my own learning studies, employing somewhat older subjects and somewhat different experimental procedures, I have often found that the performances of groups of normals and retardates of the same mental age were not significantly different. Analyzing backward learning curves, Zeaman found the slopes of the curves of the two groups to be about the same. The retardates, however, take a greater number of trials before better than chance performance begins. It is this longer lead-in that lends credence to the view that they are not attending to appropriate cues. According to Zeaman, once this attention deficit is overcome, their learning performance is much the same as that of a normal child of the same mental age. In these studies, Zeaman used a Wisconsin General Testing Apparatus. It is interesting to note that when Denny (14) replaced this impersonal, unattended learning situation with a face-to-face experimenter, he found much faster learning in the retarded than that reported by Zeaman (50), although there was still a significant difference in favor of the normals. This is hardly consistent with Zeaman's attention theory, since Denny's finding indicates that by adding another distracting stimulus, namely the experimenter, the retardate's performance improves. Even more provocative is Denny's further finding that, if non-institutionalized rather than institutionalized children are run in the face-to face procedure, the remaining significant difference in performance between retardates and normals vanishes. It thus appears that the retarded child is not generally suffering from a defective attention-directing mechanism, but rather that in certain situations he is attending to something other than what the experimenter would like him to. The problem would appear to be one of the experimenter's egocentricity rather than the child's attention-directing ability.

My own research with the institutionalized retarded child provides some clues as to what might be happening when the Wisconsin Apparatus is used. I think he is much more interested in the adult behind the apparatus than is the normal child; the unavailability of the adult and the total anxiety produced by this particular situation are such that they interefere with the child's learning. Once the experimenter is in view and is available to the child, as in the Denny situation, the retarded child's performance improves.

Let me give another example. It concerns inhibition notions which are currently rather popular. It has been said of the retarded child that he cannot overcome or inhibit a position bias. Thus, if he is given a simple two-choice size-discrimination problem, he keeps making a position response. When we see a child unable to master such a simple learning problem, it is tempting to conclude that there is something radically wrong with him. Dr. Leon Eisenberg, however, advanced at a recent Orthopsychiatry meeting the view that the position bias observed in the retarded child had little to do with any defect in the child, but was instead related to the child's expectation of reinforcement, a variable that Harold Stevenson and I (41) investigated some years ago. Eisenberg's explanation, which makes the inhibition notion superfluous, was as follows: if a normal child is given a two-choice problem, his conception of solving the problem involves finding the reward on each trial. Given his long history of failure, the retarded child is willing to settle for a much lower degree of success. Thus, on a two-choice problem, the retardate merely has to maintain a position, and he will be rewarded 50 per cent of the time. Eisenberg went on to report a simple expedient that results promptly in the child's giving up his position response and learning the problem: the candy reward is simply taken back each time the child is wrong, so that the child must learn the problem before he can accumulate any reinforcers.

My object is to point up the danger of leaping from such behavioral data of learning scores to some defect in the child's head. We have to be very careful in examining the motivation of the retarded child, his particular history, and his own structuring of the experimental situation.

I think the kind of reinforcement used is a crucial matter in work with retardates. We have been too ready to view being right for the sake of being right, which certainly motivates us, as also motivating the retarded child. I have not found this to be a particularly effective reinforcer for retardates; there are many things more reinforcing for them than a desire to be correct. This state of affairs is not unique to retarded children. I will forgo reporting my own data on this matter and refer, instead, to the work of Terrell, Durkin & Wiesley (43). Working with lower- and middle-class children of normal intellect, they discovered that middle-class children performed better on a simple discrimination-learning task in order to be right than to receive a tangible reward. Lower-class children did better in the tangible-reward condition than in one in which they were simply informed of their correctness. These findings have important implications for the field of mental retardation, and especially for our views concerning the familial retarded, who are drawn from the lowest socio-economic segment of our society. Some of Terrell's work has been confirmed in our own laboratory, where we have discovered that a simple change in the reinforcer quickly alters a behavior thought to be the inexorable product of some hypothesized defect.

I would like to discuss briefly one other factor that has clouded research in our area, namely institutionalization. For some reason, there has been a tendency to conceptualize institutionalization as representing some homogeneous psychological variable. Such is obviously not the case. Institutions for the retarded differ markedly in their social-psychological characteristics. In our own work we are now turning our attention to exactly how institutions differ, and how such differences affect the behavior of retarded children. This factor is relevant to the many inconsistencies found in the research literature dealing with institutionalized retardates. When an investigator tries to reconcile an inconsistency between his findings and those of another investigator, he notes every difference (e.g., age of the subject, etiology, age upon admission, etc.) except the most obvious of all: that the studies were conducted in institutions that might have differed greatly in respect to the institutional milieu. Ellis has reported findings* which indicate rather marked differences in discrimination learning of retardates as a function of the nature of the institution. We, too, have discovered notable differences in performance on motivational-type tasks between retardates in two institutions (11).

Allow me to conclude by reasserting that, as long as the typical experimental paradigm is as I have outlined, great care must be taken before differences in performance between normals and retardates are attributed to some postulated, and as yet not directly validated, physiological defect.

Birch: In many ways I look upon comparisons between so-called retarded and non-retarded individuals as an exercise that may or may not be fruitful in building up our body of knowledge. From what Doctors Zigler and O'Connor have said, we certainly are not dealing with homogeneous groups of individuals except insofar as they have been socially identified as either having attained a given score on an intelligence test, having been dismissed from school, having caused trouble for their parents, or a variety of other circumstances. Those of us who have worked with total populations of mentally subnormal children—I do not like to call them retardates or defectives; their function is subnormal in terms of the expectation of a population—cannot help but become convinced of their diversity and concerned with ways in which relatively more homogeneous groupings of individuals can be identified. So, we turn to the problem of attempting to homogenize them with respect to IQ, which is probably the weakest method of homogenization we could use, and which, in a sense, is homogenizing to a mixture rather than to anything else. We say, then, that we have relatively equal end products of the mix rather than specific entities. Or we try to homogenize with respect to etiology—again, a very dangerous procedure; if we take a very specific etiology such as phenylketonuria (which we know occurs in approximately 1 in 10,000 individuals in the population), we are confronted with a relatively wide range of intellectual functions within the afflicted group, and we may even identify untreated individuals with very high blood phenylalanine levels who are functioning well within the normal intellectual range. Thus the assumption of a clear, specific genetic defect based upon one gene-single enzyme interrelation probably does not hold even for phenylketonuria, one of the most sharply differentiated of disorders.

If we have a total body of information on all of the obstetrical factors relating to total population of births and try to identify children with respect to having been at risk during pregnancy, labor, delivery, or perinatal period, we again end up with very diverse groups of functioning individuals. It appears that we must try to identify these individuals first with respect to

---

* Personal communication.

patterns of dysfunction, and second with respect to any of a background series of disturbances that may have contributed to these dysfunctions.

Surely, if we are going to look at groups of mentally subnormal and normal individuals with respect to any variety of problems, we will find certain
differences or, if we modify conditions, will not find them. But are there any
individuals within the mentally subnormal group who have identifiable patterns of disturbance in function? To the degree this can be found, we approach the problem of mental subnormality, which interests me most. Scientifically, there is less of interest in the social welfare of mentally subnormal
children. I am more concerned with a very different kind of question: To
what degree does the study of a group of individuals with pathologies or
disturbances in function illuminate aspects of the learning process? Does it
in any way illuminate mechanisms that are involved in or underlie the organization of learning? In the same sense, for example, the biochemist is interested in an individual who has a specific enzymatic defect, not so much
from the point of view of whether he is going to have a hematologic crisis at
a given time, or whether or not he is going to die younger than someone
else, but as a subject offering the opportunity to work out a metabolic
chain, a knowledge of the sequences of events in the metabolism of
different substances derived from the identification of individuals who fail
to metabolize them beyond certain points and who have accumulations of
end products.

If we look at various subgroups or even various individuals in the mentally subnormal population, I think we become increasingly convinced, as I
believe Dr. O'Connor did, of the possibility that there may be certain fundamental disturbances in input, and in relationships among inputs, that
characterize some individuals in this group. With certain mentally subnormal individuals we are struck by the fact that, even though we may be presenting them with beautiful, large cards containing visual stimuli, their response is to smell them or, as I think Dr. O'Connor has also experienced, to
rub their hands over them. In other words, the available input systems utilized by subnormal individuals are quite different from those customarily
utilized by normals. In addition, we know that in many instances, when
there are auditory or olfactory stimuli available in the environment, the
subjects are preponderantly responsive to these and are unresponsive to the
very aspect of the environment that we wish them to respond to at a given
moment in time.

A comparative psychologist like myself is struck by the similarity of such
individuals to certain outstanding phylogenetic differences in the development of behavior, and to intraclass differences in the development of organisms. For example, an understanding of fish behavior indicates that to
catch a catfish it is best to tie an old piece of pork rind or a rotten piece
of some other fish to a hook and drag it along the bottom of the water.
Visual stimuli such as fly lures will never catch catfish, while they will

attract trout or salmon. In other words, within a class of vertebrate organisms such as fish, there are hierarchal organizations of significant input
systems. These are direct characteristics of these organisms, and they differ
from one another in terms of what constitutes their effective environments,
to use a term that we heard a little earlier here. In this connection then, the
first question is whether or not the effective environment of the learner is
the first step for us to be concerned with in the study of learning. It becomes obvious, for instance, that, to the degree that we know the effective
environment of an organism, we know the stimulus system inputs which
may be effective in directing its behavior. To this degree do we really begin
to deal with the organism. If we do not present the appropriate kinds of inputs, or if we present them in the presence of a second phenomenon, namely when hierarchically more important or dominant inputs for the organism
are also occurring, we get interference function. When this happens, we are
not going to find a response organized around our presented stimulus, but
evidence of so-called "distraction".

Two things, then, emerge from careful study of mentally subnormal
groups—groups with damaged brains or a number of other defects: first, in
the course of the learning process, we have to account for stimulus input,
stimulus input preponderance, and hierarchical organizations among the
sensory systems; second, we have to account for the differential ability of certain stimuli which we will call, for the moment, preponderant stimuli with
respect to a given modality, to interfere with the active functioning of what
could be called subordinate input systems. Consequently, in any of our
learning experiments, whether the classical conditioning situation or any
other kind of associative learning situation, we always speak of presenting
an effective stimulus paired with a neutral stimulus, by which we mean that
we are going to be presenting stimuli which are hierarchically different from
one another in their arousal properties for the subject organism.

We also know that we have to be concerned with the temporal relationship between stimuli in the two systems. For example, if we present the so-
called unconditioned stimulus in the dominant system first, and then present the conditioned stimulus, we have great difficulty in establishing association. I think there is an increasing amount of evidence (and I would hypothesize there would be more if we looked at the problem somewhat more
electrophysiologically) that the effect of introducing this UCS is to inhibit
this activity in the subordinate stimulus organization itself. What we get is
an active inhibition or interference, then, with the subordinate stimulus.
This may account for our temporal relationships.

As a comparative psychologist, again, I have become concerned, in looking at mentally subnormal individuals, with a second order of problem,
namely the nature of the primary change which takes place in learning situations. If we look at the development of adaptive organizations in the animal phyla, one of the findings that emerges most strongly is that the phe-

nomenon most closely associated with the expansion of adaptive capacities is the development of interrelations among the different sense systems. As a comparative physiologist, Sherrington was aware of this when he asked, in his book *Man on his Nature* (37), what it is that characterizes the strategy of the evolution of the nervous system. He said that the naive among us would have expected evolution, in its course, to have developed a nervous system characterized by increasing numbers of avenues of sense. However, the strategy, he says, has been quite different, namely not the multiplication of avenues of sense, but the increase in the refinement of liaison among the so-called original five, six, ten senses. He goes on to say that it is this phenomenon of intersensory liaison that the cerebral cortex has represented in the course of evolution. I think we can go beyond this and say, in a very real sense, that this has been the evolutionary process characterizing the emergence of the mammalian nervous system.

Voronin & Guselnikov (45) have recently been investigating a series of comparative transphyletic studies of evoked potential and evoked potential interference, obtaining beautiful findings from the point of view of the understanding of learning mechanisms in a phylogenetic sense.

One of the most striking phenomena of learning in the entire phylogenetic scale is demonstrated by the frog. We know full well, as Abbott (1) showed back in the 1880's, that if we take a frog and place it on a stand in front of a wiggling fly impaled upon a pin which is surrounded by a palisade of sharpened stakes, the frog will flip its tongue out at the moving fly, hitting the stakes, and rapidly withdrawing it. As long as the fly is moving, the frog continues to flip its tongue, even though the tongue is eventually ripped into shreds. In other words, the frog does not inhibit a visually determined response on the basis of tactile and other kinds of information.

Pribram: You do not mean intersensory communication in the sense I thought you did.

Jensen: I thought there was some recent work on frogs done with robber flys and bees, in which frogs passively inhibited as a result of being stung by the bees (8).

Birch: In my own laboratories and in the field, we have studied another phenomenon altogether, involving a hairy caterpillar which is extremely bitter to the taste. A frog presented with such a caterpillar flips out its tongue, touching the caterpillar, and in 10 to 12 trials inhibits its striking response.

In my laboratories, if we take a target hooked up to an eccentric cam, put pins all over it and use it as the striking target with the fly, the frog continues to strike at it without inhibition. However, if we coat the fly with quinine sulfate, then within relatively few trials the frog inhibits its response. Furthermore, if we connect this target to one pole of an electric circuit, and the water pan in which the frog is sitting to the other pole, so that, when it contacts this target it now gets a shock to the tongue which stimu-

lates the whole of the vomerogustatory system, the striking response is
again inhibited within a very few trials. There is a common discharge for
organ and visual systems, but no such common discharge for tactile and
visual systems. There is also the interesting finding that we can influence
the latency and the magnitude of the evoked potential to a given auditory
input in the frog to gustatory stimulation, but it is unmodified by either
concurrent or antecedent tactile stimulation. We begin to find that that organism, the frog, which had a transition point is starting to show ability to
modify and not to modify behavior, a beginning basic mechanism of interrelation among afferent systems as a primary mechanism in the learning process.

There are several different kinds of questions with which we must be
concerned, then, if we are going to look at learning, its retention, its interference, its acquisition, and so on. We can begin by considering the manner
in which there is an interrelationship among afferent systems themselves,
and the manner in which afferent activity results in modifications of the organization of behavior.

As Demb and I (5) have shown, if we develop a conditioned response to a
light-sound relationship in different varieties of mentally subnormal children (hyperactive mentally subnormal children as contrasted with non-hyperactive), we do not find a great deal of difference in their course of acquisition of the conditioned reflex. However, if we now look at their extinction
course, the repetition of the unreinforced light stimulus to the hyperactive
group of children leads to regularly increased body activity, eventually
resulting in movements of sufficient magnitude to tear them loose from the
electrodes in the measurement situation. In contrast, when the non-hyperactive children are presented repetitively with an unreinforced extinction
stimulus, they grow increasingly quiescent and, if this persists for a
sufficient period of time, half of them go to sleep. They fall asleep in
sufficient depth so that a weak electric shock introduced as a reinforcer does
not awaken them.

There is yet another phenomenon, that of an intrasensory organization or
the degree to which activation within a sensory system results either in
spreading depression or excitation. In one group this set of interrelations
involves the elimination and the diminution of behavior; in another group it
is one that involves the disorganization and outward expansion of behavior.
In one group we see something almost characteristic of what Pavlov called
"internal inhibition," extending into sleep, and in the other group, disinhibi-
tion with increased movement characteristics.

I would like to submit that the material Dr. O'Connor has presented, and
many of the phenomena in the functioning of mentally normal children,
cause us to focus not so much upon the stardard paradigm of S-R connection, but upon the interrelationships among sensory systems and that, in
this relationship, we have the primary problem of the mechanism of associ-

ation, whatever that may be. I think our associations are inter- and intrasensory, and are not related directly to response. At any rate, I think this is what the study of mentally subnormal children begins to call to our attention.

Hernández-Peón: I have been extremely interested in listening to the results presented by Dr. O'Connor and, also, to the very stimulating ideas presented by Dr. Birch. I would like to comment briefly from work in our laboratory on some recordings of average evoked potentials in a group of mentally retarded subjects. These were all males from 13 to 15 years of age who would be classified as imbeciles of the non-hyperactive type. The stimulus was a single shock or a very short train of pulses applied to the skin of the forearm. We recorded the average evoked potentials through scalp electrodes, from the opposite hemisphere. Some differences were certainly found in the management of sensory information by the brain of subnormal subjects as compared to normal subjects during distraction and during focusing of attention.

In Figure 75 the spontaneous activity is represented on the left side. Each picture corresponds to the average of 40 successive stimuli; by comparing the first two sets of 40 stimuli, one may see the process of habituation in this subject. Then, at a given moment, we distracted him by either asking him to solve a very simple problem or telling him to describe some moving picture he had seen. The first effect was just the opposite of what happens in the normal subject: the potentials became enhanced. It was only after 40 seconds that the potentials diminished, as happens in normal subjects during distraction. The last picture is the control after the distracting procedure. Comparing the potentials during the control period with the poten-

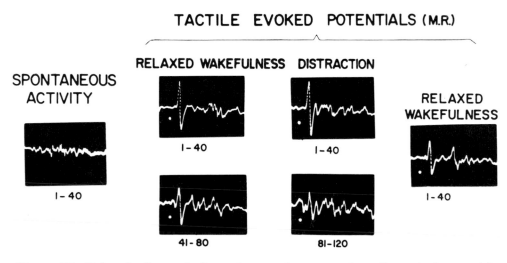

TACTILE EVOKED POTENTIALS (M.R.)

SPONTANEOUS ACTIVITY

RELAXED WAKEFULNESS DISTRACTION

RELAXED WAKEFULNESS

1-40
1-40
1-40
1-40

41-80
81-120

Figure 75. Delayed effects of distraction on the averaged tactile evoked potentials recorded in a mentally retarded subject 16 years old. Each picture represents the average of 40 consecutive sweeps at the rate of 1/sec. Note that at the onset of the distracting stimulus the potential was enhanced, and diminished only after 40 seconds.

tials recorded during distraction, the latter is larger than the first. There-fore, the reduction produced by distraction in mentally retarded subjects appears with some delay as compared to normal subjects, in which reduc-tion occurs immediately after the initiation of the distracting procedure.

Zigler: This poses a question that has been raised by others, of whether such a stimulus was equivalent in arousal qualities for two different types of subjects. The differential anxiety-producing features could affect the evoked potential. I wonder whether the same effect would be obtained if some care were taken to equate the value of the distracting stimulus for the two types of subject.

Hernández-Peón: The same distracting procedure in normal subjects produced a reduction of the first 40 potentials, with no such delay being ob-served in the mentally retarded.

Zigler: Did you equate them on chronological or mental age?

Hernández-Peón: On chronological age.

Zigler: That is interesting. The kind of theoretical issue I was raising be-fore is whether you would get the differences at the same mental age, which is more tied to the development of physiological or cognitive intellec-tual structures than is chronological age.

Hernández-Peón: We have not done that yet. On the other hand, if we tell the subject to pay attention to the arm where the stimulus is being ap-plied, the first effect is also just the opposite from the one seen in the nor-mal subject: there is first a diminution of the potentials as compared to the control, and only later on, after at least 40 seconds, there is an enhancement of the potentials before they again become reduced.

Donchin: I think we can interpret these data in another way to support a different theory. We have found (15, 47) that for visual stimulation the am-plitude of some components of the average evoked potential is inversely re-lated to stimulus intensity. Thus, with a stimulus of a lower intensity, we might obtain larger amplitudes than with brighter stimuli. It is difficult at this stage to draw inferences from the amplitude of the evoked potentials about the underlying data-processing activity. While you obviously have found differences between the normals and the retardates, they cannot be interpreted without much more data on the behavior of the evoked poten-tials recorded for various stimulus and situational parameters.

Hernández-Peón: We are only comparing these types of events in the mentally retarded with normal subjects, and we have seen a difference from the beginning. Of course, the findings may be open to several interpretations.

Zigler: It should be emphasized that with a chronological age match there is no person in the mental retardation field who would not predict a difference on just about every truly intellectual function. With such a match, I would be amazed if you could not find some difference, whatever it might mean, with your physiological measure. To fail to do so would be inconsistent with the view that every cognitive process has some physiolog-ical underpinning.

Galambos: Before we leave this, I would like to point out that, according to Bickford (3), these evoked responses may not be derived entirely from the cortex. With scalp recording, electrophysiologists are uncertain about how much of the activity is derived from muscles or skin.

Donchin: Dr. Bickford obtained his potentials with clicks of intensities ranging up to 150 dB above threshold. Replications with lower intensities have not been too successful.*

Galambos: These are not clicks but shocks to the skin.

Lindsley: We have control recordings from the muscles all around the head and neck, with flashes of light, and we simply do not get any response.

Galambos: As should be evident to the non-physiologists here, there is some controversy over whether this phenomenon arises from the skull or from the brain itself.

Donchin: There are a number of reports of simultaneous recordings from the scalp and the dura, or from the scalp and the cortical surface (23), in which substantially similar results were obtained.

Galambos: There are some data from cats where simultaneous recording from electrodes inside and outside the head show the two responses to vary in opposite directions (36).

Donchin: We have records in which we placed electrodes on the neck while recording from the scalp. It can be seen clearly that, while large responses are obtained from the occipital electrodes, no corresponding potentials can be recorded from the neck.

REFERENCES

1. ABBOTT, C., The intelligence of batrachians. *Science*, 1882, **3**: 66-67.
2. BERKSON, G., HERMELIN, B., and O'CONNOR, N., Physiological responses of normals and institutionalised mental defectives to repeated stimuli. *J. Ment. Def. Res.*, 1961, **5**: 30-39.
3. BICKFORD, R. G., JACOBSON, J. L., and CODY, D. T. R., Nature of average evoked potentials to sound and other stimuli in man. *Ann. N.Y. Acad. Sci.*, 1964, **112**: 204-223.
4. BINET, A., and SIMON, T., *Mentally Defective Children*. Longmans Green, New York, 1914.

---

* *Added by Dr. Donchin after the conference:* I was informed by Dr. Bickford that his intensity specifications refer to the amplitude of the maximum peak-to-peak deviation of his stimulus waveform, which is damped oscillation. Given this stimulus waveform, the absolute auditory threshold was found to be at about 50 dB on the scale used in the published reports. It should be noted that, even with this correction applied to the cited values, the click intensities were quite high.

It appears that the crucial point neglected in the interpretations of Dr. Bickford's results and their implication for evoked potential studies is the fact that the myogenic potentials reported by Dr. Bickford and his coworkers (3) can be extracted only from EEG records obtained from tense subjects, which abound in "muscle" activity. Averages extracted from records obtained from relaxed subjects who are substantially free of "muscle" activity are probably free of myogenic artifacts. Thus, rather than reflecting on the validity of average evoked potential studies, Dr. Bickford's work underlines the validity of records obtained under proper EEG practice.

5. BIRCH, H. G., and DEMB, H., The formation and extinction of conditioned reflexes in "brain-damaged" and mongoloid children. *J. Nerv. Ment. Dis.*, 1959, **129**: 162-170.

6. BOARD OF EDUCATION (Great Britain), *Report on The Education of the Adolescent.* H. M. Stationery Office, London, 1926.

7. BROADBENT, D. E., *Perception and Communication.* Pergamon, London, 1958.

8. BROWER, L. P., and BROWER, J. V. Z., Investigations into mimicry. *Nat. Hist.*, 1962, **71**(4): 8-19.

9. BROWN, J., *Immediate Memory.* Ph.D. Thesis, Cambridge Univ., Cambridge, 1955.

10. BRYANT, P. E., *The Effects of Language on the Formation of Concepts in Imbecile Children.* Ph.D. Thesis, Univ. of London, London, 1963.

11. BUTTERFIELD, E. C., and ZIGLER, E., The influence of differing institutional social climates on the effectiveness of social reinforcement in the mentally retarded. *Am. J. Ment. Def.*, 1965, **70**: 48-56.

12. CONRAD, R., Decay theory of immediate memory. *Nature*, 1957, **179**: 831-832.

13. CROME, L., Some morbid-anatomical aspects of mental deficiency. *J. Ment. Sci.*, 1954, **100**: 894-912.

14. DENNY, M. R., Research in learning and performance. In: *Mental Retardation* (H. A. Stevens and R. Heber, Eds.). Univ. of Chicago Press, Chicago, 1964: 100-142.

15. DONCHIN, E., and LINDSLEY, D. B., Visually evoked response correlates of perceptual masking and enhancement. *EEG Clin. Neurophysiol.*, 1965, **19**: 325-335.

16. ELLIS, N. R., The stimulus trace and behavioral inadequacy. In: *Handbook of Mental Deficiency; Psychological Theory and Research* (N. R. Ellis, Ed.). McGraw-Hill, New York, 1963: 134-158.

17. GELLERMANN, L. W., Chance orders of alternating stimuli in visual discrimination experiments. *J. Genet. Psychol.*, 1933, **42**: 206-208.

18. GOLDSTEIN, K., Concerning rigidity. *Char. & Pers.*, 1942, **11**: 209-226.

19. HERMELIN, B., *Studies on Learning and Trainability in Imbeciles.* B.A. Thesis, Univ. of London, London, 1956.

20. ———, Effects of variation in the warning signal on reaction times of severe subnormals. *Quart. J. Exp. Psychol.*, 1964, **16**: 241-249.

21. HERMELIN, B., and O'CONNOR, N., Recognition of shapes by normal and subnormal children. *Brit. J. Psychol.*, 1961, **52**: 281-284.

22. HERMELIN, B. M., and VENABLES, P. H., Reaction time and alpha blocking in normal and severely subnormal subjects. *J. Exp. Psychol.*, 1964, **67**: 365-372.

23. HIRSH, J. F., PERTUISET, B., CALVET, J., BUISSON-FEREY, J., FISCHGOLD, H., and SCHERRER, J., Études des réponses électrocorticales obtenus chez l'homme par des stimulations somesthésiques et visuelles. *EEG Clin. Neurophysiol.*, 1961, **13**: 411-424.

24. HOUSE, B. J., and ZEAMAN, D., Position discrimination and reversals in low-grade retardates. *J. Comp. Physiol. Psychol.*, 1959, **52**: 564-565.

25. INHELDER, B., and PIAGET, J., *The Growth of Logical Thinking from Childhood to Adolescence.* Routledge & Kegan Paul, London, 1958.

26. KOUNIN, J. S., Experimental studies of rigidity. I. The measurement of rigidity in normal and feebleminded persons. *Char. & Pers.*, 1941, **9**: 251-272.

27. LEWIN, K., *A Dynamic Theory of Personality.* McGraw-Hill, New York, 1935.

28. LEWIS, E. O., Types of mental deficiency and their social significance. *J. Ment. Sci.*, 1933, **79**: 298-304.

29. LURIA, A. R., *The Role of Speech in the Regulation of Normal and Abnormal Behavior* (J. Tizard, Ed.). Pergamon, New York, 1961.

30. ———, Psychological studies of mental deficiency in the Soviet Union. In: *Handbook of Mental Deficiency; Psychological Theory and Research* (N. R. Ellis, Ed.). McGraw-Hill, New York, 1963: 353-387.

31. MASLAND, R. L., Methodological approaches to research in etiology. *Am. J. Ment. Def.*, 1959, **64**: 305-310.

32. MEIN, R., and O'CONNOR, N., A study of the oral vocabularies of severely subnormal patients. *J. Ment. Def. Res.*, 1960, **4**: 130-143.

33. O'CONNOR, N., and HERMELIN, B., Discrimination and reversal learning in imbeciles. *J. Abn. Soc. Psychol.*, 1959, **59**: 409-413.

34. ØSTER, J., and SLETVED, H. V. (Eds.), *Proceedings of the International Copenhagen Congress on the Scientific Study of Mental Retardation,* Vols. I and II. Berlingske Bogtrykkeri, Copenhagen

35. PENROSE, L. S., *The Biology of Mental Defect.* Grune & Stratton, New York, 1963.

36. PRICHARD, J. W., CHIMIENTI, J., and GALAMBOS, R., Evoked response from extracranial sites in the cat. *EEG Clin. Neurophysiol.*, 1965, **18**: 493-499.

37. SHERRINGTON, C., *Man on his Nature* (2nd ed.). Cambridge Univ. Press, Cambridge, 1951.

38. SIEGEL, P. S., and FOSHEE, J. G., Molar variability in the mentally defective. *J. Abn. Soc. Psychol.*, 1960, **61**: 141-143.

39. SPEARMAN, C., Theory of general factor. *Brit. J. Psychol.*, 1946, **36**: 117-131.

40. SPITZ, H. H., Field theory in mental deficiency. In: *Handbook of Mental Deficiency; Psychological Theory and Research* (N. R. Ellis, Ed.). McGraw-Hill, New York, 1963: 11-40.

41. STEVENSON, H. W., and ZIGLER, E. F., Probability learning in children. *J. Exp. Psychol.*, 1958, **56**: 185-192.

42. STRAUSS, A. A., and LEHTINEN, L. E., *Psychopathology and Education of the Brain-Injured Child,* Vol. I. Grune & Stratton, New York, 1947.

43. TERRELL, G., JR., DURKIN, K., and WIESLEY, M., Social class and the nature of the incentive in discrimination learning. *J. Abn. Soc. Psychol.*, 1959, **59**: 270-272.

44. TEUBER, H. L., Space perception and its disturbances after brain injury in man. *Neuropsychologia*, 1963, **1**: 47-57.

45. VORONIN, L. G., and GUSELNIKOV, V. I., On the phylogenesis of internal mechanisms of the analytic and synthetic activity of the brain. *Zh. Vyssh. Nerv. Deiat. Pavlova*, 1963, **13**: 193-206 (in Russian; English abstract).

46. VYGOTSKY, L. S., *Thought and Language* (E. Hanfmann and G. Vakar, Eds. and Transl.). M.I.T. Press, Cambridge, 1962.

47. WICKE, J. D., DONCHIN, E., and LINDSLEY, D. B., Visual evoked potentials as a function of flash luminance and duration. *Science*, 1964, **146**: 83-85.

48. WOODWORTH, R. S., and SCHLOSBERG, H. (Eds.), *Experimental Psychology* (rev. ed.). Holt, New York, 1954.

49. ZANGWILL, O. L., *Cerebral Dominance and its Relation to Psychological Function.* Oliver & Boyd, Edinburgh, 1960.

50. ZEAMAN, D., and HOUSE, B. J., Discrimination learning in retardates. *Train. School Bull.*, 1959, **56**: 62-67.

51. ZIGLER, E., and UNELL, E., Concept-switching in normal and feebleminded children as a function of reinforcement. *Am. J. Ment. Def.*, 1962, **66**: 651-657.

CREATIVITY AND LEARNING

J. P. GUILFORD
University of Southern California
Los Angeles

It is quite appropriate that there should be a session devoted to creativity in a conference on learning. A broad, non-popular view of creativity recognizes an act as creative when there is something novel about it; novel, that is, for the person performing the act. The act must also be relevant, a qualification added to distinguish the creative output from the productions of the schizophrenic or manic. The qualification of usefulness, which may be appropriate in some contexts, is sometimes added—but usefulness involves value judgments, which, as scientists, we consider outside our province. Relevance, however, is a specification that does have meaning and empirical potentialities.

Novel behavior means a change in behavior, and a change means learning when "learning" is defined as a relatively enduring change in behavior as a consequence of behavior. In this conference, as in others, no complete agreement has been reached on the meaning of learning or what it entails; there are good reasons for that. I agree with Dr. Gagné that we must recognize different kinds of learning; I do not agree, however, with his idea that there is only one kind of association. I think we have to consider not only different kinds of learning, but also different kinds of association, as I shall point out later on.

The conclusion that learning and creativity are much the same phenomenon can be reached by another route. From my fifteen years of study of the intellectual aspects of creative production, it seems apparent to me that creative thinking can be equated essentially with problem solving. Identifying these two phenomena with each other does seem to deglamorize the topic of creativity, and perhaps takes away some of its mystery. On the other hand, it gives some added significance to problem solving, which has been quite commonly recognized as an important instance of learning. By its nature, a genuine problem is a cognized situation for which the organism appreciates that it has no ready coping response; something new or novel must be done—in other words, a creative act. I use the term "appreciates" here deliberately, with no implications of either conscious or human qualities.

Problems are as varied in kind as behavior itself. Having linked problem solving with creative performance and learning, we may apply the latter two concepts to behavior of almost any kind and almost wherever it is found. What I am trying to emphasize is that, in order to understand learning, problem solving, or creative performance, we must maintain a very comprehensive view of behavior itself. In other words, we need a taxonomy of learning, that is, a taxonomy of the kind of changes that take place in behavior; some of the changes may not be recognized as learning. I remember remarking at a meeting once that I thought it might be well for us to avoid using the term "learning" for a period of perhaps ten years, and talk about changes in behavior instead. I still think this idea has merit.

My other point is that creative behavior, at least in its intellectual aspects, cannot be adequately treated without consideration of intellect in general. This also holds true when we attempt to relate creative activity to brain function. Traditionally, intelligence has been defined as "learning ability," and studies of brain function have sometimes been conducted in relation to scores on orthodox types of intelligence tests, on the assumption that "intelligence" should be bound in one global package such as a general learning ability.

DIFFERENTIAL ABILITIES IN STUDIES OF THE BRAIN

In recent years, investigators of brain function, by whatever method, have properly shown distrust of the assumption that intelligence is a single ability. Halstead (7), Matthews & Reitan (10), de Mille (2) and others have considered the results of factor analysis. Teuber, Semmes and their co-workers (20, 22, 23) are among those who have taken to the approach of using special tests of abilities, not just tests of IQ or mental age, but have not given attention to factors. The need for differential testing of abilities in connection with brain investigations was summed up by Orbach (14) when he said that the major problem in an experimental program of localization or focalization of function is to determine unitary functions. Lashley has been quoted as being of the same opinion.

To me, there seems to be no rational alternative. The major problem extant is then concerned with the nature of unitary functions. As I see it, there are three important questions in science: "what", "how" and "why". The answer to "what" is in terms of concepts; the answer to "how" is in terms of operational analysis, with operations as the result; and the answer to "why" is in terms of theory. Factor analysis is well designed to answer the question of *what* the concepts should be.

THE STRUCTURE-OF-INTELLECT MODEL

I would like to offer for consideration the intellectual factors represented in my structure-of-intellect model as the first of the models and concepts generated by the theory. A glossary of the terms we use is offered in Table 17. Only the major properties of the model will be reviewed, to be followed

TABLE 17

GLOSSARY

Categories in the Structure of Intellect

I. OPERATIONS: Major kinds of intellectual activities or processes; things that the organism does with the raw materials of information.*

Cognition: Immediate discovery, awareness, rediscovery, or recognition of information in various forms; comprehension or understanding.

Memory: Fixation of information for retention or storage, with some degree of availability.

Divergent Production: Generation of information from given information, where the emphasis is upon variety and quantity of output from the same source. likely to involve what has been called transfer.

Convergent Production: Generation of information from given information, where the emphasis is upon achieving unique or conventionally accepted best outcomes. It is likely that the given (cue) information fully determines the response.

Evaluation: Reaching decisions or making judgments concerning the goodness (correctness, suitability, adequacy, desirability, etc.) of information in terms of criteria of identity, consistency, and goal satisfaction.

II. CONTENTS: Broad classes of information

Figural Content: Information in concrete form, as perceived or as recalled in the form of images. The term "figural" implies some degree of organization or structuring. Different sense modalities may be involved, e.g., visual, auditory, kinesthetic.

Symbolic Content: Information in the form of signs having no significance in and of themselves, such as letters, numbers, musical notations, and other "code" elements.

Semantic Content: Information in the form of meanings to which words commonly become attached, hence most notable in verbal thinking and in verbal communication.

Behavioral Content: Information, essentially non-verbal, involved in human interactions, where awareness of the attitudes, needs, desires, moods, intentions, perceptions, thoughts, etc. of other persons and of ourselves is important.

III. PRODUCTS: Forms that information takes in its processing by the organism.

Units: Relatively segregated or circumscribed items of information having "thing" character. May be close to Gestalt psychology's "figure on a ground."

Classes: Common ideas in sets of items of information grouped by virtue of their common properties.

Relations: Recognized connections between units of information, based upon variables or points of contact that apply to them.

Systems: Organized or structured aggregates of items of information; complexes of interrelated or interacting parts.

Transformations: Changes of various kinds of existing or known information, or in its use.

Implications: Extrapolations of information, in the form of expectancies, predictions, known or suspected antecedents, concomitants, or consequences.

---

* *Information* is defined as "that which the organism discriminates."

by a general problem-solving model showing how the intellectual abilities are related to a functioning organism. Later on I shall suggest some ways in which these concepts have been found to be related to brain function.

The structure-of-intellect model is shown in Figure 76. Under development during the past ten years, this theoretical model rests on the findings of factors, interpreted as unitary intellectual abilities. Some of them were

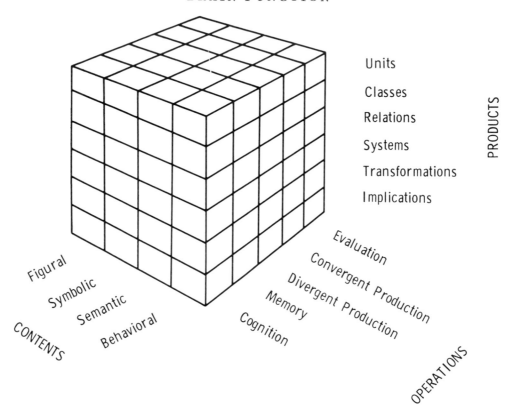

Figure 76. A theoretical model for the complete "Structure of Intellect".

first found by Thurstone (24) and his students, some were discovered by psychologists in the Army Air Force Aviation Psychology Research Program during World War II, and others were found during the last fifteen years in the Aptitudes Research Project* at the University of Southern California. The model represents an effort to see larger and more general meaning and significance in the accumulating numbers of differentiated abilities. The product of this thinking, as it now stands, is a crossclassification of the intellectual abilities in three dimensions. Each cell in the model represents a unique ability, defined by the combination or conjunction of a particular *operation* (five kinds), a particular content (four kinds) and a particular kind of *product* (of which there are six). In the top front row, for example, there are four abilities that can be described. From left to right: (*a*) cognition of *figural* units—these are *visual* figural units, i.e., objects which have properties of size, shape, color, etc; (*b*) cognition of *symbolic* units, that is, words, syllables, combinations of letters or numbers, and other signs or symbols from conventional systems; (*c*) cognition of *semantic* units, which are in the form of meaningful ideas, usually verbalized information; and (*d*) cognition of *behavioral* units.

* Supported by the Office of Naval Research, the Air Force, the U.S. Office of Education, and the National Science Foundation.

In the area of behavioral information I added a category for which there was originally no empirical evidence; fortunately, one of my students came to my rescue recently and presented six new factors found in the behavioral area. Behavioral information, as we conceive it, is the kind we get from cues other people give us (through what we see or hear) about their own states of mind, feelings, intentions, perceptions, and so on. This represents what some people call the area of "social intelligence", or the area including "empathy", which may be equated with behavioral cognition. I should say I am using the term "cognition" in this system in a much narrower sense than is common; usually it is used to represent the entire field of intelligence. I prefer to restrict it to simple awareness of knowing or being in possession of information.

Konorski: What is the difference between "cognition" and "perception"?

Guilford: In the figural area there is a very close connection. The Gestalt figure-ground phenomenon would be an example; the figure is a unit, so to speak. Many of these concepts will be elucidated in connection with the second model, in which I have tried to show how these abilities operate in the living organism. Some people refer to our factors as providing a static picture of behavior; since, actually, there is something ongoing or active about them, I have been forced, more or less, to develop a second model, putting these abilities into the context of the behaving organism. An ability is a particular mode of individual difference, a unique kind of difference shown by the ways in which people behave. That being so, an ability does reflect something that is also a property of the individual. That is the logic of going from the factor to the behaving organism.

Of 120 potentially differentiable abilities, about 70 have been demonstrated empirically by factor analysis. These recognized abilities are scattered unevenly throughout the 15 categories of the model, ranging from 23 of the 24 potential cognition abilities to 6 of the 30 potential behavioral abilities. During the past five years our analyses have used the model heuristically as a way of predicting undiscovered abilities. At least 20 abilities we have found were predicted by the model before they were demonstrated.

There are also possible extensions of the model: I think we shall probably find a set of auditory abilities parallel to the visual-figural category in the model; about four of these have already been demonstrated. There may be, in addition, some tactual and some kinesthetic abilities. Senses other than vision and audition are not as well structured in their operations and are not used as much; the extent to which there is differentiation of abilities within these areas is problematical.

Another possible extension is in the behavioral area, where factors have been conceived as abilities to know, for example, what other people are thinking. Some of the abilities involve using that information to manipulate other individuals. There may also be a parallel set of abilities pertaining to oneself, that is, knowing and managing oneself with regard to plans, strategies, and so on, as Dr. Pribram pointed out.

A General Problem-Solving Model

Previous models have been proposed for problem solving, such as those diagrammed in Figure 77. Dewey's (3) well-known model—if we want to dignify it by calling it a model—dates as far back as 1910. There is one by Graham Wallas (25) for the case of creative production, and one by Rossman (18) for invention, which indicates a set of operations in sequence that he applied to the performance of inventors. The similarity of these models is striking, whether they are for problem-solving, invention, or for creative thinking in general. One interesting difference is the step for incubation in the Wallas model, which does not appear in the other two. I find it notable —this should be of interest to Dr. Pribram, too—that every other step in the Rossman model is, I would say, an evaluation step, beginning with a testing step and alternating operating and testing steps as in the TOTE model presented by Miller, Galanter & Pribram (12).

The new model resembles the traditional ones, but with considerable elaboration, plus the benefit of enlightenment gained during recent years. Structure-of-intellect concepts play prominent roles in the model, and a few other concepts reflect the influence of findings from traditional experimental psychology, from studies of brain function, and from cybernetics. Speaking in very general terms, the model is not immediately adaptable to the preparation of a simulation program for dealing with any particular kind of problem; its proper place is in general psychological theory.

The structure of intellect places strong emphasis upon basic varieties of information, suggesting we view the living organism as a processor of information. From the psychological point of view, I would define "information" as that which the organism discriminates—a very simple definition, but the best I can provide at this point. Discriminations are in terms of different kinds of products, coming from the different kinds of content and, *within* each of these categories, differences between relations, particular systems, and so on.

Information implies discrimination. This is also reminiscent of the definitions of information theory. From here on I believe we diverge substantially, since information, from information theory as applied to psychology, is also defined as uncertainty. I would say that my conception of information in psychology seems almost the reverse: information is certainty rather than uncertainty. Whether there is a completely negative correlation between the two conceptions of information, I am not prepared to say. I recognize the value of following the uncertainty definition, but it seems to me that structure and approach to certainty would be more in line with what we need for psychological use of information in general.

Pribram: Information theorists I have questioned regarding this point answered that they use the term "meaning" or "significance" in that sense.

Grant: They use the term "intelligence" for transmitted information.

Guilford: From the point of view of brain activity, information is a spe-

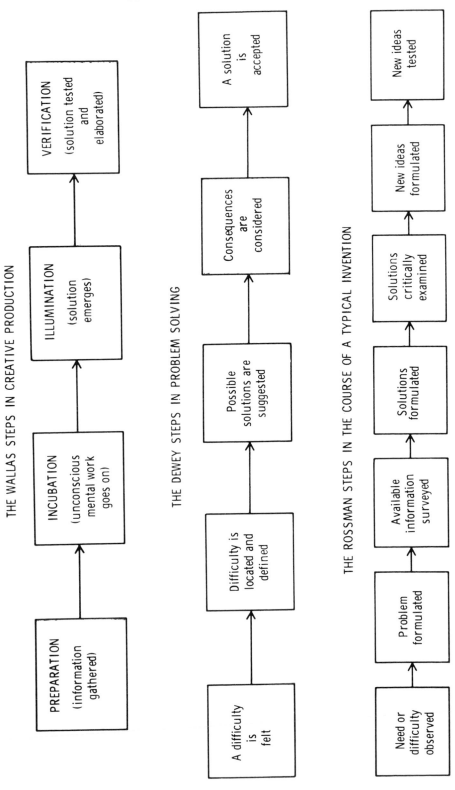

Figure 77. Three traditional conceptions of the sequence of events in creative production, problem solving, and invention.

cial manifestation of energy in the form of "triggering" functions. These triggering functions make possible the direction and regulation of much greater quantities of energy by means of built-in mechanisms. From either a psychological or a neurological point of view, information serves its communicative functions well. This implies the double-aspect view of the mind-body problem.

Let us consider now the subject of roles of the intellectual operation categories in the structure of intellect. The problem-solving model, as illustrated in Figure 78, is designed to represent a problem-solving episode, viewed as a patterned sequence of events within a system composed of a memory store and a set of operations, which include cognition, production (both divergent and convergent), and evaluation. Although these five operational categories were put in one line in the model illustrated in Figure 76, I think that here we have to differentiate memory from the others. The memory store is basic to, and has an influence upon, all operations; hence, it is represented by a long rectangle filled with items of information (I studiously avoided saying "bits" of information because of the technical meaning), indicating their general availability, but not necessarily of equal degree; this availability is there, more or less, at all stages of problem-solving.

The flow of information within the system is indicated by arrows. Between any two stations within the model the flow may be in one direction only or in both. For example, arrowheads pointing toward the memory store indicate either a searching (scanning) process when stored information is needed, or a committing of information to storage for retentive purposes. Although the general direction of flow of information in the model is from left to right, two important features modify such a simple temporal sequence. One is that many events occur simultaneously; the other is a "looping phenomenon", a concept prominent in cybernetics. Four such cycling patterns are labeled, two involving loops from cognition to memory store to evaluation and back to cognition (loops I and III), and two involving loops from production to memory store to evaluation and back to production (loops II and IV). Larger cycles include the combination of loops III and IV at the right, which resembles in form the combination of the two preceding loops, I and II. Smaller loops involve the direct interplay between cognition and the memory store, between production and the memory store, and also between cognition and evaluation, and production and evaluation as a direct transmission. I am not sure about the complete bypassing of evaluation as shown. I might have been influenced by Osborn's (15) emphasis upon suspended judgment and its consequences. Bypassing may be only a relative term.

Another major feature is the dependence of all operations upon evaluation. In general, behavior is self-regulating and self-correcting through the principle of feedback information, as illustrated in the operation of evaluation, which helps to select information at the filtering stage near the point

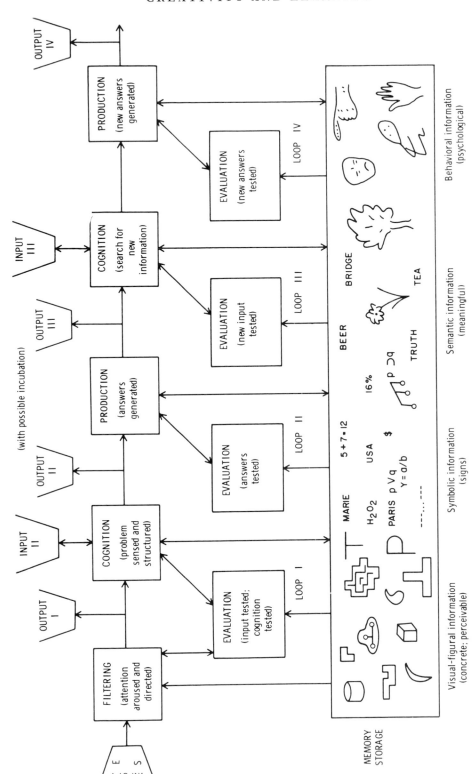

Figure 78. Schematic diagram of the flow of information in a somewhat typical instance of problem solving, from the input (from environment and from soma) to the output of accepted information. See text.

of input and to reject or accept information in the operations of cognition and production. I am not certain that the kind of evaluation that applies at the point of input is the same as the kind occurring later in the sequence, as implied by the TOTE-model theory (12).

Input of information into the system occurs in connection with the operation of cognition, either unsolicited as in Input I, or actively sought, as in Inputs II and III. Note that in the first input location (upper left) there is reference to the environment (E) and to the soma, or body (S). I think most of the motivational sources of behavior will be found in the soma input. It has struck me as somewhat humorous that some behaviorists have come to the point of saying there are stimuli in the brain; if we talk about input this does not sound so strange. I noticed at a recent convention of the American Psychological Association that there was much talk about "input" and "output" rather than "stimulus" and "response". I agreed with Dr. Hilgard when he said it would be better to talk less about stimulus and response—in fact, I think, these terms have been a source of rigidity in our thinking, in many respects; "input" and "output" allow greater flexibility. The outward-pointing arrowheads in Inputs II and III indicate active search for information at input sources. The diagram does not show filtering steps in connection with these additional inputs; these events occur, but they would complicate the picture too much.

Outputs may occur at various decision points, in the form of suspension or cessation of problem-solving efforts. Output I might represent evasion of the problem, considered then of trivial importance or beyond the prospective problem solver's coping powers; for any of these reasons he may not even attempt to understand the nature of the problem. Output II may represent a quick and easy solution, a decision to suspend operations temporarily, or a complete surrender to the problem without an effort at solution. The same alternatives may apply at Outputs II and IV, except for the occurrence of some degree of production activity. Suspension at any point may mean a resort to the condition of incubation, with eventual resumption of intentional activity with respect to the problem.

Although all five of the structure-of-intellect types of operations have been mentioned in connection with the problem-solving model, the distinction between the operations of divergent and convergent production—forced upon us by the kinds of factors we found in our research—is not explicitly expressed in the diagram (Figure 78). Both operations involve retrieval of information from the memory store. Divergent production is well implied by the cycling or looping phenomenon, i.e., in a trial-and-error process multiple solutions are offered, either by the direct connection with the memory store or through the step of evaluation; in the condition of "suspended judgment" there is much by-passing of the evaluation, as I have already indicated. Convergent production can occur only when cognition furnishes a search model of such clarity and completeness as to make possible the determination of the unique answer needed to fulfill it; that is, convergent production means arriving at a unique and fully determined answer. Although divergent production may occur before the convergent answer is determined (as in the case of mistakes in solving mathematical problems), we can conceive of a search model setting the evaluative filter so well that only one item of information can be admitted from the memory store.

The four kinds of information in the structure-of-intellect model are represented in the memory store. They were segregated for illustrative purposes, but I would point out that there is evidence of some relation to brain localization: for example, verbal or semantic information appears to be relatively more related to left-hemisphere function, and figural to right-hemisphere function (13, 27). Six kinds of products are represented. Each product by itself could be a unit, but the organism sometimes makes units out of systems by a process of chunking, of which G. A. Miller (11) speaks; close examination of some of the units shows that they have systematic internal markings. When we analyze, we often make systems out of units; we understand inner arrangements, inner workings, and interrelationships we did not differentiate before.

Classes are represented in Figure 78, starting with the four major kinds of information. Within each of these there are further groupings or classifications. I would say that hierarchal models are rather typical of our memory storage. This is very important in retrieval: i.e., each stored product has an "address" determined to a great degree by its position in the hierarchy. Relations are also shown; for example, "5 + 7" would be a relationship, and "a/b" another. Implications are shown, a very obvious one being "p implies q"; the tree implying the flower might be another, since flowering trees are known. Incidentally, I regard a classical conditioned response as a case of implication. An implication could be paraphrased by saying "expectancy" or "anticipation".

No sample of a transformation is actually shown in Figure 78. An example could be the transposing of the numerical equation to give "$5 = 12 - 7$" and the altering of the literal equation to give "$a = bY$".

You may note my avoidance of the term "association" throughout this discussion. I submit that it is time we become more discriminating and replace the concept of association with the various products of information. Incidentally, the six kinds of products are also concepts shared by modern logic. The implication product is the nearest approximation to what we ordinarily call association; in stressing this kind of association almost exclusively, we have been too rigid, ignoring a number of phenomena such as units. Titchener and Wundt failed in their attempt to account for units in terms of associations of elements of experience. We also have to recognize, along with the Gestalt psychologists, that there are such things as relations and systems as well as units, and that "association" as ordinarily conceived will not account for these mental events.

CREATIVE ASPECTS OF PROBLEM SOLVING

Factor-analytic studies aimed more specifically toward the intellectual activities believed to be most pertinent to creative performance led to the isolation of various abilities under the headings of fluency, flexibility and elaboration. Since the development of the factor model, we have recognized that the category of divergent production encompasses the traits of fluency, elaboration, and some sorts of flexibility, while other kinds of flexibility belong in the category of transformations, which are alterations of products. It is somewhat tempting to say that this is where learning occurs; transformations do constitute one important kind of learning event, but I would not say they are the only learning locus nor the only learning kind. My general definition is that learning is the achieving of information, which means both new discriminations and organizations. Not all such acquisitions are by way of transformations as presently conceived.

In terms of more familiar mental operations, fluency is the facile production of ideas. It is a matter of retrieval of information from memory storage. How readily can we search, or dig into memory storage, and retrieve items at will? Incidentally, fluency abilities seem to be less trainable than flexibility; although each person does not tend to become more fluent with training, his speed in producing ideas may be quite variable with time. Measurable changes in flexibility with different kinds of practice can be demonstrated. Flexibility is also a matter of retrieval of information, and this is what I would call "transfer recall" as distinct from the "non-transfer recall", the type that has received most attention in learning studies where a subject's recall of information is tested. In most creative responses there is transfer: the response is retrieved in relation to some other cue. The process of stimulus generalization, of similarity and its effects, comes immediately to mind, and similarity does play a role, but sometimes, in the very creative thinker, some of the similarities are extremely remote, as if the idea came by dint of the thinnest thread of connection between two items of information. I would urge experimental psychologists to devote much more effort to the study of transfer recall or retrieval.

Flexibility also means the revamping, recombining or reorganizing of information to meet new needs; in other words, transformation. Novelty of behavior occurs in similar ways and, hence, originality or creativity.

SOME POSSIBLE BRAIN-FUNCTION IMPLICATIONS*

In this closing section I should like to consider briefly some possible relationships between known brain functions and the psychological pictures that have been painted. This is on the basis of my limited reading in the field of information about the brain. Is there anything to be gained in attempts to find parallels between intellectual functioning and the brain,

---

* *Editor's Note:* The following portions of Dr. Guilford's paper could not be presented at the Conference due to lack of time. The other participants, therefore, had no opportunity to discuss them.

when intellectual functioning is envisaged in terms of the structure of intellect and its basic concepts? To be sure, none of us would still expect to find the brain compartmentalized to correspond to the intellectual factors, à la Gall (cf. 1), but the search for compartments of some kind is by no means a dead issue, and enough correspondences have been found here and there to keep alive the localization (or focalization) type of investigation.

Operations Categories and the Brain

To start with the five kinds of operations, we may say that because there can be no production (either divergent or convergent) without memory, and no memory without cognition, these three kinds of operations might involve the same brain elements. This would not necessarily be so, for there are rich interconnections within the human cerebral cortex, but studies by different methods seem to implicate especially the parietal and temporal lobes in connection with all three operations. Possibly, the frontal lobes cannot be ruled out entirely, at least the anterior intrinsic centers mentioned by Dr. Pribram (17), for which the interesting suggestion is made that a focal place for self-cognition or cognition of one's own plans, strategies, and tactics (implying overt behavior) can be found there.

More interesting, more difficult to investigate, and in the long run probably more illuminating than correlations in the form of localizations, are correlations in terms of varieties of brain activities—intercellular or intracellular, electrical or chemical. The new interest in the form in which memories are stored is one indication of research in this direction. I gather that models in terms of associative pathways and cell assemblies are being questioned, and that we may eventually see them replaced by concepts such as molecular assemblies, molecular structures, resonances, and so on. In this connection, we can ask what kind of cell or molecular activity it is that makes possible the cognition of a unit, a class, a relation, and each of the other products of information.

Agnosias, Aphasias, and Intellectual Abilities

At this point I should like to call attention to some speculations of John Elmgren (4) concerning varieties of aphasias and certain intellectual factors. Some recent findings call into question the apparent neatness of some of the older concepts of aphasia and agnosia, but their parallels with intellectual factors seem very attractive still. When combinations of symptoms associated with accidental brain injuries are not uniform or clear-cut, we have to remember that nature pays little attention to scientific concepts when it performs its "experiments" in the form of brain injury.

According to Elmgren, Head distinguished three kinds of aphasia: "semantic aphasia", involving loss of comprehension or words, which can be aligned logically with the factor of cognition of semantic units; "syntactic aphasia", a disturbance of the formation of sentences, which is suggestive of the two factors concerning production of semantic systems (we have found that in some contexts sentences satisfy the label of semantic system); and "nominal aphasia", which presents a difficulty in naming things or in finding words, and suggests the two factors involving production of semantic units. The description of another disorder, "jargon-aphasia", attributed to Pierre Marie, the French neurologist, shows that the mentally deficient may excel in giving verbal associations of a purely superficial or alliterative kind without knowing the word meanings, which suggests a high level of the ability Thurstone (24) called "word fluency", and which is now recognized as the divergent production of symbolic units.

Although Elmgren did not mention the agnosias in his factor analysis (4), it can be hypothesized that *alexia* is a loss of the ability of cognition of symbolic units. If this were the only loss, factorially, the alexic should be able to name the letters of a word but not the word. If he cannot name letters and other objects that he should know from experience, he has lost ability to recognize visual, figural units.

It is true that Schuell et al. (19) and Jones & Wepman (9) failed to find the classical varieties of aphasia by factor analysis and other procedures, but in neither investigation was the choice of experimental variables appropriate. I should like to see those studies repeated with the test battery composed of marker tests for factors in the structure of intellect; the results should be very different.

In considering relations to brain functions, the operation of evaluation has some interesting possibilities. There is some evidence for associating evaluation with the frontal lobes and their underlying structures. Damage to the frontal lobes has been noted clinically to be affiliated with loss of judgment and circumspection with respect to personal conduct. Pribram (17) speaks of a comparison of plans for the purpose of sensing errors and incongruities in connection with the frontal lobes; the description of comparing something for "sensing errors and incongruities" describes essentially many of our evaluation tests. Weiskrantz (26), in effect, attributes some evaluative behavior to the limbic system.

Content Categories and the Brain

There seems to be much corroborated evidence that the right hemisphere in man is more concerned with sensory, i.e., figural, information (at least visual and auditory) in the way of cognition, and that the left hemisphere is concerned with semantic information from visual and auditory inputs (13, 27). The category of symbolic information has not been given the recognition it deserves in view of the factor-analytic distinction of an entire category of abilities parallel to the figural and semantic abilities.

Conventional symbols evolved in connection with language, and in common with language in general they are based on visual or auditory inputs. We might, therefore, consider some kind of cooperation between the right and left hemispheres in looking for focal areas underlying operations with symbolic information. Or we might expect to find the left hemisphere to be chiefly involved, as a general language organ and including a basis for symbolic information. All language has both semantic and syntactic aspects.

Behavioral information is of quite a different kind. Because of the extent to which feeling and emotion enter into the picture, it is possible that some subcortical regions are involved in the rather direct, empathic understanding of one person by another, with intellectual aspects of behavioral information somehow related to the frontal lobes. The possible relation of cognition of self behavior in connection with the anterior intrinsic centers (17) has already been mentioned.

Product Categories and the Brain

In accounting for different kinds of products in connection with the brain, there are only a few facts pointing in certain directions. Some findings seem to link the product of implications with the frontal lobes (but probably not exclusively): for one thing, implications are regarded as an important basis for foresight. The Porteus maze tests (16) seems to show rather consistent losses in cases of damage to the frontal lobes. We have found such tests to measure prominently the factor of cognition of figural implications; while other interpretations have been made as to the kinds of psychological deficit shown by the Porteus maze tests, I know of no support for those hypotheses from factor analysis or even from simple correlational studies of construct validity.

Deficiency in the drawing of inferences has also been reported in connection with frontal lobe damage (6). Drawing inferences (if the term can be taken literally) should be in the area of production of implications from given information, usually semantic. In lower animals, loss in delayed reactions tests is sometimes a symptom in connection with frontal lobe damage (21, 22). Such a test may involve cognition of implications (expectancies), depending upon how the problem is set up for the experimental subjects. Incidentally, if a certain test gives positive findings only some times, it may be that subtle changes in test conditions have altered the basic ability emphasized.

These few suggestions as to hypothetical brain-factor correlations are very limited, but they indicate the kind of implications and the kind of thinking that are called for by knowledge of the intellectual abilities. Only time, and a great deal of empirical investigation, will tell whether hypotheses generated from structure-of-intellect theory will bear fruit in connection with the study of brain functions.

Discussion

Miller: Dr. Guilford, suppose I had some financial backing, a staff, and the idea that the visual ability you mentioned was divided into urban abilities for identifying city figures and rural abilities for identifying country figures; were I to send a group of testers to do this, would I be able to sub-divide that ability and add a new category to your factor analysis model?

Guilford: That is a possibility, but I do not think it would be very exten-sive or very uniform over different countries, for example. It would be a fac-tor different in kind from those I described. The latter are found by se-lecting populations of rather homogeneous characteristics by employing ex-perimental controls—relatively uniform age, sex, education, etc. The abili-ties you would add would be very specific; those I have been talking about have some generality.

In one of our recent studies on evaluation abilities the model predicted an ability to evaluate semantic units. "Evaluation" means testing, as Dr. Pri-bram uses the term, or determining whether or not information measures up to standards, or meets certain requirements. We are yet unsure of the extent of this evaluative kind of ability, but we are sure that matching and making decisions as to the identity of two things (whether they are identical or not) leads to a very dependable kind of decision that we can use.

Koestler: How does the model in Figure 76 make its prediction?

Guilford: There is a cell at the intersection of the evaluation and the sem-antic categories and the category of units. The unique ability is indicated at the point where those three come together.

Jensen: I think the static model you describe is so simple that most of us would not think of it as being a model at all.

Guilford: It is not an operational model.

Lumsdaine: The model is organized like the periodic table—there is some-thing at each spot. I think it is a very good model.

Zigler: Is that a model for any one person's intellect, or for everybody's intellect combined? Would all of these factors be found in one person or in diverse groups of people?

Guilford: As far as we know, it applies only to the populations in which we have found the factors. We cannot say how general they are; these fac-tors have been found in adult males, adult females, and in high-school youngsters down to the ninth grade; we also found some of them in the sixth grade. Not every factor is found in every population, but when the same factors are investigated in somewhat different populations, they are almost always found in all those populations.

Zigler: Thinking of Jones' (8) factor analysis of the Stanford-Binet tests at different ages, and of Garrett's APA presidential address (5), when he talked about the changing factorial structure of intelligence with age, a question could be raised. Your model representing the structure of intelligence is a constant one—we know, however, that the structure of intelligence is not constant. A test that would fall within one factor at one time lands on an-other factor at another time.

Guilford: I must say that the Binet collection of tests is not a very good one for a factor analysis. Anybody using only those tests would, I think, be defeated before he started, and would not be expected to find very stable factors. Most of the experimental results have been against the Garrett hypothesis.

Miller: My question about rural *versus* urban factors was concerned with the degree to which cultural variables determine the kinds of factors that will be extracted. An anecdote, which I trust is true, will illustrate the point: When Nissen went to Africa to study chimpanzees he took some form boards along. At first he was confined to his camp by rain, so he tested his African guides on the form boards. Their performance was terrible—much worse than that of American infants. He wondered whether he had feeble-minded guides, which would defeat his whole expedition. Then the rain stopped. Each day the guides took him to where the chimps were and each day this was a different place. He was amazed and asked the guides, "How do you find where the chimps are?" The guides looked at him as if *he* were feeble-minded and said: "Can't you see? The chimps leave a big trail. Up in that tree the twigs are broken, and here on the ground are the seeds of the fruit they have been eating. It is obvious the chimps went this way." Apparently the Africans had some visual-figural abilities that Nissen did not have, and vice versa. These differences probably were the result of different cultural training. If we gave a group of Yale professors and native guides batteries of form boards and chimpanzee-tracking tests, would we not obtain a jungle factor as well as a professorial factor in visual ability?

Guilford: Are you suggesting that whites and African natives be used in the same analysis?

Miller: Yes.

Guilford: You could probably generate factors. However, I would not combine them. Your professor and his guides simply had different funds of information in storage.

Pribram: Another way of asking the question might be: are these differences that you are trying to focus on intraindividual or interindividual?

Guilford: Our data are from interindividual differences, but the implication is that intraindividual differences of the same kind also occur, as can be seen in an individual's profile of scores, each score representing his status on a different factor.

Lumsdaine: But I take it that everybody in the population would have a score on *each* of the dimensions: a three-dimensional profile would be obtained. So, it is not quite right to say it is inter-, not intraindividual; it is both.

Pribram: It shows up the individual with respect to his group.

Koestler: Dr. Guilford, in defining divergent production as "generation of information from given information, where the emphasis is upon variety and quantity of output from the same source", does the "source" involve not only the information input but the memory store as well?

Guilford: The major source is from input, modified by the contents of the memory store. Here I am thinking in the context of the psychological tests, in which the item given provides input or source, and the examinee's reaction is the information produced. As an illustration, I might distinguish between divergent and convergent thinking in terms of test items: if a subject is asked to give a word meaning the opposite of "dry", the conventional answer is "wet". If, however, he is asked to give as many words as he can that mean almost the opposite of "dry", then he might say not only "wet", but "moist", "watery", "saturated", etc.; this is divergent production. In convergent production, there is enough information input determining and regulating the processes to lead to one right answer.

Jensen: Do I understand that there are temporal relations and sequence orders across the diagram in Figure 78 involving Output I, Input II, Output II, and so forth?

Guilford: Yes; the direction is generally from left to right. The memory store is just there, available anywhere, anytime. The temporal order does not apply to the memory store as illustrated.

Grant: That is a very general sort of model, in a sense. In tackling a tough problem, we certainly would have to go through nearly all the steps, and work over the loops. Some people, however, working on some kinds of problems, seem to use shortcuts.

Guilford: There can be cognition of shortcuts, as when a person sees immediately what known strategy to apply. Any strategy, I would say, is a kind of system. A trained person would have a stock of problem-solving strategies in his memory store.

Grant: If a mathematician is not satisfied with the solution you give him, for example, he may say, "Have you ever thought of doing it another way?" He does not stop where we usually do. Would you call that somatic input? It is built into his traits; it is a habit of thinkng, for he looks at the problem in a way different from ours.

Guilford: I would say he suddenly achieves new cognitions and these generate new strategies.

Grant: Or, indeed, he has tools that I do not have. He also has a different aspirational level; he is not satisfied with the kind of solution that would satisfy me. Where does that come into the model?

Guilford: Where standards are involved, we have evaluation.

Grant: In the first cognition step we say the problem is sensed and structured. Perhaps some people sense-structure in different ways from others.

Guilford: This would mean that we are solving different problems.

Koestler: Am I correct in assuming that what you call "soma" implies differences in the personal criteria of relevance and in the structuring?

Guilford: I think the source would be the memory store rather than input from the soma outside the nerve cells.

REFERENCES

1. Boring, E. G., *A History of Experimental Psychology* (2nd ed.). Appleton-Century-Crofts, New York, 1950.

2. de Mille, R., Intellect after lobotomy in schizophrenia; a factor-analytic study. *Psychol. Monogr.*, 1962. **76**(1): No. 535.

3. Dewey, J., *How We Think*. Heath, Boston, 1933.

4. Elmgren, J., Some fundamental problems in psychological factor analysis. *Acta Univ. Gothoburg.*, 1958, **64**: No. 3.

5. Garrett, H. E., A developmental theory of intelligence. *Am. Psychologist*, 1946, **1**: 372-378.

6. Gray, G. W., "The great ravelled knot". *Sci. Amer.*, 1948, **179**(4): 26-39.

7. Halstead, W. C., *Brain and Intelligence*. Univ. of Chicago Press, Chicago, 1947.

8. Jones, L. V., A factor analysis of the Stanford-Binet at four age levels. *Psychometrika*, 1949, **14**: 299-331.

9. Jones, L. V., and Wepman, J. M., Dimensions of language performance in aphasia. *J. Speech Hear. Res.*, 1961, **4**: 220-232.

10. Matthews, C. G., and Reitan, R. M., Correlations of Wechsler-Bellevue rank orders of subtest means in lateralized and non-lateralized brain-damaged groups. *Percept. Mot. Skills*, 1964, **19**: 391-399.

11. Miller, G. A., The magical number seven, plus or minus two: some limits on our capacity for processing information. *Psychol. Rev.*, 1956, **63**: 81-97.

12. Miller, G. A., Galanter, E., and Pribram, K. H., *Plans and the Structure of Behavior*. Holt, New York, 1960.

13. Milner, B., Intellectual function of the temporal lobes. *Psychol. Bull.*, 1954, **51**: 42-62.

14. Orbach, J., "Functions" of striate cortex and the problem of mass action. *Psychol. Bull.*, 1959, **56**: 271-292.

15. Osborn, A. F., *Applied Imagination; Principles and Procedures of Creative Problem-Solving* (3rd ed.). Scribners, New York, 1963.

16. Porteus, S. D., and Peters, H. N., Maze test validation and psychosurgery. *Genet. Psychol. Monogr.*, 1947, **36**: 3-86.

17. Pribram, K. H., A review of theory in physiological psychology. *Ann. Rev. Psychol.*, 1960, **11**: 1-40.

18. Rossman, J., *The Psychology of the Inventor; A Study of the Patentee* (2nd ed.). Inventors Publ. Co., Washington, D.C., 1931.

19. Schuell, H., Jenkins, J. J., and Carroll, J. B., A factor analysis of the Minnesota Test for Differential Diagnosis of Aphasia. *J. Speech Hear. Res.*, 1962, **5**: 349-369.

20. Semmes, J., Weinstein, S., Ghent, L., and Teuber, H.-L., Correlates of impaired orientation in personal and extrapersonal space. *Brain*, 1963, **86**: 747-772.

21. Stanley, W. C., and Jaynes, J., The function of the frontal cortex. *Psychol. Rev.*, 1949, **56**: 18-32.

22. TEUBER, H.-L., Neuropsychology. In: *Recent Advances in Diagnostic Psychological Testing; A Critical Summary.* Thomas, Springfield, 1950: 30-52.

23. ———, Some alterations in behavior after cerebral lesions in man. In: *Evolution of Nervous Control from Primitive Organisms to Man* (A. D. Bass, Ed.). American Association for the Advancement of Science, Washington, D.C., 1959: 157-194.

24. THURSTONE, L. L., *Primary Mental Abilities.* Univ. of Chicago Press, Chicago, 1938.

25. WALLAS, G., *The Art of Thought.* Harcourt, New York, 1926.

26. WEISKRANTZ, L., Neurological studies and animal behaviour. *Brit. Med. Bull.*, 1964, **20**: 49-53.

27. ZANGWILL, O. L., Neurological studies and human behaviour. *Brit. Med. Bull.*, 1964, **20**: 43-48.

THE ACT OF CREATION

ARTHUR KOESTLER
London

I will take as my text a quotation attributed to Karl Friedrich Gauss, mathematician: "I have had my solutions for a long time but I don't know yet how to arrive at them."

My points will be three: a model of creativity which I think is complementary, not contradictory, to Dr. Guilford's model; the extraconscious factors in the decisive stage of the creative act; and an attempt to put creativity into a wider biological frame.

Creative activity could be described as a type of learning process where teacher and pupil are located in the same individual. Some creative people like to ascribe the role of the teacher to an entity they call the unconscious, which they regard as a kind of Maxwell demon; others deny its existence, and still others are prepared to admit it but deplore the ambiguity of the concept. I belong to the last group, and I believe that the ambiguity is mainly due to a venerable tradition that applies the same word to a variety of phenomena.

The first of these is awareness of an ongoing activity. It is a trivial fact of experience that awareness is not an all-or-nothing affair but a matter of degrees, a continuum extending from the unconsciousness that results from being hit on the head, through the extraconsciousness of visceral processes, through tying one's shoelaces absent-mindedly, through fringe-conscious perceptions and routines, up to the laser beam of focal consciousness. These states can be arranged on a linear gradient—white through gray to black. But this gradient should not be confused with the sleep-drowsiness-full wakefulness levels. The gradient I am talking about refers to awareness of an ongoing activity—a motor activity such as tying shoelaces, or a cognitive activity. So, in the same wide-awake state one can carry on an activity in the preconscious or extraconscious ranges of that gradient. Possibly we have here a distinction between specific reticular projections, which would account for a given process being in focal consciousness, as opposed to non-specific cortical-reticular interaction, which would simply account for the level of wakefulness of the subject, regardless of any specific process.

Bright new skills, acquired by learning—whether perceptual, motor or cognitive—tend to condensate into habits and to migrate to the twilight zone. I can carry on a conversation while driving the car, and hand over control to the automatic pilot in my nervous system. Gastaut & Beck (7) have suggested that well-established habits may be handed down from the cortico-reticular level to the limbic system and other structures in the dien-cephalon; this mechanism seems a bit too crude to account for the fine shadings along the gradient. However that may be, I would like to under-line the fact that automatized skills do not necessarily become rigid and stereotyped. Driving a car without paying attention requires a flexible strat-egy; the night club pianist who transposes a tune into a different key or syn-copates Chopin while carrying on a flirtation with the barmaid displays great virtuosity, although he functions semi-automatically, on the lower reaches of the gradient of awareness.

Thus, habit formation entails a constant downward traffic along the gra-dient, as on a moving escalator. But this downgrading does not necessarily involve an impoverishment of the skill, nor does it exclude virtuosity of a kind which is often mistaken for creativity. Watch a locksmith at work as he feels his way with a simple bent wire in a complicated lock and snaps it open, as if guided by some mysterious intuition: there is certainly no crea-tivity here, but there certainly is a kind of virtuosity. To ride a bicycle over a tightrope or to perform the feats of a calculating prodigy are admirable achievements, but at the opposite pole to creative originality. The much-ad-mired masters of the various Zen arts, from fencing to caligraphic painting, have always aimed at precisely this kind of virtuosity, confusing uncon-scious automatisms with unconscious inspiration.

If we then say that creativity relies, at certain critical moments, on inspi-rations of unconscious origin, we mean some kind of *upward* traffic on that escalator. This can be interpreted in more than one way. "Inspiration" can be taken as a message received from the unconscious conceived as an auto-nomic agency—a separate compartment of the mind where the Maxwell demon does your homework for you. I believe this view to be untenable, although it was upheld not only by romantically inclined artists, but by mathematicians like Poincaré. The very term "the unconscious", used as a noun, is rather misleading because it implies a structural entity, a kind of box inside which certain activities take place, whereas, in fact, awareness is but a variable *dimension* of activities, though an important one. One and the same activity can be accompanied by varying degrees of awareness. Visceral functions can apparently be brought under conscious control by certain Eastern techniques or by the Valsalva maneuver (22). The opposite happens when, on awakening, one tries to hang on to the remembrance of a dream which runs away, like quicksand, out of conscious reach; I think this phenomenon, with which we are all familiar, deserves to be dignified by a Greek name, and I suggest *oneirolysis*—from "oneiros", dream, plus "lysis", dissolution; more about it later on.

If we discard the notion of "the unconscious" as a noun, acting as a *deus ex machina,* we can adopt a more sober view, in which the apparently spontaneous creative act appears as the result of mental events of a known and definable type which, however, took place below the reaches of focal or even peripheral awareness. The puzzling question remains, of why these dark interludes are apparently a *sine qua non* in the wide-awake pursuits of science. The first rough answer suggesting itself is that the particular type of mental activity which takes place in the so-called period of incubation does not meet the criteria of articulateness and logical decency required for admission into the wide-awake state, for the very good reason that, if given unrestricted access, it would play havoc with our everyday thinking routines. But to quote Arnold Bennett, "A dirty mind is a continuous feast"—"dirty" meaning of course semantic impurity, or the logical impurity of these twilight processes. When the routines of normal thinking break down, a temporary regression to these pre-rational forms of mentation often does just the trick.

Let me discuss first what *kind* of trick it is that the creative act is supposed to perform; and then how it can profit from such regression.

Original discoveries in science range from the highly dramatic to the deceptively simple, but there is a basic pattern underlying the entire range. It can be summed up in the verb to cogitate, derived from "coagitare", co-agitate, to shake together what has previously been separated. Köhler's (14) chimpanzees were skilled in grabbing bananas placed outside the cage by squeezing an arm or leg through the bars; call this skill No. 1. They had also acquired the habit of using sticks playfully to scrape the earth or to push objects around; call this skill No. 2. When a banana was placed outside the chimpanzee's reach, the animal would persist for a long time in hopeless attempts to reach it by applying the routines of skill No. 1, until the dramatic moment when its eyes focused on the stick lying in the cage, grabbed it and used it as a rake, for the first time combining the two hitherto separate skills.

An impressive number of human discoveries is based on the same pattern, where some playful *l'art pour l'art* technique provides the unexpected solution to a problem in a quite different field. Galileo astonished the world when he turned a primitive toy invented by Dutch opticians into a tool for astronomers. The geometry of conic sections, studied by Apollonius of Perga in the fourth century B. C. just for the fun of it, provided Kepler two thousand years later with his elliptical orbits. The mathematics of probability originated in Pascal's interest in the Chevalier de Méré's passion for gambling. Relativity and quantum mechanics owe almost everything to the non-Euclidian geometries and other absurd games played by mathematicians, *seul en l'honneur de l'esprit humain,* as one of them said. The act of creation does not create something out of nothing; it reshuffles, combines, synthesizes already existing facts, ideas, frames of reference, cognitive skills. Hebb's phase sequence hypothesis led him to similar conclusions (9). Perhaps Schmidt or Hydén will one day come up with a model of superimposed frequency-modulated patterns.

Newton combined Kepler's laws of planetary motion with Galileo's laws of the motion of projectiles; he put two and two together to make five. The more familiar the parts, the more striking the new whole. The motions of the tides and the phases of the moon had been separately known for time immemorial but, again, it took a Newton to put them together.

Gutenberg invented the printing press with movable type by combining the techniques of the coin stamp with the technique of the wine press, both of which were equally well known. He described (11) his being tortured by the problem of how to use coin stamps cast in lead to make lasting imprints, which he could not do because the only technique of printing then available was the carved woodcut, placed over vellum and rubbed with a dabber. For a year he tried various solutions vainly, until: "I took part in the wine harvest. I watched the wine flowing, and, going back from the effect to the cause, I studied the power of the wine press, which nothing can resist. At that moment it occurred to me the same steady pressure as that exerted by the wine press might be applied to the pressing of paper, and owing to the pressure the lead would leave an imprint on the paper. To work then! God has revealed to me the secret I demanded of Him in a ray of light."

The pattern is found again and again. Darwin was looking for an agency which would bring a selective principle into the process of evolution; he read Malthus' essay on human populations, and there was the click. Maxwell borrowed from hydrodynamics to make a model for the propagation of electromagnetic waves.

This act of cross-fertilization or, rather, self-fertilization between two cognitive matrices in a single brain, seems to me the essence of the creative act. I have proposed for it the barbaric term "bisociation" to distinguish it from the routines of associative thinking within the framework of a single matrix. This may sound tautological, so I had better specify that the term "matrix" is used here to refer to any ability, habit or skill governed by a fixed set of rules of the game (the code) which lends it coherence and stability, but leaves sufficient degrees of freedom for flexible strategies adapted to the environmental input. I have tried to show elsewhere (13) that the concept of the matrix as an open behavioral system, with an invariant code and variable strategies, has a wide range of applicability on all levels of the organic hierarchy.

Think, on the level of instinct behavior, of a spider weaving its web; it suspends the web on anything from three to twelve points of suspension, according to the lay of the land, but the radial threads will always intersect the laterals at equal angles, and the geometric center of the web will always be its center of gravity. Think of playing a game. It has a code: the rules of the game define the ensemble of permissible moves. The actual moves will be a result of the interplay of the rules of the game with the features of the environment (the lay of the land, the chessmen on the board). Whenever we speak, certain rules of the game, such as grammar, syntax and common or garden logic, direct the process in the gaps between the words, though we are unaware of it.

Anyone can ride a bicycle but nobody can explain how it is done, not even the bicycle manufacturers; it is a very complicated formula. The code, the set of rules which govern the performance, always functions on a lower level of awareness than the performance itself. I do not think there is so much difference between verbal skills and bicycle riding, for we are as little capable of defining the rules which govern verbal thinking as of explaining the riding of a bicycle. Specialists, semanticists and linguists, are needed to crack the code. But we are concerned only with *cognitive matrices*, the term "matrix" here being used as a unifying formula to include what we variously call frames of reference, associative contexts, universes of discourse, mental sets, schemata, etc., including those vestigial forms of mentation which reflect an earlier phase in the development of the individual or of the species. The convenient ambiguity of the term "code"—highway code, coded message—reflects the property of the nervous system to control bodily activities by means of coded signals.

When life presents us with a problem, it will be attacked in accordance with the code of rules which enabled us to deal with similar problems in the past. These rules range from manipulating sticks by chimpanzees to operating with ideas, verbal concepts, visual forms, and mathematical entities. When the same kind of task is repeatedly encountered under monotonous conditions, in the same kind of setting, the subject's responses become stereotyped and degenerate into rigid patterns. He may be compared to an engine driver who must drive his train along fixed rails according to a fixed timetable. Vice versa, a variable environment will tend to create flexible behavior patterns, with a high degree of adaptability to circumstances. The driver of a motor car has more degrees of freedom than an engine driver. But the challenge of the environment can be carried, by life or in the laboratory, to a point where the situation still resembles in some aspects other situations encountered in the past, but contains new features, data, or complexities which make it impossible to solve the problem by the same rules of the game that were applied to past situations. When this happens, the situation is blocked, though the subject may realize this fact only after a series of hopeless tries, or never at all. Our motorist is heading for a frontier to which all approaches are barred, and all his skill as a driver will not help him, short of turning his car into a helicopter. In other words, he must find a second mediating matrix governed by different rules of the game and combine it with the first to unlock the situation. This is the essence of the bisociative act, I submit.

Thus we arrive at the crucial question: how does the mediating matrix achieve that happy combination of ideas which nobody before had thought of combining, and which looks so heartbreakingly obvious after it has been done?

A blocked matrix obviously creates stress. When all promising attempts at solving the problem by traditional means (the period of "conscious preparation") have been exhausted, thinking tends to run in circles, until the whole personality becomes saturated with the problem. At this stage (the period of incubation) the single-mindedness of the creative obsession produces a state of receptivity, a readiness to pounce on favorable chance constellations and to profit from any casual hint. Dr. Pribram gave us a beautiful example, with his sitting and watching the chimp do what it did; it was a hint, no more, and there was the click. As Lloyd Morgan said, "Saturate yourself through and through with your subject—and wait". In discoveries of the type in which both rational thinking and the trigger-action of chance play a noticeable part, the main contribution of extraconscious activity is to keep the problem constantly on the agenda while conscious attention is occupied elsewhere—watching the grape harvest or reading an essay by Malthus. Our friend, the demon, seems to have "bugged" all cortical receptor areas to make sure that no bit of information of any conceivable use to him is lost— which is just another way of quoting Pasteur: "Fortune favors the prepared mind."

But, in the more dramatic forms of discovery, unconscious mentation seems to intervene in more specific active ways: first, to encourage a kind of promiscuous mixing of ideas, then to act as a matchmaker. Or, to put it more respectably, it has a catabolic and an anabolic aspect.

The catabolic aspect of this regressive process is characterized by the re-linquishing of certain conscious controls which are necessary to maintain the disciplined routines of articulate thought but prevent the creative leap when routine is blocked. The result of this relaxing of controls is, metaphorically speaking, a kind of de-differentiation of the cognitive tissues, a regression from highly specialized, articulated levels of thinking to earlier, less disciplined forms of ideation, governed by more tolerant rules of the game. A frequent form of this phenomenon is the retreat from precise verbal thinking to vague visual imagery. Jacques Hadamard's (8) inquiry among American mathematicians led to the striking conclusion that nearly all of them thought neither in verbal terms nor in precise algebraic symbols, but relied on visual imagery of a vague, hazy kind. Typical was Einstein's oft-quoted statement: "The words of the language as they are written or spoken do not seem to play any role in my mechanism of thought . . . which relies on more or less clear images of a visual and some of a muscular type. . . . It also seems to me that what you call full consciousness is a limit-case which can never be fully accomplished because consciousness is a narrow thing" (8).

As far as one can gather from the record, the majority of scientists who have bothered to describe their working methods were visualizers who seem to have shared Woodworth's opinion: "Often we have to get away from speech in order to think clearly." Watson was very naive indeed, and so are those among his successors who still equate thinking with "implicit verbal behavior". Words crystallize thoughts, they give articulation and precision to vague images and hazy intuitions; but a crystal is no longer a liquid. Language can act as a screen between the thinker and reality, and creativity often starts where language ends, that is, by regressing to preverbal levels in the mental hierarchy.

More generally, this process of *reculer pour mieux sauter*—of a temporary regression preparing the forward leap—seems to trigger into action cognitive structures of a type prevalent in childhood and in primitive societies and, up to a point, in dreaming or daydreaming, which are normally under restraint in the civilized adult. Anthropology, psychiatry, and particularly the school of Piaget, have familiarized us with some common features of these otherwise varied thought matrices. I certainly do not want to lump together, as it is sometimes done, the particular logic of the dream, the logic of the Primitive, and the logic of the various stages in the development of the child, but there are certain common characteristics, common denominators, which hold these otherwise very different pre-rational matrices together. A few of these are: indifference to contradiction and to formal logic in general, the subjectivization of space and time, "thinking" in pictures in preference to words, regression from physical causality to magic causality and animism, the symbolization, concretization and dramatization of cognitive processes, and a tendency to combine apparently incompatible ideas, to perceive hidden analogies between cabbages and kings.

The negative benefits of such regression are obvious. The code of rules which governs a routine performance, whether riding a bicycle or verbalizing, always operates on a lower level of awareness than the performance itself; the code is a hidden persuader. Lashley's dictum, "In all our perceptions we are aware of an organized structure; the organizing is never experienced" (16) seems to apply all along the way, from the visual constancies and rules of grammar and syntax to the prejudices and hidden axioms built into our reasoning matrices. Regression means a temporary suspension of these codes. The mind in labor is liberated from the tyranny of rigid, over-precise schemata; it is enabled to unlearn and acquire a new innocence of the eye, a greater fluidity of thought. (But, of course, a greater gullibility also. False inspirations carry the same spontaneous convincingness as the legitimate ones which outnumber them a thousandfold. The acid test is verification, but verification comes after the act.)

So much for the catabolic aspect. It dissolves the stubborn embeddedness of ideas—I am using the word "embeddedness" in the technical sense of adherence to a matrix. During the regressive phase, the embeddedness of ideas in their traditional context is dissolved, enabling us to perceive a familiar event from an unexpected angle, in a new light. But the unbedding of unsuitable partners is not enough; the word "intuition" implies some positive guiding factors at work, but we can have only indirect intimations of how they work. To illustrate: I mentioned among the features of this prelogical type of thinking, the *symbolization and concretization* of abstract concepts. You may remember Kékulé's dream of the benzene ring while he was struggling with a very abstract problem; he described (cf. 6) very vividly how, sitting in a daze in front of a fire he saw the little sparks going around "like luminous atoms", then the sparks uniting into a kind of a snake, which twisted around, finally the snake bit into its own tail, and the ring was there. Kékulé ended the lecture in which he related his dream with the admonition, "Let us dream, gentlemen."

To avoid a popular fallacy, I hasten to say that to find one's solutions in a dream is an exceedingly rare phenomenon. As far as we know, Kékulé was in a half-dream when that happened. And so was Coleridge when the gentleman from Porlock interrupted his phantasy of Kubla Khan. The fertile region is not in the dream itself, but apparently (there is a great consensus on that) in that marshland between the liquid dream and the firm earth of wakefulness, in the hypnagogic state.

Let me give you another example. Faraday saw the lines of force as curves in space as real as if they had consisted of solid matter, and the whole universe was patterned with these lines; he had a nervous breakdown at the end of his vision. Kékulé's serpent reminds one of a painting by William Blake, while the curves which crowd Faraday's universe recall the vortices in Van Gogh's skies.

I also mentioned *magic causation*, which certainly does not seem very helpful to a scientist. Yet Kepler founded modern astronomy on his belief that there is a virtue or force emanating from the sun which drives the planets, as God the Father operates through the Holy Ghost. And when Kepler first suggested that the tides are due to the attraction of the moon, Galileo, an eminently rational man, rightly rejected this as an occult fancy, a return to animism. Newton himself adopted action-at-a-distance with the utmost reluctance (as his letters to Bentley show), and for the same reason. Post-Heisenberg physics is certainly not a regression to ancient magic, but it is a retreat from the rigid mechanistic conception of physical causality of the nineteenth century. The basic paradoxes of Heisenberg's Uncertainty Relation, the paradoxes of indeterminancy, the relativization of space and time—not to mention negative time and holes in space—are easier to approach by that fluid type of thinking which permits one, like Alice, to believe in six impossible things before breakfast. The recent prediction of the omega minus particle was prompted by a hunch strongly reminiscent of Pythagorean number lore. So were some of Eddington's speculations. Even more striking are the ever-recurrent assertions by physicists and mathematicians (Planck, Poincaré, Einstein, Hardy, Hadamard, to mention a few) which are summed up in the laconic pronouncement, "It is more important to have beauty in one's equations then to have them fit experiment." That was Dirac speaking in the *Scientific American* (4), reproving Schrödinger for not having published his first correct equation of the electron because it contradicted data as known at the time.

Thus we hear again and again, mathematicians asserting that it is not logic, it is not reason: it is beauty which guides them. Now, beauty is one of the few things about which Cro-Magnon man knew as much as we do, and it seems that the road to the discovery of the positron led through the caves of Lascaux.

It has been said that the essence of discovery is to see an analogy where nobody had seen one before. And no doubt the most important kind of unconscious guidance is the unearthing of *hidden analogies*. But where was the analogy hidden, and how is it found? Mathematics began, wrote Bertrand Russell, when it was discovered that a brace of pheasants and a couple of days have something in common: the number 2. An analogy of this kind is not hidden somewhere in a cupboard, it is created in the mind by abstracting a feature X present in two phenomena, an inconspicuous feature further obscured by its embeddedness in two different contexts. It is not a logical procedure but a bisociative act; once a new analogy has been created, it is of course there for all to see—just as a poetic metaphor, once created, soon fades into a cliché.

Regression is apt to produce a rich harvest of wayward analogies. One example is the pun—analogy by sound—manifested in the dream, in slips of the tongue, and in the punning mania of children. Incidentally, Freud's emphasis on punning in the dream has recently been vindicated by the experimental studies of Berger (1). The pun's benefits to the poet are evident: the rhyme is merely a glorified pun, two strings of ideas bisociated in an acoustic knot. The same is true of what one might call optical puns: when Solomon compares the Shulamite's neck to a tower of ivory, he bisociates a visual form with two different meanings. While there are a few discoveries on record which have apparently been inspired by such purely visual analogies (Harvey, Kelvin, Mitcherlich, the ubiquitous Kékulé), these too dramatic and pat cases are rather the exception.

A form of less direct unconscious guidance seems to me of much greater importance to our subject. But it is also less easy to describe. The dream, or the drowsy daydream, drifts effortlessly from matrix to matrix; it constantly bisociates cabbages and kings in a kind of passive, free-wheeling manner. It churns out analogies which are useless except for serving some intimate, private ends; analogies which disintegrate when the dreamer awakes and which he is unable to put into a concise verbal shape, except by muttering, "Something reminded me of something, but I don't know what reminded me of what, and why." This is what I have called "oneirolysis." In the throes of the creative obsession, when thinking on all levels is harnessed to the purpose, this process may perhaps be reversed into a kind of *oneirosynthe-sis*. This is only meant as a speculative pointer to the manner in which those "somethings" vaguely reminding one of other "somethings" may condense into a nascent analogy. It may be a hazy, tentative affair, like Einstein's muscular sensations, and its shape may be changing from camel to weasel as Hamlet's cloud. The unconscious reaches of fertile minds must be pullulat-ing with such nascent analogies, hidden likenesses, and the cloudy forms of things unknown. But most clouds form and dissolve again. Only a few intui-tions can be assumed to reach the stage of "seeding the cloud" which results in the formation of verbal drops. And cloudbursts are a rarity.

To put it in another way, fifty years have passed since Ariëns Kappers coined the term "neurobiotaxis" for the growing towards each other of func-tionally related nerves until they make contact. In its original form, the the-ory did not stand up to time. It was followed by a variety of others—chemi-cal gradients, contact guidance, and what-have-you—to account for the puz-zling mechanism which guides nerves to their functional destination. And there was Paul Weiss' (26) remarkable salamander with its fifth transplanted leg which, within a short time, functioned in perfect synchronism with the adjacent normal limb, although its muscles were supplied by nerve fibers which had split up in the scar at the graft and whose branches had pressed forward until some of them met the degenerated nervepaths in the trans-plant's muscles in a completely random manner. When I first looked at the diagram of the branching, groping nervetree of the Weiss salamander, I was reminded of a famous passage in the *Logique de Port Royale* concerned with problem solving, to the effect that, if somebody wanted to discover whether he was a descendant of St. Louis, he could follow one of two meth-ods, or a combination of both: he could trace St. Louis' descendants as they branch out downwards, or he could trace his own ancestors branching out and up, or he could start at both ends and see whether the branches met. The authors were equating the upward process with analysis, the downward with synthesis, but that formal distinction does not concern us. Problem-solving can be described in terms of bridging the gap between the initial sit-uation and the target by means of a mediating matrix, the search for which probably proceeds in much the same way as in the St. Louis case, by a fan-ning out of tentative hypotheses, groping in a vaguely sensed direction, guided by nascent analogies, following some unknown gradients. In other words, here opens a splendid vista of ignorance. All I wanted to say is that, when we hear repeatedly statements of the kind, "I have got my solution, but I don't know how I arrived at it", then we have no justification to reject out of hand the possibility of some such principle operating below the level of awareness—a kind of neurobiopsychotaxis.

This brings me to my concluding remarks. It seems to me that the phe-nomenon of human creativity is foreshadowed on lower levels of the evolu-tionary scale, in the very prototype of the *reculer pour mieux sauter* process, namely organic regeneration. The organism lives by constant transactions with its environment, which presents challenges of varying intensity. So long as the challenge can be met by adaptive routines which do not entail major changes in the pattern of the organism as a whole, it can be said to be in a state of dynamic equilibrium. But under abnormal conditions—traumatic challenges—only what one might call adaptations of the second order can restore the balance. These involve the reshaping of bodily structures and the reorganization of functions, revealing the existence of unsuspected regenerative potentialities in animal and man which are dormant under normal conditions. The regeneration of bodily structures imitates the processes of embryonic development. It is essentially a regression of tissues to an embryonic or juvenile phase of development, with the resulting liberation of genetic potentials normally inhibited in adult tissues. Progressive specialization in morphogenesis is paid for by the loss of creative potential. The traumatized tissues must retrace their steps on the genetic gradient, as it were, to make a fresh start.

As we proceed from lower to higher organisms, the capacity to regenerate physical *structures* decreases, and is replaced by the ability to counter traumatic challenges with reorganizations of *function* on an equally dramatic scale. In Lashley's rats (16), the intact parts of the brain take over the functions of the ablated parts; in Bethe's crab (2), another leg deputizes for the amputated pacemaker and the whole pattern of locomotion is automatically readjusted in a geometrically elegant way. Hingston's mason-wasp (24) repairs a damaged clay-cell, after its habitual building methods have failed, by a technique it has never employed before. Some birds, if their young are taken away, start the mating cycle out of season.

Lastly, a quote from Tinbergen (25): "If, in a colony of bees, all the foragers are taken away—the foragers are usually bees of twenty days or over—young bees scarcely six days old fly out and become foragers. If all the building workers are taken away, that task is taken over by older bees who had already been builders before. To this end they not only change their behavior, but also regenerate the wax-glands."

We have here a series of environmental challenges: in the Lashley rats it was physical mutilation; in the last three examples I mentioned it was a kind of mental shock—if you allow me this shorthand expression—which could not be met by routine measures, only by adaptations of a second order. If we extrapolate the series to the human level, we get traumatic challenges in the form of new data which shake the foundation of some well-established theory, observations which contradict each other, problems which cause frustration and conflict—or else the artist's perplexities in trying to communicate his experiences through the blocked matrices of conventional techniques. Psychotherapy aims at inducing a temporary regression of the emotionally traumatized patient in the hope that he will regenerate into a pattern which eliminates the conflict. The creative act is a kind of do-it-yourself psychotherapy, where the traumatic challenge, the problem to be solved, is cognitive instead of emotional.

To sum up, *réculer pour mieux sauter* in regeneration, as in creativity, are superadaptations which owe their striking character to the sudden liberation of morphogenetic or psychogenetic potentials, potentials which are normally under restraint. The period of incubation corresponds to the catabolic phase in organ regeneration; the latter triggers off embryonic growth processes inhibited in the mature organism—the former releases ontogenetically or phylogenetically earlier, intuitive modes of ideation from the censorship imposed by the conscious mind. And, finally, to extrapolate the series, we find the same pattern of regression followed by progressive rebound reflected in the death and resurrection motif in mythology: Joseph is thrown into a well, Mohammed goes out into the desert, Jesus is resurrected from the dead. It seems that *réculer pour mieux sauter* is a principle of universal validity in the evolution of individuals and cultures, guiding their progression by feedback from the past.

Discussion

Konorski: One of the two parts in which Mr. Koestler's very interesting and stimulating paper can be divided consists in presenting the well-known models of what he calls creative thinking, and others call problem solving, insight, intelligence, or reasoning. He began by presenting Köhler's classical experiments (14), and I think that, quite rightly, he said that creativity occurs when an animal or man suddenly connects two sequences of activities which until this time were quite apart and had nothing to do with each other, and a problem is solved. Of course, this point of view is well known in animal psychology. It was Norman Maier (17, 19) who proposed the theory and carried out many interesting experiments to support it in both animals and man. So, I think that we are familiar with this point of view, and many of us share it.

In the second part of the paper, an explanation of the creative thinking process was proposed in the principle *réculer pour mieux sauter*, in that creative thinking is supposed to involve some sort of regression to more primitive types of thinking. I have some doubts regarding the substantiation of this point of view. It is far from being the case in the primitive model, namely Köhler's chimpanzees or Maier's rats: I believe that the chimpanzee, rather than returning to some prelogic or preverbal way of thinking in his solution of the problem of the out-of-reach banana, utilizes a very elaborate mechanism of its higher nervous activity, a mechanism that lower animals probably do not possess. The situation with rats is even clearer: we know that only bright rats in Maier's experiments were able to solve the reasoning problems (17). Even small cortical lesions made the rats unable to do so, and they returned to the more primitive type of behavior, i.e., that based on the already established habit (reasoning *versus* learning).

Therefore, we cannot say that the rats solved the problem by *réculer;* I see no evidence for this, and I would say the same about human beings. I do not know whether it really can be said that there is some prelogic or preverbal thinking in problem-solving behavior. Apparently there is some misunderstanding about verbal and preverbal thinking; I understand verbal thinking or internal speech to mean just the type of thinking where we do not verbalize aloud what we have to say.

Simon: What is the evidence for the use of words?

Konorski: This is introspective evidence.

Simon: Mine is also introspective, and they are not words.

Konorski: To my mind, this does not mean that the non-verbal is lower than the verbal.

For instance, I remember some very interesting episodes in Mr. Koestler's book, *Darkness at Noon* (12). It struck me as a very interesting novel. I was much impressed by it but I forgot in which language it was written because I lost totally the words which were there, and I have only the images, the visual images, and these visual images I have preserved. I do not remember words as in remembering a poem. Nevertheless, I would not say that remembering the subject of the novel is "preverbal", since our visual thinking is as highly developed as our verbal thinking.

Mr. Koestler said, and I agree with him, that a great deal of scientific thinking is nonverbal, as Einstein pointed out (as in playing chess). But this does not mean that such thinking is preverbal or prelogic and that it is more primitive than verbal thinking; on the contrary, I believe that a scientist fortunate enough to discover something does it in his best frame of mind, when his mental horizons are particularly broad and his images are particularly vivid. Only then can one bridge the gaps between various apparently separate phenomena. I do not believe that bridging the gaps goes through prelogic or magic thinking and through *réculer.*

Birch: Maier (18, 20, 21), and also I, have conducted experiments on pendulum problem-solving, in which the subjects are asked to tie together two strings hanging far from each other, way out of reach. The subjects grab them, reach out, try a series of things; they do not solve the problem at all unless they walk down the hall or across the room, brush against the window shade and set the bob of the window shade moving. As soon as this happens, 80 to 90 per cent of the subjects tie a weight to one of the hanging strings, set it swinging, then walk over and get the other one and tie the two strings together. When asked how they solved the problem, none of the subjects is able to tell anything about brushing against the window shade and setting the bob in motion. They used it; it was an essential condition for the solution of the problem. It was not in their awareness; introspection is no help in understanding it.

I submit that the introspective or biographic method of trying to elucidate the process of problem solving is an illusion, that a problem solver cannot tell how he solved his problem; he merely gives a rationalization of his solution, which is a very, very different matter. In my own experiments, half the subjects used a switch as the weight because they had certain kinds of pretraining, the meaning of which they did not understand. The other half used a relay as the weight. When I asked one group, "Why did you use the switch?" they said, "Any fool knows that a switch is heavier and ties better", and so on. The equally intelligent group which tied the relay answered, "Any fool can see this."

There is, of course, the question of reorganization in problem solving, which may be studied with rats and chimpanzees, and which has more features than have been described. But we cannot speak of these reorganizations as being either verbally or consciously mediated: these are philosophic presumptions rather than positions that give any information as to problem solving. I think we have several processes, some of which can be identified, but not by introspection; this is not an appropriate method.

Koestler: I agree that these discoveries or reorganizations are neither verbally nor consciously mediated.

Going back to Dr. Konorski's question, he said that there is full agreement on these matters among experimenters. I do not think so. There is endless controversy in the literature on the question of whether Köhler's chimpanzee (14) finds the solution of putting two matrices together by "insight" in one trial, or whether the solution is preceded by trial and error, whether the learning curve is continuous or discontinuous. Hilgard summarized this controversy beautifully in *Theories of Learning* (10). The problem is really very complicated, and there is far from being agreement on what I call the bisociative act. I do believe there is a continuous gradient between implicit trial-and-check attempts, or hypothesis-making in the Krechevsky sense, and the insightful solution at the other extreme. But whether or not trial and error precedes the final fusion of the two matrices, this fusion is the essence of the thing. It is more impressive if it happens dramatically, but even if it does not, it still remains the essential factor through which novelty has come into the world.

Dr. Konorski objected to the regression hypothesis as applied to chimpanzees, Lashley's rats, and the human record, and said, furthermore, that regression from verbal to visual thinking is not a regression. He is correct in saying that the chimpanzee does not regress. I said that extraconscious processes intervene to varying extents, and the first stage of intervention occurs in the type of discovery where, in the obsessive phase, the extraconscious processes merely keep the problem on the agenda until a favorable chance turns up. In the chimpanzee's case, his gaze falls by chance on the stick, and no more is claimed; but there are varying degrees of intervention in the processes which I discussed. Incidentally, this example also shows that, if the situation is ripe for a discovery, meaning that an animal (or a given human culture) has a command of both the matrices necessary for a discovery, and both matrices are independently well established, then the statistical probability of their fusing together is enormously increased; some kind of chance, some trigger-event, will sooner or later present itself. Hence the phenomenon of multiple discoveries found so often in history.

When I mentioned Lashley's rats (16) I wanted to show that there is a gradient from organ regeneration, e.g. the salamander's limb, to functional regeneration. The gradient starts with primitive organisms which regenerate a whole individual from a single segment; higher up, the amphibian regenerates a limb; even higher up, the rat cannot regenerate an organ, but when part of its brain is ablated, then (we cannot explain this any other way) there occurs a functional de-differentiation of other brain tissues regaining their equipotentiality, and these areas become available to take over the functions of the ablated parts. The *reculer pour mieux sauter* is quite clear here; that was the only point I wanted to make.

Lastly, on the human level, there are two types of evidence for the regression to preverbal and prerational levels. One is the cumulative record of all those creative people who have reported the fact that this twilight state intervenes. Then we have the Duncker experiments (5), and the pendulum experiments described by Dr. Birch, in which, quite clearly, brushing against the curtain bob results in 90 per cent of the subjects solving the problem, though all they were given was the merest hint. So, we do have evidence that the lucky combination which will unlock the problem and lead to the appropriate second matrix among a million possibilities—that this rendezvous of ideas is mediated not by logical reasoning, but by "underground" processes because of the greater fluidity of "underground thinking".

Phylogenetically, visual thinking *is* a regression: pictorial-thinking does precede verbal thinking in the child, and in the language of primitives there is visual dominance—what Kretschmer (15) called a picture-strip language. Instead of abstract statements, the primitive makes statements of the type, "Tommy here runs. White man there beat Tommy." It is like a comic strip. So, visual thinking does precede verbal thinking and, in this sense, is a regression.

Pribram: Dr. Birch raised a side issue. If he is right, the introspective method for finding out what is going on in problem solving is one that will lead nowhere, which, incidentally, should make Dr. Simon's approach difficult to pursue. This is an old issue in psychology, and a bit of history might be useful at this point. The Würtzburg school (cf. 3) showed that the *content* of thinking or problem-solving could be reached through the introspective technique of just asking people the answers to problems—but this approach did not work for the *process* of thinking.

Brentano in Vienna and William James at Harvard are especially identified with pursuing the problem of the "process," "act," or "stream" of thought. And they were blocked, just as Dr. Simon has said, because people just do not know what is going on; they are not aware of their thought processes. A solution was proposed by one of Brentano's students (although he never admitted to being such), a neurologist by the name of Sigmund Freud. Freud suggested that by simply allowing people to verbalize whatever came to mind in what he came to call the free association method, their thought processes could become uncovered. On the basis of his observations with this technique he suggested that the thought process was hierarchically organized, its roots in the experiences of infancy, only its most recent branches available to awareness. I have the feeling that the current methods of computer simulation, based on asking a chess player, "Why did you do this? How did you do it?" are not too far removed from this time-honored and much maligned technique—and by this statement I do not mean to imply anything about its therapeutic efficacy.

Simon: In our studies we never ask our subjects why. We simply have them make moves on the chess board, accompanied by such verbalizations as they wish to utter. The verbalizations are among the data to be predicted. We do not care a whit about the subject's theory of his behavior.

Pribram: Even better. You sound just like a psychoanalyst. That is exactly the procedure in the analytic situation: you never ask a patient why. You take his "free" verbal productions and his behavior, and from these try to reconstruct a useful model to explain his behavior. Unfortunately, the psychoanalytic model has only recently been opened to testing at the biological level (23). And, of course, there is always a considerable distance between a model and its predictable usefulness in any specific instance. But this should not damn the model if its explanatory value is high.

Simon: The issue of introspection is a red herring. Thinking aloud is not introspection. The task of a psychological theory is to explain and predict human behavior. A theory that makes many predictions per minute of the subject's behavior can be tested and, if wrong, refuted much more easily than a theory that makes few predictions, provided the predictions can be compared with the behaviors. "Thinking aloud" is simply a form of verbal behavior. A subject who thinks aloud while performing a task emits many more observable behaviors per minute than a subject who performs the task silently. The information processing theories make specific predictions about these verbal behaviors, hence provide many opportunities for testing their correctness for each minute of the subject's laboratory time.

In our laboratories at the Carnegie Institute of Technology, one of our principal aims is to externalize as much of the subject's behavior as possible in order to increase the "density" of the observable stream of behavior. After all, we are trying to understand a system that operates at millisecond speeds; we are not likely to find out much about its processes by taking one reading every five minutes, or even every five seconds. Allen Newell and some of my other colleagues (27) have been supplementing the thinking-aloud data with data from an eye-movement camera. This work demonstrates that for significant problem-solving tasks the evidence from what the subject is looking at is highly consistent with the evidence from what he is saying. At some later date, I expect that we shall want to tie in EEG data as well. At present, we would not know how to interpret that in relation to the simulation data.

REFERENCES

1. BERGER, R. J., Experimental modification of dream content by meaningful verbal stimuli. *Brit. J. Psychiat.*, 1963, **109**: 722-740.
2. BETHE, A., Plastizität und Zentrenlehre. In: *Handbuch der normalen und pathologischen Physiologie* (A. Bethe, G. v. Bergmann, G. Embden and A. Ellinger, Eds.), Vol. 15,2. Springer, Berlin, 1931: 1175-1220.
3. BORING, E. G., *A History of Experimental Psychology* (2nd ed.). Appleton-Century-Crofts, New York, 1950.
4. DIRAC, P. A. M., The evolution of the physicist's picture of nature. *Sci. Amer.*, 1963, **208**(5): 45-53.
5. DUNCKER, K., On problem-solving. *Psychol. Monogr.*, 1945, **58**(5): No. 270.
6. FINDLAY, A., *A Hundred Years of Chemistry* (3rd ed.). Duckworth, London, 1965.
7. GASTAUT, H., and BECK, E., Brain rhythms and learning. *New Scientist*, 1962, **13**: 496-499.
8. HADAMARD, J., *An Essay on the Psychology of Invention in the Mathematical Field*. Dover, New York, 1954.
9. HEBB, D. O., *A Textbook of Psychology*. Saunders, Philadelphia, 1958.
10. HILGARD, E. R., *Theories of Learning* (2nd ed.). Appleton-Century-Crofts, New York, 1956.
11. HÖFER (Ed.), *Histoire de l'Invention de l'Impremerie par les Monuments*. Höfer, Paris, 1840.
12. KOESTLER, A., *Darkness at Noon*. Macmillan, New York, 1941.
13. ———, *The Act of Creation*. Macmillan, New York, 1964.
14. KÖHLER, W., *The Mentality of Apes* (2nd ed.). Routledge, London, 1948.
15. KRETSCHMER, E., *A Text-Book of Medical Psychology*. Hogarth, London, 1952.
16. LASHLEY, K. S., *Brain Mechanisms and Intelligence*. Hafner, New York, 1964.
17. MAIER, N. R. F., Reasoning in white rats. *Comp. Psychol. Monogr.*, 1929, **6**: 1-93.
18. ———, Reasoning in humans. I. On direction. *J. Comp. Psychol.*, 1930, **11**: 115-143.
19. ———, Reasoning and learning. *Psychol. Rev.*, 1931, **38**: 332-346.
20. ———, Reasoning in humans. II. The solution of a problem and its appearance in consciousness. *J. Comp. Psychol.*, 1931, **12**: 181-194.
21. ———, Reasoning in humans. III. The mechanisms of equivalent stimuli and of reasoning. *J. Exp. Psychol.*, 1945, **35**: 349-360.
22. McCLURE, C. M., Cardiac arrest through volition. *Calif. Med.*, 1959, **90**: 440-441.
23. PRIBRAM, K., Freud's Project: an open, biologically based model for psychoanalysis. In: *Psychoanalysis and Current Biological Thought* (N. S.

Greenfield and W. C. Lewis, Eds.). Univ. of Wisconsin Press, Madison, 1965: 81-92.

24. THORPE, W. H., *Learning and Instinct in Animals.* Methuen, London, 1956.
25. TINBERGEN, N., *Social Behaviour in Animals.* Methuen, London, 1953.
26. WEISS, P., Experimental analysis of co-ordination by the disarrangement of central-peripheral relations. *Symp. Soc. Exp. Biol.,* 1950, 4: 92-111.
27. WINIKOFF, A. W., *Eye Movements as an Aid to Protocol Analysis of Problem Solving Behavior.* Ph.D. Thesis, Carnegie Institute of Technology, Pittsburgh, 1967.

INDEXES

NAME INDEX

SUBJECT INDEX

A

Abilities, 309
  auditory, 311
  behavioral, 310, 311
  cognition, 310, 311
  content, 310, 312, 320, 321
  differentiation of, 310, 311
  elaboration of, 318
  fluency, 318
  kinesthetic, 311
  operation, 310, 314
  product, 310, 312, 321
  semantic, 310, 320
  symbolic, 310
  tactual, 311
  visual figural, 310, 311, 320, 321, 323
Ability, 330
  definition, 311
Abstract concepts, symbolization and concretization of, 334
Abstraction, 110, 111, 157, 173
Acetylcholine, 1, 5, 68
Acetylcholinesterase (AchE), 1, 3, 5, 14, 17
Acid-in-the-mouth experiment, 148, 163
Acquisition, 28, 53, 54, 58-61, 64, 112, 156, 238, 239, 318
Acquisitional learning, 59
Adaptation, 49, 215, 232, 298, 299, 331, 337, 338
  sensory, 215-219
Adenine ratio, 13
Adrenalin, 70
Agnosia, 109, 319, 320
Alertness, 112
Alexia, 320
Alimentary reflex, 148
  conditioned, 163
Alimentary system, 130-140
  consummatory subsystem, 132-134, 136, 138, 140
  hunger subsystem, 132-137, 139, 140
Alpha rhythm, 236, 283, 284
Alternation behavior, 89-92, 110, 156
Amino acids, 3, 7, 8

Amnesia, 74
Amygdala, 50, 89, 133
Anencephalic infants, 236
Anesthesia, 59, 71, 74
Animal experimentation, 6, 7, 11, 19-34, 82-87, 105, 112, 133, 160, 272
  environmental influence, 5, 17
  physiological state of organism, 29-33, 37, 59, 62
  selection of animals, 36
Animal learning, 204, 205
Animal psychology, 34, 338
Animism, 334
Anthropology, 333
Anticipation, 175, 205, 275, 317
Anxiety, 294, 302
Aphasias, 188, 319, 320
  nominal, 320
  semantic, 319
  syntactic, 319
Arousal, 70, 225, 235, 298, 302
  conditioned, 135
  habituation of, 69
  mental retardates, in, 283, 284, 298, 302
  motor, 132, 135
Association, 12, 15, 25, 26, 29, 33-35, 65-67, 110-112, 146, 149, 160-162, 164, 171, 176, 191, 192, 194, 196-200, 266, 271, 272, 298, 300, 301, 307, 317, 331
  directional nature of, 203, 205
  formation of, 6, 7, 9, 54, 132, 203, 271, 273
  forms of, 307
  free, 342
  plastic, 65, 70
  sensory, 85
  verbal, 320
Association cortex, 80, 85, 87, 101, 105, 106, 108, 109, 111
Association systems, 111, 234
  corticofugal model, 109
Associative conditioning, 24-27
Associative learning, 26, 27, 29, 34, 38, 61, 145, 147, 149-151, 219, 233, 271, 298

Memory (cont.)
  decay function, 187
  deposition, 51, 61, 74
  immediate, 171, 179, 205, 280, 282-284, 287
  intermediary processes, 179
  long-term, 57, 178, 179, 181, 194, 195, 198, 202, 235, 280, 281
  mechanisms of, 49-51, 60, 61
  mental retardates, in, 282
  molecular approach to, 39, 40
  molecule, 1, 2, 39-42, 52
  permanent, 178, 234
  permanent basis for, 5
  retrieval, 51, 53, 73, 74, 204, 280, 316-318
  RNA as substrate, 1, 2
  short-term, 73, 74, 109, 151, 179, 181, 194, 195, 198, 199, 201, 202, 204, 235, 285
  standing D.C. potentials in, 59
  timing problem in, 40
  trace, 39, 42, 61, 187
    decay, 283, 284
    localization, 19
  verbalizing, through, 289
  visualizing, through, 289, 333
Mental retardates, 281
  arousal in, 283, 284, 298
  attention-directing mechanism, 292-294
  biochemical anomalies in, 280
  CNS damage in, 279, 281, 289-292, 298
  cognitive functions in, 287
  discriminability in, 288
  educability of, 279
  familial retardate, 290, 291, 295
  idiot, 289
  imbecile, 281, 289, 301
  learning ability, 269, 270, 282
  memory of, 282
  mongoloid, 281, 282, 285, 292, 295, 296
  motivation, 295
  organic retardates, 291
  rigidity, 292
  training of, 279
Mental retardation, 189, 269, 270, 320
  defect notion in, 189, 279, 290-293, 295-298
  etiology, 290, 291, 295, 296
  institutionalization, 293-296
  learning and, 279-303
  neurological correlates of, 289
  perinatal factors, 212
  phenylketonuria, 296
  phenylpyruvic oligophrenia, 290
  psychology of, 279, 280
  theories, 290-292
Mentality, structure of, 174
Metabolic gradient, 35, 37
Metabolic variability, 35, 36
Metabolism, 297
Meta-molecular phenomena, 39
Midbrain, 18, 50, 60, 64, 69, 71, 140
  reticular formation, 56, 64, 65

Migratory pattern, innate, 157
Mind-body problem, 314
Mind-brain problem, 39
Mitochondria, 14, 18
Molecular biology, 2, 7, 8, 41, 204
Molecular neurology, 49
Molecular psychobiology, 1, 49
Monotony, 112
Mood, 136
Morphine, 71, 148
Morphogenesis, 337, 338
Motility, 31, 32
Motivation, 138, 153, 158, 239, 240, 282, 285, 292, 295, 296, 316
  developmental changes in, 240
Motivational state, 29
Motor activity, 2, 6, 10, 11, 17, 159, 327
Motor arousal, 132, 135
Motor-learning, 289
Motor pathways, extrapyramidal, 51
Motor response, 126-130, 136-138, 140, 152, 153
Motor system, 292
  cortical, 112
  projection, 111
Muller cells, 16

N

Negative learning, 64
Neocortex, 64, 132, 140
Nerve impulse, 42
  transmission, 14
Nervous system, 162, 170
  coding in, 70, 71, 331
  electrical activity, 236
  evolution of, 299
Neural axis, 18
Neural satiation, 292
Neural system, model of, 79, 111-118
Neurobiopsychotaxis, 336
Neurobiotaxis, 336
Neuroglial relationship, 17
Neurograms, 115
Neurology, 161, 164, 200
Neuron, 3, 15, 16, 41, 51, 52, 170, 185, 204
  association, 17
  cortical, 3
  culture studies, 5
  growth in, 5, 15, 203
  intercommunication between, 5, 113
  intracellular recordings, 115, 118
  membrane thickness, 14
  motor, 3, 115-117
  Nissl substance, 3
  physiology, 111
  pseudopods, 15
  recovery of, 107-109, 111, 112, 114, 115
  RNA-DNA mechanisms, 54
  sensory, 117
Neurophysiology, 5, 70-72, 79-118, 149-158, 169, 200, 202-206, 211, 231, 240, 270
Neuropil habituation, 69
Neuropsychology, 185

DATE DUE